£21.55

1.3.85

Modelling
Fluctuating Populations

Modelling
Fluctuating Populations

R. M. NISBET and W. S. C. GURNEY

University of Strathclyde

A Wiley–Interscience Publication

JOHN WILEY & SONS

Chichester · New York · Brisbane · Toronto · Singapore

Library of Congress Cataloging in Publication Data

Nisbet, R. M.
  Modelling fluctuating populations.

  "A Wiley–Interscience publication."
  Includes index.
  1. Population biology—Mathematical models.
I. Gurney, W. S. C. II. Title.
QH352.N57   574.5'248'0724   81–14668
ISBN 0-471-28058-5   AACR2

British Library Cataloguing in Publication Data:

Nisbet, R. M.
  Modelling fluctuating populations.
  1. Population biology—Mathematical models
  I. Title   II. Gurney, W.S.C.
  574.5'248   QH352

  ISBN 0 471 28058 5

Typeset by Preface Ltd, Salisbury, Wilts., and
printed in the United States of America.

Contents

PART III   CASE STUDIES

APPENDIXES

x

Preface

This book is intended as a 'do-it-yourself' manual to enable readers of widely varying levels of mathematical sophistication to formulate, analyse and interpret their own population models. One of our primary aims is to help reverse the increasing division of population biologists into those who possess mathematical self-confidence and those who do not. The seeds of this unwholesome split are sown early and we have therefore provided a route through the book (Chapters 1, 2, 4, 8 and 9) which should be readily accessible to those, such as final year life-science students, whose mathematics does not extend beyond simple calculus and probability.

For the initially less adept reader whose confidence increases after working through the more elementary material and for those readers who are already mathematically practised, we have set out in Chapters 3 and 5 some considerably more challenging deterministic material and in Chapters 6 and 7 give an extensive discussion of the state of the art in stochastic modelling. To assist in the learning process at all levels, each chapter in which new techniques are introduced is provided with a set of problems, many of which are based on models recently published in the population-biology literature.

Despite the heated philosophical debate which re-emerges from time to time over the role which mathematics ought to play in the life sciences, we believe that mathematical modelling should be judged on the same grounds as any other scientific tool, namely on what it can deliver. We thus conclude with three detailed case studies (Chapters 8, 9, and 10) drawn from our own research experience, in which we discuss not only the practical use of the analytic techniques described in the earlier parts of the book, but also the equally vital phases of model formulation and final interpretation. We lay particular emphasis in this section on the testing and verification of our models, and have therefore chosen as our examples laboratory populations which are sufficiently carefully controlled and closely documented for detailed model testing to be a practicable proposition.

R.M.N.
W.S.C.G.

Acknowledgements

Many people have helped us in the preparation of this book: our wives, who encouraged us to finish it when it seemed we never would; Jean Lindores, who with endless patience transcribed our illegible handwriting into elegant typescript; Alex Cunningham and Stephen Blythe who collaborated in the original research described in Chapters 9 and 10; Professors Edward Eisner and Alan Dandy who, together with all our colleagues at the Universities of Strathclyde and the South Pacific, gave unstinting support and encouragement; Joan Finch, Madhu Narayan and Sobhana Narayan, who traced artwork and typed drafts for us; Mike Hassell, John Lawton, Bob May, Norman MacDonald, Jim McKinstry, Ross McMurtrie, Mike Pettipher, and many others, who read parts of the manuscript and provided helpful and encouraging comment. We thank them all.

Chapter 1

Introduction

1.1 AIMS OF THEORETICAL POPULATION DYNAMICS

Our aim in this book is to present a number of mathematical techniques which have proved useful in analysing models of fluctuating populations. Such mathematical models are of three broad types:

(a) 'tactical models' which are designed to yield accurate short-term forecasts of population changes;
(b) 'strategic models' which are simple, mathematically tractable, models constructed with the aim of identifying possible ecological principles, i.e. to answer the question 'Could it happen?' as opposed to 'Will it happen?';
(c) testable models of laboratory data.

Tactical models, sometimes called 'simulations', require precise and detailed information on the species involved. In skilful hands such simulations yield good short-term predictions of population trends provided that the estimates of the parameters involved (for instance the life-tables used in human demography) are continuously updated. However, these models are normally so complex that there is little hope that they will lead to testable generalizations concerning the mechanisms underlying any population changes.

On the other hand strategic models, whose design is strongly influenced by considerations of mathematical simplicity, will seldom withstand detailed comparison with any one system. They are constructed with the aim of 'providing a conceptual framework for the discussion of broad classes of phenomena' (May, 1974b, p. 11). A good example is provided by the logistic equation which, treated as a crude representation of density-dependent population growth, is in poor agreement with empirical data on many species, but which can serve as a starting point for qualitative investigations of the effects of time-delays, population growth in periodically and randomly fluctuating environments, optimal harvesting strategies, and even evolutionary questions such as whether natural selection will favour efficiency or speed of resource utilization. Strategic models of natural populations can seldom be tested against field data, though they are frequently of value in selecting *a posteriori* explanations of observed phenomena.

Neither tactical nor strategic models are truly 'scientific' in the sense that this term is conventionally used, i.e. neither yields testable formulae which can be used to reject scientific hypotheses. Although tactical models do yield predictions of population changes, these predictions are not based on fundamental hypotheses concerning the mechanisms responsible for these changes. The primary aim of tactical modelling is thus statistical forecasting and not scientific prediction. The primary function of strategic modelling is the generation of hypotheses and the elucidation of their possible consequences; the testing of these hypotheses on natural populations cannot be based on the very simple idealized models used in their construction.

We believe that the current 'state of the art' in population dynamics is that at present we can make quantitative testable models only of laboratory systems which are themselves a caricature of reality. Contact with the real, natural, world is achieved by simulation or by strategic models. This situation may be improved a little as the distinction between strategic and tactical models becomes less well defined but in our opinion no major breakthrough will occur until we have a far greater understanding of the relationships between the properties of laboratory and natural populations. This in turn involves being able to construct and model more realistic laboratory ecosystems which mimic natural populations better than do existing experimental systems. It is thus probable that over the lifetime of this book the main thrust of population modelling will be directed at laboratory systems. For this reason, although the techniques to be presented are applicable to all three types of models, we have chosen as our major case-studies (Chapters 8–10) three examples of laboratory populations.

1.2 CHOICE OF VARIABLES

For most of this book we shall use as the principal variable in our modelling the number of individuals of a particular species in a given region of space. We make this choice in order to base our population dynamics on knowledge of, or guesses at, 'per capita' birth and death rates. Furthermore by choosing this representation we open the possibility of using the well-developed mathematical theory of stochastic 'birth and death' models. The price we pay for constructing models in terms of population numbers is that we make more difficult the task of identifying how thermodynamic or evolutionary factors influence a given population. We comment on these in turn.

The birth, growth and maintenance of an individual organism all require the input of a readily measurable quantity of energy. The prolonged existence of populations of organisms requires in addition the constant recycling of various elements (see, for example, Fig. 1.1), a process which itself depends on a constant input of solar energy (primarily for photosynthesis) and on the

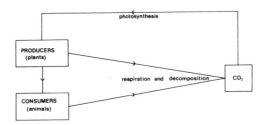

Fig. 1.1. A schematic representation of the
carbon cycle.

radiation away from the earth of energy dissipated as heat. Thus the bio-
sphere appears superficially very similar to the type of system analysed in
non-equilibrium thermodynamics, especially in a chemical context. There is
certainly no difficulty in interpreting rates of energy flow or material conversion as thermodynamic fluxes, but to apply the results of non-equilibrium
thermodynamics would require the fluxes to be related to some thermodynamic forces (just as chemical reaction rates are controlled by differences in chemical potential). No satisfactory identification of such forces has
yet been achieved and ecological energetics still lacks a 'dynamics'. In general
terms, therefore, there is much to be lost and little to be gained by constructing dynamic models exclusively in terms of energy or material content,
although, in particular situations sufficient experimental information may be
available for such models. For example, in Chapter 9 we analyse one model of
a laboratory population which is controlled by the availability of nitrogen.

The properties of *individuals* in a population are generally believed to have
evolved through the action of natural selection. Consequently there are constraints on the properties of *populations* which ought to be incorporated into
any ecological theory. However, to base population models on the dynamics
of individual genes is clearly impossible as many thousands of genes may be
involved in determining any one of the large number of phenotypic characteristics whose distribution within a population is in turn responsible for
population regulation. How to incorporate evolutionary constraints in population models is thus unclear; perhaps the most useful recent development
here has been the concept of the 'evolutionarily stable strategy' due to Price
and Maynard Smith (1973). Techniques based on this idea yield criteria for
determining whether the parameters in a population equation retain their
values for evolutionarily significant lengths of time, provided we can specify
the form of a 'fitness set' which quantifies the relative importance of different
attributes to an individual in the population. Although we shall not emphasize
such evolutionary problems in this book, the techniques which we describe
are readily applied to them.

A second and more controversial evolutionary consideration is more
directly connected with the work in this book. We shall place considerable
emphasis on calculations of the intensity of fluctuations in population num-

4

bers and shall show that this leads to an estimate of the likelihood of the population becoming extinct during a given time interval. Various biologists have argued that those population regulatory mechanisms which are concerned with avoiding over-exploitation of resources might have evolved through natural selection acting on groups of individuals rather than on the individuals themselves. One possible mechanism for group selection involves extinction of those groups whose imprudent use of resources leads to large population fluctuations. The debate on group selection has centred on the question of whether it could ever act sufficiently fast to dominate individual selection. Again this is not a problem we shall emphasize, but the relevance of Chapters 6 and 7—where we calculate approximate extinction times—is obvious. Perhaps a little less obvious is that the 'patchy' environments considered in Chapters 5, 6, and 10 constitute situations in which group selection might be effective and rapid.

1.3 DETERMINISTIC AND STOCHASTIC PHENOMENA

Under optimum conditions, most populations have a very high potential for growth. However, in spite of this potential, the numbers observed in populations of many species appear to be 'regulated' or 'controlled' within certain limits. The sheep population in Tasmania which is illustrated in Fig. 1.2 is a good example of a 'controlled' population; after an initial period of very rapid growth the population has fluctuated around a mean of about $1\frac{1}{2}$ million for a century. A second example of the same phenomenon but with much smaller random fluctuations is shown in Fig. 1.3, which depicts the growth of a laboratory culture of yeast.

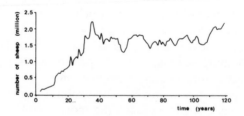

Fig. 1.2. Number of sheep in the island of Tasmania. (Reproduced from Davidson, 1938; copyright the Royal Society of South Australia Inc.)

Given data like that on the Tasmanian sheep it seems natural to represent it as a superposition of a *deterministic trend* and *random fluctuations* (see Fig. 1.4). Even when the population does not settle down and fluctuate about a stationary level, this separation can still be made though the precise criteria which define the trend are obviously somewhat arbitrary. Statistical techniques for isolating trends can be found in any text on time series analysis,

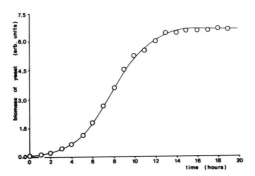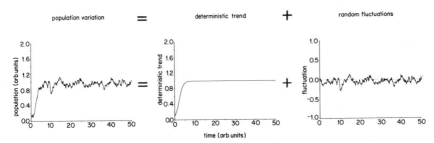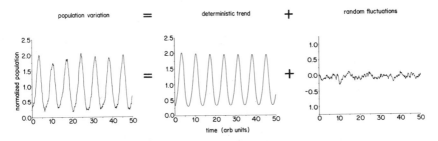

Fig. 1.3. Growth of yeast in a laboratory culture. (After Allee, Emerson, Park, Park, and Schmidt, 1949.)

Fig. 1.4. Representation of a population plot as the sum of deterministic and random components.

e.g. Box and Jenkins (1970) or Chatfield (1975). An example involving an apparently cycling population is shown in Fig. 1.5.

With some populations (e.g. the yeast in Fig. 1.3 or the algae of Chapter 9) the random fluctuations are small, and for many purposes it is sufficient to construct a model, which we call a *deterministic model* which only describes the trend. The most important property of deterministic models is that, if we know the history of the population up to the present time, we can predict its

Fig. 1.5. Representation of an apparently cycling population as the sum of deterministic and random components.

exact value at any future time. A model which describes both the trend and the fluctuations is called a *stochastic model* and in all the stochastic models in this book we shall treat the fluctuations statistically. Whereas with a deterministic model it is possible to make exact predictions of future populations, a stochastic model is only able to predict the *probability* that at a given time, the population will be of a particular size.

Wherever an assumption of randomness is made in a stochastic model, it implies neglect (often reflecting ignorance), of some of the details of the system being modelled. In Chapters 6 and 7 we discuss in some detail the validity of this procedure; however, at present it is useful to note that the transition to a probabilistic approach is valid when considering large numbers of statistically independent factors. One such situation arises if the external factors which cause population fluctuations are uncorrelated in time; we then use a mathematical idealization known as 'white noise' which enormously simplifies the analysis.

We shall apply stochastic methods to population fluctuations with two distinct origins:

(a) *demographic stochasticity*, which is the name given to fluctuations which arise because populations contain a discrete number of members, with population changes being caused by a succession of individually unpredictable births and deaths;

(b) *environmental stochasticity*, which is the name properly applied to aperiodic environmental variation and often also applied loosely to the resulting population fluctuations.

Both types of fluctuations will be analysed in Chapters 6 and 7. Meanwhile we note that the pattern of the fluctuations in a population is intimately linked to the deterministic properties of the same system. Suppose that after experiencing a single perturbation a population takes a time T_R to return to a value close to its original value. Since this quantity T_R is a property of the trend, it can be calculated from a deterministic model. Intuitively we would expect the population to be able to respond easily to any environmental changes (including random ones) which take place over time intervals much longer than T_R, but to be sluggish in its response to changes which involve times significantly less than T_R. Careful analysis of stochastic models shows that this is in fact the case and is but one example of the numerous interrelationships that exist between deterministic and stochastic properties. For this reason, by developing techniques for constructing and analysing deterministic models (in Chapters 2–5) we shall have completed much of the groundwork necessary for work on the more complex stochastic models which are the subjects of Chapters 6 and 7.

1.4 CYCLIC, QUASI-CYCLIC AND NON-CYCLIC FLUCTUATIONS

So far we have referred rather vaguely to 'random fluctuations' in population without defining 'random' and without investigating whether there is a distinct pattern to any observed fluctuations. In particular it is of interest to question whether a specific set of fluctuations is in any sense cyclic.

The mathematician's concept of cyclic or periodic variations is of little use in population dynamics. Mathematically, a population exhibits cyclic fluctuations with period P if at any time t the population contains exactly the same number of individuals as it did at time $t - P$, and obviously no real population is as well behaved as this. A much more useful characterization of pattern in fluctuations is provided by the *autocovariance function* (AC_0F) or the *autocorrelation function* (ACF) which are measures of the correlation between the population fluctuations at a time t and at a later time $t + \tau$. If $N(t)$ is the population at time t and $\langle N \rangle$ the average population over a very long time interval then the AC_0F is defined by

$$C(\tau) \equiv \langle (N(t) - \langle N \rangle)(N(t + \tau) - \langle N \rangle) \rangle \qquad (1.4.1)$$

where $\langle \ \rangle$ again denotes an average over a very long interval of time. The ACF is a normalized form

$$\rho(\tau) \equiv C(\tau)/C(0) \qquad (1.4.2)$$

defined so as to have a value of one when $\tau = 0$. The interpretation of this function is assisted by noting the resemblance to a standard correlation coefficient. If r is the correlation coefficient between any two quantities x and y then r^2 (which is sometimes called the coefficient of determination) is the fraction of the variation in y which could be predicted from the variation in x. Similarly $(\rho(\tau))^2$ represents the fraction of the variation in population at time t which could be predicted from knowledge of the variation at time $t - \tau$.

For mathematically perfect cycles of period P the correlation coefficient between the population value at time t and at time $t \pm P, t \pm 2P$ etc. is exactly 1. Thus, as we illustrate in Fig. 1.6(a), a perfectly cyclic fluctuation has an ACF which is itself perfectly cyclic. Real population fluctuations are never perfectly periodic and, therefore, never exhibit this form of mathematically cyclic ACF. However, two kinds of partially repetitive behaviour, which we shall call 'quasi-cycles' are observed in nature.

(a)   A population may respond to some external or internal factor which is itself dependent upon an underlying process exhibiting mathematically perfect cycles. An obvious example is seasonal climatic variations which are ultimately driven by the rotation of the earth round the sun, a process whose minute deviations from perfect periodicity are ecologically irrelevant. In such cases the population fluctuations maintain a loose but not infinitely elastic relationship with the underlying 'metronome', and their ACF (see Fig. 1.6(b)) reflects this by exhibiting a cyclic 'tail' at large values of τ. We call fluctuations with this kind of ACF *phase-remembering quasi-cycles*.

(b)   A population may vary in a quasi-periodic manner without any cyclic factor to 'drive' the oscillations. In such cases the system has only a short-term 'memory' of its previous history and thus the values of the

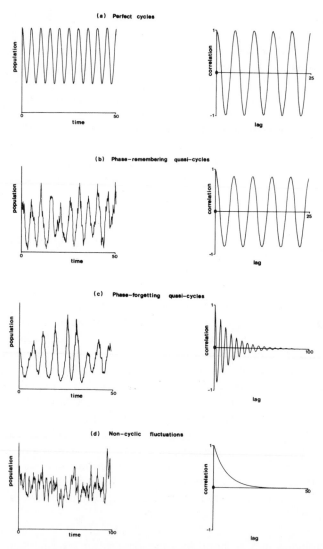

Fig. 1.6. Population fluctuations and their autocovariance functions. The left-hand plots show segments of four distinct population histories and the right-hand plots show the equivalent theoretical ACFs determined from the entire time history.

population fluctuation at instants widely separated in time are unlikely to be significantly correlated. The ACF of these fluctuations, which we shall call *phase-forgetting quasi-cycles* thus exhibits damped oscillations (see Fig. 1.6(c)) whose amplitude decays to zero as the lag, τ, becomes large.

As far as is known the great majority of animal population fluctuations are *non-cyclic* and thus have an ACF of the general form shown in Fig. 1.6(d). Why then has the relatively uncommon phenomenon of population cycling attracted so much attention? There seem to be two main reasons. First, if a population exhibits *endogenous* (internally generated) quasi-cycles, we might hope to be able to extract from the characteristics of these cycles information about the mechanisms of population regulation. This is particularly true for populations such as the laboratory cultures of the water flea *Daphnia pulex* which yielded the data shown in Fig. 1.7, whose oscillations can be suppressed by a change of environmental conditions. Secondly, where a population is 'driven' by periodic environmental variations to exhibit *exogenous* (externally generated) quasi-cycles, then a careful comparison of the characteristics of the population cycles with those of the environmental variation, may provide a powerful tool for identifying casual relationships. Such techniques are particularly useful for laboratory experiments, such as those of Ollason (1977) (see Fig. 1.8), where the general environmental conditions can be very closely controlled.

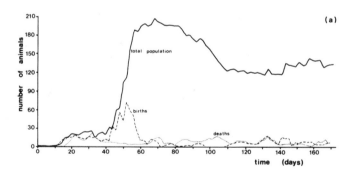

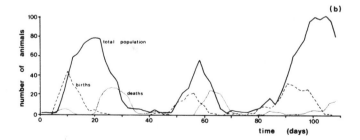

Fig. 1.7. Population growth in the water flea *Daphnia magna* at, (a) 18 °C, and (b) 25 °C in 50 cc of pond water. (Reproduced by permission of The Marine Biological Laboratory, Woods Hole, Mass. from Pratt, 1943 reproduced by Krebs, 1972.)

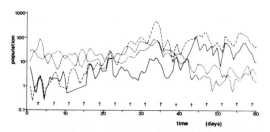

Fig. 1.8. Four populations in an aquatic micro-
cosm subjected to sinusoidal variations in light
intensity (arrows indicate maxima of light intensity). (From Ollason, 1977; reproduced by permission of OIKOS.)

1.5   ECOLOGICAL AND MATHEMATICAL STABILITY

Few concepts in ecology have more successfully eluded acceptable, formal definition than stability. The problem is partly due to the fact that the term is regularly applied to communities and complete ecosystems as well as to single populations. In this book we shall only concern ourselves with population stability and *we define as ecologically stable a population which persists for a large number of generations, and as ecologically unstable one which persists only for a few generations.*

Ecological stability thus defined is a property of real (as opposed to model) populations but it is clearly within the scope of stochastic models to predict the ecological stability or instability of a model population, by predicting the probability of extinction within a given time interval. We can thus calculate the mean time which elapses before the occurrence of a fluctuation large enough to drive that population extinct. If this time, which we denote by τ_E, is many generations we say the model population is ecologically stable, while if it is only a few generations we say the model population is ecologically un-stable. Evidently this definition is incomplete until we assign orders of mag-nitude to the terms 'many' and 'few', and this choice will depend on the particular system being modelled. However, in many cases the aim of model-ling is to determine whether a particular influence has a 'stabilizing' or 'de-stabilizing' effect on a population, and for such comparisons it is convenient to define a *stability index*.

$$\xi \equiv \ln \tau_E. \tag{1.5.1}$$

We define ξ in terms of the logarithm of the mean extinction time because it is only order of magnitude changes in this quantity which are likely to be intuitively recognizable as 'stabilizing'.

Our definition appears to place questions of stability well outwith the scope of deterministic models. However, we shall see in Chapters 6 and 7 that if a population described by a deterministic equation possesses the property of *deterministic stability*, then under certain restrictive conditions a relatively simple stochastic modification of the model yields useable estimates of the ecological stability index.

With a deterministic model we say the population has a *deterministic steady state* if its value stays constant with time. We say that the steady state is *deterministically stable* if, after the population is perturbed from its steady state value, it ultimately returns to, or infinitesimally close to, that value. Otherwise it is *deterministically unstable*.

The approach to a deterministically stable state may involve a succession of damped oscillations in which case the population is said to be *underdamped*, or it may be non-oscillatory in which case it is said to be *overdamped*. An overdamped population, if perturbed, need not return monotonically to its steady state value, but there will only be a finite number of overshoots or undershoots; ultimately the approach to equilibrium will be monotonic with time. Similarly with an unstable population the divergence from the steady state may be oscillatory or non-oscillatory. Each of these possibilities is illustrated in Fig. 1.9.

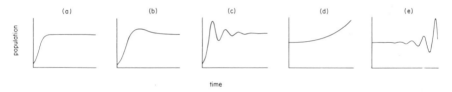

Fig. 1.9. Different types of deterministic steady state: (a) and (b) stable overdamped, (c) stable underdamped, (d) unstable, exponentially diverging, (e) unstable, divergent oscillations.

Obviously in any discussion of deterministic stability the size of the initial perturbation is important. A deterministic steady state is said to be *globally stable* if after any perturbation, however large, the population returns to its steady state. (We exclude in this definition perturbations which correspond to the complete removal of a species from the region under consideration.) A necessary condition for global stability is obviously *local stability*, i.e. that the population returns to its steady state after small perturbations. However, a steady state may be locally but not globally stable as is easily seen from the following biologically plausible example.

Consider a population with overlapping generations in which $B(N)$ and $D(N)$, the *total* numbers of births and deaths per unit time, vary with total population, N, in the manner shown in Fig. 1.10. At a deterministic steady state the total birth and death rate must be equal and there are thus two non-zero steady states (N_1 and N_2 in Fig. 1.10). Clearly N_1 is unstable and N_2 is locally stable; however, if the population is perturbed from N_2 to a value less than N_1 it will decline further and never return to N_2. Hence N_2 is not globally stable.

12

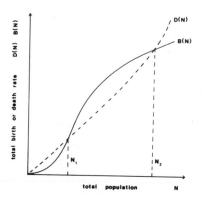

Fig. 1.10. Number of births and deaths per unit time as a function of total population in a hypothetical population with two deterministic steady states.

Concepts of mathematical stability developed for deterministic models are obviously inappropriate to stochastic models with which we cannot predict future population values but only the probability distribution of these values. We say that a stochastic model has a *statistically stationary state* if the probability distribution of population values is constant over a long time interval.

Consider now a population in some 'closed' region, i.e. a region across whose boundaries there is no immigration or emigration. In such situations it is common to find that the population probability distribution, which we denote by $P(N)$, varies with time in the manner displayed in Fig. 1.11. In the short term the probability distribution quickly settles down to a very slowly changing shape, but after very long times the most likely population is zero.

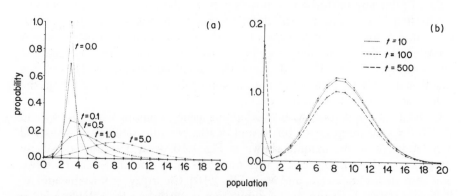

Fig. 1.11. Population probability distribution for a hypothetical population whose value was known exactly at $t = 0$. (a) Transient behaviour. (b) Quasi-stationary behaviour.

However, in many cases the time which elapses before the probability of extinction becomes appreciable is so long that although mathematically there is no statistically stationary state, in practice the distribution is almost unchanging over all ecologically relevant periods of time. We say this system has a *statistically quasi-stationary state*, a concept which is formally defined as a stationary state for the *conditional probability distribution* (conditional on $N \neq 0$). This point will be developed in Chapter 6 when we shall show that from a quasi-stationary probability distribution we can estimate mean extinction times and hence discuss ecological stability in terms of the index of equation (1.5.1).

1.6 NON-LINEAR MODELS

It is evident from the preceding discussion that in most realistic models of a stable (or potentially stable) population the total birth and death rates will vary with population in a non-linear manner. Consequently, any representation of the population dynamics will involve non-linear mathematical equations of some type (usually differential, difference, integral or some combination of these). Solving non-linear equations on a computer can with luck be a fairly straightforward exercise, but it is notoriously difficult to obtain insight into the qualitative behaviour of a system from numerical analysis. To see why this is so consider a model with three parameters. Even considering as few as 10 values for each parameter leads to 1000 combinations requiring investigation. On the other hand analytic (i.e. 'pen-and-paper') investigation of non-linear equations tends to require difficult mathematics and constitutes a broad niche occupied by an ecologically stable population of mathematicians. We must, therefore, ask to what extent is non-linear mathematics essential in modelling fluctuating populations?

The answer to be argued in this book is that while non-linear *models* are fundamental to population dynamics, there are only a few occasions when significant progress cannot be made with the aid of purely *linear mathematics*. The reason for this is that from non-linear models we can construct *locally linear* approximations which are valid near a steady state. The resulting equations are linear in the *deviation* of the population from its steady-state value. In principle such equations are only valid for infinitesimally small deviations from the steady state but in practice we have found the following to be true.

(a) With deterministic models a locally linear approximation can only be used to *prove* local stability. However, in models with only one 'feasible' steady state, i.e. one in which all populations take non-negative values, this is usually a strong indicator of global stability.

(b) With stochastic models whose deterministic analogues have a single, stable, deterministic steady state, locally linear approximations lead to an estimate of the conditional probability distribution (conditional on the population not becoming extinct) from which we can calculate such

14

quantities as the intensity of population fluctuations and their ACF. In principle the results ought to be valid only for infinitesimally small fluctuations but in practice we find them to be good approximations even if the population fluctuations are quite large. It is even possible to use this approximation to make qualitatively acceptable estimates of extinction probabilities, and hence to investigate ecological stability.

We shall use the term *robust* to characterize approximations which are useful over a much wider range of circumstances than those for which they were originally derived.

There are two situations in which we *are* forced to use non-linear mathematics as the basis for modelling, namely with models which have an unstable steady state and with models which have two or more locally stable steady states. We discuss these in turn.

It is evident from Fig. 1.9 that when a population diverges from an unstable steady state its ultimate behaviour will be governed by the nature of the birth and death rate functions at populations far from the steady state, and can thus only be accurately determined by analysis of the non-linear dynamic equations. However, in most population models the form of the non-linearities implies an eventual limitation on the continued growth of the perturbation, so that oscillatory divergence from an unstable steady state normally leads to a series of persistent oscillations (*limit cycles*) of the type shown in Fig. 1.12. The amplitude and frequency of such limit cycles is entirely independent of the size of the initial perturbation and, being determined by the non-linearities, is usually very hard to calculate. However, since the frequency is often very close to the frequency of the original divergent oscillations, which

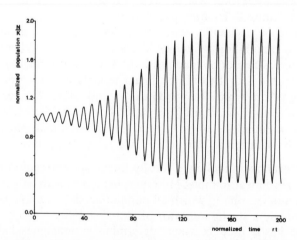

Fig. 1.12. An example of a limit cycle calculated from the time delayed logistic equation $N(t) = rN(1 - N(t - T_D)/K)$ with $rT_D = 1.7$.

can easily be calculated in the locally linear approximation, it is often possible to use the latter quantity as a first estimate of the limit-cycle frequency.

The other situation where it is necessary to take explicit account of non-linearities concerns models with multiple steady states. We give an example of such a model in Chapter 6; meanwhile we point out that they are most likely to arise in situations where a predator 'switches' its preferred diet in response to large changes in availability of prey.

SOURCES AND SUGGESTED FURTHER READING

General: Most authors of texts on population models give some exposition of the philosophy behind their work. Those by May (1974b) and Maynard Smith (1974) are particularly pertinent to this book.

Choice of variables: The theory of birth and death processes mentioned in Section 1.2 is the subject of Chapter 6. A biologically oriented reference is Bartlett (1960). An introduction to ecological energetics is Philipson (1966). Nicolis, and Prigogine (1977) and Prigogine (1980) present biological applications of non-equilibrium thermodynamics and include a little on ecological energetics. The point on group selection in patchy environments is mentioned by Gilpin (1975) who gives an extensive bibliography on group selection.

The remainder of this chapter has introduced material for which references are given in later chapters.

Part I

Deterministic Models

Chapter 2

Single-Species Models

2.1 THE FUNDAMENTAL EQUATION

There is one elementary principle which underlies all population modelling, a principle which is all too easily forgotten when battling with complex mathematics, namely that the total number of individuals (N) in a fixed region of space can only change for four reasons:

(a) births,
(b) deaths,
(c) immigration,
(d) emigration.

In a small time interval Δt the change in population (ΔN) can thus *always* be written as

$$\Delta N = (B - D + I - E)\Delta t, \qquad (2.1.1)$$

where $B\Delta t$, $D\Delta t$ are respectively the total numbers of births and deaths during Δt, while $I\Delta t$ and $E\Delta t$ are the total numbers of individuals entering and leaving the region during the same time interval. The wide variation in the mathematical form of population equations found in the literature corresponds to different assumptions concerning the terms, B, D, I and E in this fundamental equation.

These assumptions are of two types. First we need to specify the type of information on B, D, I, or E which is to be incorporated in the model. This determines the class of mathematical equations which will be used. Then we must specify the *functional form* for each of the quantities. For instance, if we are modelling a population with density-dependent, age-specific mortality we must specify the death rate as a function of age and of population size. It is important that this should be done as late as possible in the analysis in order to distinguish general principles from special results caused by particular choices of B, D, I or E. For this reason we have tried to keep our mathematical exposition as general as possible, leaving for the most part the substitution of specific functional forms for B, D, I and E to the problems at the end of the chapter.

In this chapter we consider population models in which immigration and emigration play no significant role. We specify the assumptions on B and D that are necessary to obtain particular types of deterministic model of the population of a single species and then develop mathematical techniques for the analysis of the resulting equations.

2.2 DIFFERENCE AND DIFFERENTIAL EQUATIONS

The simplest type of population to model is one in which individuals appear in discrete generations with no adults surviving from one generation to the next. We denote by N_t the number of individuals in the population at time t. If a fraction f of these are female and if each female produces on average b offspring which survive to be the adults of the next generation, then

$$N_t = fbN_{t-\tau}, \tag{2.2.1}$$

where τ is the time between generations. In the language of equation (2.1.1)

$$B = \frac{fb}{\tau}N_{t-\tau}, \qquad D = \frac{1}{\tau}N_{t-\tau}, \qquad I = E = 0. \tag{2.2.2}$$

If f and b are constant, equation (2.2.1) represents a population which grows or declines without limit (depending on whether $fb > 1$ or $fb < 1$). However, as we saw in the previous chapter many populations appear to show density-dependent regulation, in which case we should expect b to depend on $N_{t-\tau}$. Furthermore, there is no reason why some adults should not survive from one generation to the next and it is likely that the number of survivors would also depend on $N_{t-\tau}$. It is thus clear that equation (2.2.1) is merely a representative of a large class of equations, known as *difference equations*, with the general form

$$\Delta N \equiv N_t - N_{t-\tau} = \{B(N_{t-\tau}) - D(N_{t-\tau})\}\tau \tag{2.2.3}$$

where B and D are arbitrary functions of $N_{t-\tau}$. Even equation (2.2.3) is not in the most general biologically relevant form since with some species (e.g. small invertebrates) a few individuals may remain in the resting state (diapause) between generations for a time considerably longer than τ and thus 'skip' a generation. B and D then depend on both $N_{t-\tau}$ and $N_{t-2\tau}$.

Although difference equations are extensively used to model both plant and animal populations their use is only strictly justified where it is possible to identify clearly marked, discrete, non-overlapping generations. Where the generations overlap it is more plausible to approximate the fundamental equation (2.1.1) by a *differential equation* obtained by assuming that we may consistently let ΔN and Δt become very small, and hence regard N_t as a continuous function of time $N(t)$. We then write

$$\frac{dN}{dt} = B(N) - D(N). \tag{2.2.4}$$

Both equations (2.2.3) and (2.2.4) are extreme idealizations and we cannot expect to model many real populations in such simple terms. For example, if there is a gestation period between conception and birth, density-dependent factors can only influence the birth rate after a time delay. Instead of the differential equation (2.2.4) we then obtain a *differential-delay* equation; techniques for analysing such equations will be introduced in Section 2.7. Another complication is that we can only expect birth and death rates to be functions of total population if the *age-structure* of the population remains constant. We investigate the effects of age-structure in Chapter 3.

2.3 SCALING AND DIMENSIONAL ANALYSIS

Any quantity which appears in a population equation will normally have units which are products or ratios of the fundamental quantities time, distance, and population of a particular species. Occasionally (e.g. in Chapter 9) we shall use other fundamental quantities such as energy or quantity of a particular element. The fundamental quantities from which others are derived are frequently given the name *dimensions*. A pure number or a ratio of quantities with the same dimensions is described as *dimensionless* or *normalized*.

Any equation representing a real biological system should be valid irrespective of the units in which we measure the quantities involved in the system. This will only be the case if both sides of the equation have the same dimensions and if, on either side of the equation, quantities to be added or subtracted have the same dimensions. Perhaps surprisingly this somewhat philosophical observation is of considerable practical importance.

First, there is the obvious, but still very useful, point that regular checking of dimensions in the course of a long calculation provides a rapid check on algebraic accuracy. While a dimensionally correct equation need not be correct, *a dimensionally incorrect equation is invariably nonsense*! Slightly more subtle and just as useful is the fact that an equation involving m different quantities can normally be reduced to an equation involving a small number of dimensionless quantities. In physical systems where normally only four dimensions (mass, length, time and electric current) are involved, it is possible to state precisely how much simplification can be achieved in any particular case, the result (known as Buckingham's theorem) being of particular use in engineering applications involving scale models. We have no such precise guideline in population modelling but as a general rule, in models which do not involve demographic stochasticity, the final equation will involve $m - k$ dimensionless quantities where k is the number of independent dimensions involved in the original model. For example the logistic equation

$$\frac{dN}{dt} = rN\left(1 - \frac{N}{K}\right) \tag{2.3.1}$$

relates *four* quantities—the population N, the carrying capacity K which has the dimensions of population, time t, and the intrinsic growth rate r which has the dimensions of $(\text{time})^{-1}$. There are thus two independent dimensions—population and time—and we should be able to convert equation (2.3.1) into an equation involving *two* dimensionless quantities (four minus two). One possible choice of dimensionless variables is

$$N' \equiv N/K, \qquad t' \equiv rt, \qquad (2.3.2)$$

in terms of which equation (2.3.1) becomes

$$\frac{\mathrm{d}N'}{\mathrm{d}t'} = N'(1 - N'), \qquad (2.3.3)$$

an equation relating the two dimensionless quantities N' and t'.

The mathematical simplification achieved by using dimensionless variables frequently leads to some biological insight even without solving the equations. This is because dimensional analysis can reveal groups of parameters which can be thought of as 'controlling' the behaviour of the system. Thus if the logistic equation were a reasonable description of the population dynamics of some species, knowledge of its population would convey very little information while knowledge of the ratio N/K would be very useful.

The reduction of equations to a dimensionless form is also of particular value when it is intended to solve them on the computer. Not only can much computer time be saved by reducing the number of variables under investigation, but in addition the accuracy of the computations may be improved. This is because computers only perform arithmetic operations to a certain finite accuracy and significant difficulties can arise if working with quantities differing by many orders of magnitude. The point is particularly important if using a program from a computer library in which case one is often ignorant of the precise order in which operations are being performed. There is no foolproof method of avoiding this type of numerical problem but scaling the equations to a dimensionless form in which all the variables have values (say) between 0.001 and 1000 (thus spanning not more than six orders of magnitude) is a very worthwhile precaution. If numerical difficulties are still found it is either because an inappropriate technique is being used to solve the equations or because of a peculiarity of the equations themselves (e.g. a large amplitude limit cycle) which may well be of biological significance.

2.4 DETERMINISTIC STEADY STATES, STABILITY AND DECAY OF FLUCTUATIONS

The first stage in the analysis of any population model is to ask whether there is any particular size at which the population will stabilize. In formal mathematical terms we wish to know if our model possesses any stable steady states. It is normal to answer this question in two parts. We first remark that the size of a population will only remain constant over time if, at all times, the birth and death rates (B and D) in the fundamental equation are exactly equal. Thus a model in which B and D are functions only of $N(t)$ exhibits a deterministic steady state if there is some value of N for which

$$B(N) = D(N) \qquad (2.4.1)$$

at all times.

The steady state is deterministically stable if after experiencing a perturbation the population ultimately returns to its steady state value. For a population obeying a differential equation which has only one deterministic steady state (say N^*) it is intuitively clear that this will happen if

$$B(N) > D(N) \quad \text{whenever} \quad N < N^*, \qquad (2.4.2a)$$

$$B(N) < D(N) \quad \text{whenever} \quad N > N^*. \qquad (2.4.2b)$$

Conversely the steady state is unstable if these inequalities are reversed. Examples of birth and death functions leading to stable and unstable stationary states are illustrated in Fig. 2.1 from which we can see that for stability it is necessary that at the steady state the gradient of the graph of D against N is greater than that of B against N, i.e.

$$\left[\frac{dB}{dN} - \frac{dD}{dN}\right] < 0 \quad \text{when} \quad N = N^*. \qquad (2.4.3)$$

We can derive this result more formally by a procedure known as *neighbourhood stability analysis* in which we assume that the population is displaced slightly from its steady state value and follow its subsequent behaviour. If we define

$$n \equiv N - N^*, \qquad (2.4.4)$$

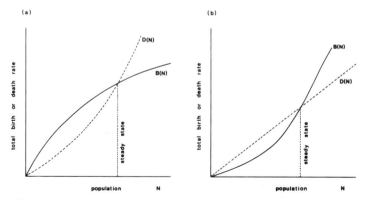

Fig. 2.1. Examples of forms for the total birth and death rate functions $B(N)$ and $D(N)$ which result in, (a) stable, and (b) unstable, steady states for a single species population obeying a differential equation.

24

then on expanding about the steady state we obtain

$$B(N) = B(N^*) + n\left(\frac{dB}{dN}\right)_{N=N^*} + 0(n^2), \qquad (2.4.5)$$

and

$$D(N) = D(N^*) + n\left(\frac{dD}{dN}\right)_{N=N^*} + 0(n^2), \qquad (2.4.6)$$

where we have used the notation $0(n^2)$ to denote all terms of order n^2 or higher. Substitution from these equations into the original differential equation (2.2.4) yields

$$\frac{dn}{dt} = \{B(N^*) - D(N^*)\} + n\left(\frac{dB}{dN} - \frac{dD}{dN}\right)_{N=N^*} + 0(n^2). \qquad (2.4.7)$$

However, at the steady state birth and death rates are equal, and near the steady state terms of order n^2 should be negligible compared with terms of order n. Hence, after a small perturbation the population fluctuation should to a good approximation follow the linear differential equation

$$\frac{dn}{dt} = \lambda n, \qquad (2.4.8)$$

with

$$\lambda = \left[\frac{dB}{dN} - \frac{dD}{dN}\right]_{N=N^*}. \qquad (2.4.9)$$

If the perturbation at time $t = 0$ is n_0 then the solution of equation (2.4.8) is

$$n = n_0 e^{\lambda t}, \qquad (2.4.10)$$

which shows that fluctuations decay exponentially provided $\lambda < 0$, in agreement with the condition (2.4.3).

For a population obeying a difference equation, the stability analysis is a little more complicated. Obviously for stability it is again necessary that deaths should exceed births whenever the population is greater than its steady-state value (and vice versa if it is lower than the steady-state level). Even when this condition is satisfied, however, because of the finite time interval that elapses between generations it is possible for a population to *overcompensate* for fluctuations to such an extent that it oscillates away from its steady state. To see this we perform a neighbourhood stability analysis, exactly analogous to that just given for differential equations, but starting with the difference equation (2.2.3). The analogue of equation (2.4.8) is now the linear difference equation

$$n_t = (1 + \lambda\tau)n_{t-\tau}, \qquad (2.4.11)$$

where λ is still defined by equation (2.4.9). Clearly the population fluctuations decrease in magnitude only if $|1 + \lambda\tau| < 1$, and hence for stability we require

$$-2 < \lambda\tau < 0. \tag{2.4.12}$$

Two distinct situations are contained within the range of values of $\lambda\tau$ in this inequality. If $-1 < \lambda\tau < 0$, then from equation (2.4.11) we see that n_t and $n_{t-\tau}$ have the same sign. The return towards the steady state is then non-oscillatory and we say that the population is *overdamped*. On the other hand, if $-2 < \lambda\tau < -1$ then n_t and $n_{t-\tau}$ have opposite signs, the return to the steady state involves damped oscillations, and we say the population is *underdamped*.

Strictly speaking, our locally-linear analysis is only valid for infinitesimally small displacements from the steady state, so our next step is to investigate its usefulness in situations where the population fluctuations are not small. Obviously this is not an aspect that can be approached in general terms since the robustness of the linear approximation depends on the magnitude of the non-linear terms which are neglected, and this of course will vary from model to model. Consequently we must consider examples, and we start with the best known, and one of the simplest models of a single species with density-dependent population regulation—the logistic model. In differential equation form this is

$$\frac{dN}{dt} = rN(1 - N/K), \tag{2.4.13}$$

where r is the intrinsic growth rate of the species and K is the carrying capacity of the environment for this particular species. Where the generations are discrete the model is written in difference equation form as

$$N_t - N_{t-\tau} = r\tau N_{t-\tau}(1 - N_{t-\tau}/K). \tag{2.4.14}$$

Thus, in the notation of the previous analysis,

$$B(N) - D(N) = rN(1 - N/K), \tag{2.4.15}$$

and it is straightforward to calculate from (2.4.13) and (2.4.9) that

$$N^* = K, \qquad \lambda \equiv \left[\frac{dB}{dN} - \frac{dD}{dN}\right]_{N=N^*} = -r. \tag{2.4.16}$$

Linear analysis thus predicts that the steady state of the differential equation model is stable as long as $r > 0$. Now the differential equation (2.4.13) can actually be solved exactly without making any linear approximation. If N_0 is the population at time $t = 0$ then the exact solution is

$$N(t) = \frac{K}{1 + [(K - N_0)/N_0]e^{-rt}}, \tag{2.4.17}$$

from which it is clear that, irrespective of the magnitude of the initial perturbation, N ultimately approaches the steady state (K) provided that $r > 0$. As

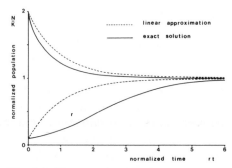

Fig. 2.2. Exact and approximate solutions
to the logistic differential equation for two
different initial conditions N_0/K = 2.0 and
N_0/K = 0.1.

Fig. 2.2 shows, the precise details of the return to the steady state are influenced by the non-linearities, but the qualitative result that there is stability whenever $r > 0$ turns out to be generally true.

A similar situation prevails with the difference equation (2.4.14) where the linear analysis predicts stability if $0 < r\tau < 2$. Exact solutions here (see Fig. 2.3) show that for biologically acceptable initial conditions the return to the steady state is ultimately non-oscillatory if $0 < r\tau < 1$ and involves damped oscillations if $1 < r\tau < 2$. However, the divergent oscillations predicted by the linear analysis for $r\tau > 2$ obviously cannot persist indefinitely. Examples of what actually happens are given in Fig. 2.4. Again the qualitative prediction that the steady state is unstable turns out to be sound but the details of the dynamical behaviour are complex. We shall return to this situation in Section 2.8.

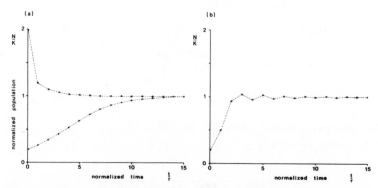

Fig. 2.3. Exact solutions of the difference equation $N_t = N_{t-\tau} + r\tau N_{t-\tau}$
$(1 - N_{t-\tau}/K)$ with parameters chosen to give a stable steady state. (a)
$r\tau$ = 0.4, overdamped return, two initial conditions. (b) $r\tau$ = 1.8,
underdamped return, one initial condition.

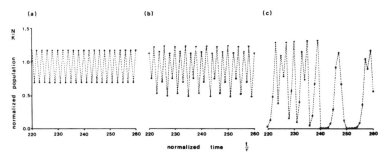

Fig. 2.4. Oscillatory solutions of the difference equation
$N_t = N_{t-\tau} + r\tau N_{t-\tau}(1 - N_{t-\tau}/K)$. (a) $r\tau = 2.3$, two-point limit cycle. (b)
$r\tau = 2.55$, eight-point limit cycle. (c) $r\tau = 3.0$, 'chaos'.

Analogous investigations can be performed with other models (the reader
might attempt Problem 3) and lead to the general conclusion that provided
the population equations have only one steady-state solution, then the
stability of this steady state will be adequately determined by a
neighbourhood stability analysis.

2.5   SYSTEMS 'DRIVEN' BY FLUCTUATING PARAMETERS

A. General principles

So far we have assumed that birth and death rates are constant functions of
the population N. Obviously this is an extreme idealization even of laboratory
conditions, while in the real world outside laboratories birth and death rates
clearly depend on parameters such as temperature and humidity which vary
with time. For simplicity we first consider the effects of a single time-
dependent parameter $\phi(t)$, and to emphasize the dependence of B and D on
$\phi(t)$, we write the basic differential equation (2.2.4) in the form

$$\frac{dN}{dt} = B(N, \phi(t)) - D(N, \phi(t)), \qquad (2.5.1)$$

We now suppose that the average value of ϕ over a long time interval is ϕ^*. If
ϕ were to remain constant with a value ϕ^*, then the equation (2.5.1) would be
of the type analysed in the previous section and we shall assume that it would
have a deterministic steady state N^*. Provided this steady state is stable, small
fluctuations in ϕ about the value ϕ^* will cause small population fluctuations
about the value N^*. If

$$n(t) = N(t) - N^*, \qquad f(t) = \phi(t) - \phi^*, \qquad (2.5.2)$$

then to first order in n and f

$$\frac{dn}{dt} = \lambda n + \alpha f(t), \qquad (2.5.3)$$

where, as in the previous section

$$\lambda = \left[\frac{\partial B}{\partial N} - \frac{\partial D}{\partial N} \right]_{\substack{N=N^* \\ \phi=\phi^*}}, \tag{2.5.4}$$

while

$$\alpha = \left[\frac{\partial B}{\partial \phi} - \frac{\partial D}{\partial \phi} \right]_{\substack{N=N^* \\ \phi=\phi^*}}. \tag{2.5.5}$$

The properties of the linear differential equation (2.5.3) are well known. It can be shown formally that the general solution is of the form

$$n(t) = \text{'complementary function'} + \text{'particular integral'}, \tag{2.5.6}$$

where (i) *the complementary function* is the solution of the equation obtained by setting $f(t) = 0$ in equation (2.5.3). This of course is just equation (2.4.8), the equation which defines the *transient* dynamics of the population.

(ii) *the particular integral* is defined as any solution of the differential equation which is independent of the initial conditions. Provided the steady state is stable, this solution represents the *persistent* behaviour of the system which is determined by $f(t)$ but is independent of any initial perturbation.

Thus biologically, the solution of the equation is of the form

$$n(t) = \text{transient solution} + \text{persistent solution.} \tag{2.5.7}$$

We can similarly analyse the effect of variations in some environmental parameter on populations described by a difference equation. This analysis is seldom used in practice since difference equations are such crude approximations to reality that detailed investigations of temporal variations in their parameters is seldom meaningful. In particular, where the equation refers to a population with one generation per year the parameters in the model already reflect all environmental variations with a period of 1 year or less, while with an equation modelling a population with several generations per year great care must be taken before introducing time-dependent parameters as the generations themselves are certainly not separated by constant time intervals.

Nevertheless suppose we have a model of the form

$$N_t - N_{t-\tau} = \tau \{ B(N_{t-\tau}, \phi_{t-\tau}) - D(N_{t-\tau}, \phi_{t-\tau}) \}. \tag{2.5.8}$$

Proceeding exactly as with the differential equation and considering small fluctuations about a hypothetical deterministic steady state we obtain in place of equation (2.5.3) the linear difference equation,

$$n_t = (1 + \lambda\tau)n_{t-\tau} + \alpha f_{t-\tau}. \tag{2.5.9}$$

The general solution of a linear difference equation of this type is again the sum of a transient and a persistent solution.

Frequently more than one environmental quantity will be varying with time, but fortunately the extension of our analysis to the general case of many fluctuating parameters is completely straightforward. Mathematicians use the notation $\{\phi_i; i = 1, 2, \ldots m\}$ to represent the *set* or collection of quantities ϕ_1, $\phi_2, \phi_3, \ldots \phi_m$, and after m has once been defined in a given model this can be abbreviated to $\{\phi_i\}$. Thus to make explicit in our basic differential equation the dependence of B and D on m parameters which themselves are functions of time we write

$$\frac{dN}{dt} = B(N, \{\phi_i(t)\}) - D(N, \{\phi_i(t)\}). \qquad (2.5.10)$$

Equation (2.5.1) is obviously a special case of this equation corresponding to $m = 1$. Provided *all* the fluctuations are small enough for the present linear analysis to be valid, the linearized differential equation (2.5.3) generalizes to

$$\frac{dn}{dt} = \lambda n + \sum_{i=1}^{m} \alpha_i f_i(t) \qquad (2.5.11)$$

where

$$\alpha_i = \left[\frac{\partial B}{\partial \phi_i} - \frac{\partial D}{\partial \phi_i} \right]_{\substack{N=N^* \\ \{\phi_i\}=\{\phi_i^*\}}}, \qquad (2.5.12)$$

$$f_i(t) = \phi_i(t) - \phi_i^*, \qquad (2.5.13)$$

and ϕ^* is the average value of ϕ_i over a long time interval. It can be shown that the persistent solution of (2.5.11) is simply the sum of the solutions which would be obtained if each $f_i(t)$ were present on its own. We may therefore consider each fluctuating parameter $\phi_i(t)$ to be 'causing' fluctuations in N, the total fluctuation in N at any instant being the sum of the contributions from each parameter. A similar result holds for linear difference equations.

B. An illustrative example

In Section 2.6 we shall consider general mathematical techniques for analysing linear differential and difference equations. Meanwhile we consider an example which illustrates the theory developed so far and which permits us to introduce several concepts which we shall require later. Suppose a population obeys the logistic differential equation (2.4.13) but that the carrying capacity (K) varies periodically with time because of either diurnal or annual influences. If T is the period of the oscillations in carrying capacity then the *frequency f* of the oscillations is defined to be $1/T$, and the *angular frequency* ω is defined by

$$\omega = 2\pi f = 2\pi/T. \qquad (2.5.14)$$

The units of ω are radians per unit time, an angle of one radian being equal to $180/\pi = 57.3$ degrees. The simplest possible example of a carrying capacity oscillating with angular frequency ω is obtained by assuming

$$K(t) = K_0(1 + b \cos \omega t), \qquad (2.5.15)$$

so that

$$\frac{dN}{dt} = rN\left[1 - \frac{N}{K_0(1 + b \cos \omega t)}\right]. \qquad (2.5.16)$$

This equation can be scaled assuming $N' = N/K_0$ and $t' = rt$, the result being

$$\frac{dN'}{dt'} = N'\left[1 - \frac{N'}{(1 + b \cos \omega't')}\right], \qquad (2.5.17)$$

where

$$\omega' = \omega/r. \qquad (2.5.18)$$

From equation (2.5.15) the average value of K over a long time interval is seen to be K_0 and hence the corresponding steady state value of N' is one. From equations (2.5.4) and (2.5.5) reinterpreted for the scaled equation (2.5.17),

$$\lambda = -1, \qquad \alpha = 1, \qquad f(t') = b \cos \omega't'. \qquad (2.5.19)$$

Hence if

$$n' = N' - 1, \qquad (2.5.20)$$

then

$$\frac{dn'}{dt'} = -n' + b \cos \omega't', \qquad (2.5.21)$$

provided $b \ll 1$, i.e. provided the fluctuations in K are small relative to K_0.

We have already seen that the complementary function must simply be proportional to $e^{-t'}$, with a constant of proportionality determined by the initial conditions. Although for simplicity we shall continue to denote this constant by n_0 it is important to note that it no longer simply represents the perturbation at $t' = 0$. To obtain the particular integral we adopt the well-tried procedure of making an intelligent guess at its form and substituting in the original equation to see if it fits. This is quite legitimate since the general theory guarantees that the sum of a particular integral and the complementary function is the most general solution of the differential equation—there are no restrictions on using devious or underhand methods to find the particular integral. Intuition suggests that if the carrying capacity varies sinusoidally, then so too will the population. However, the population oscillation will probably be out of phase with the 'driving' oscillations in K because of the time required for the population to respond to changes in its habitat. We thus assume a solution

$$n'(t') = p \cos(\omega't' - \varepsilon), \qquad (2.5.22)$$

where p and ε are unknown constants. Substituting in equation (2.5.21) we find after a few lines of very tedious algebra that

$$\cos \omega' t' \{\omega' p \sin \varepsilon + p \cos \varepsilon - b\} + \sin \omega' t' \{p \sin \varepsilon - \omega' p \cos \varepsilon\} = 0$$
(2.5.23)

However, if this equation is to be true *at all times* then the individual expressions in brackets multiplying $\cos \omega' t'$ and $\sin \omega' t'$ must themselves be zero and hence

$$\omega' p \sin \varepsilon + p \cos \varepsilon - b = 0,$$
(2.5.24)

and

$$\sin \varepsilon - \omega' \cos \varepsilon = 0.$$
(2.5.25)

From the second of these equations it is obvious that

$$\tan \varepsilon = \omega' = \omega/r,$$
(2.5.26)

and thus that

$$\sin \varepsilon = \frac{\omega'}{\sqrt{(1 + \omega'^2)}}, \qquad \cos \varepsilon = \frac{1}{\sqrt{(1 + \omega'^2)}}.$$
(2.5.27)

Substituting back in equation (2.5.24) and performing a little more algebra leads finally to

$$p = \frac{b}{\sqrt{(1 + \omega'^2)}} = \frac{rb}{\sqrt{(r^2 + \omega^2)}}.$$
(2.5.28)

We have thus obtained values of p and ε (equations (2.5.28) and (2.5.26)) which will make equation (2.5.22) a particular integral of the linearized equation. The complete solution of the linearized equation (2.5.21) must then be

$$n'(t') = n'_0 e^{-t'} + \frac{b}{\sqrt{(1 + \omega'^2)}} \cos(\omega' t' - \varepsilon)$$
(2.5.29)

with ε given by equation (2.5.26). That this solution is an acceptable approximation to the actual behaviour of the system described by equation (2.5.17) is illustrated in Fig. 2.5, which compares an exact numerical solution of this equation with the equivalent approximate solution calculated from equation (2.5.29) by recalling that $N' = 1 + n'$.

A number of general points can be drawn from an examination of our linear approximate solution (2.5.29), which illustrates the interconnection between deterministic stability and response to environmental fluctuations mentioned in Chapter 1:

(a) For times which are long compared to the 'natural' time scale of the system ($t' \gg 1, t \gg r^{-1}$) the 'transient term' $n'_0 e^{-t'}$ is very small. The population has thus effectively 'forgotten' its initial perturbation and the persistent behaviour is wholly described by the particular integral we derived above.

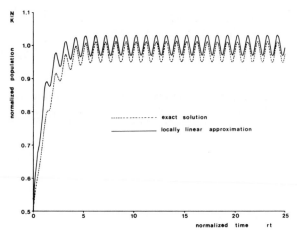

Fig. 2.5. Approximate and exact solutions for the logistic equation with a sinusoidally varying carrying capacity. $\omega' = 6.28$, $b = 0.2$.

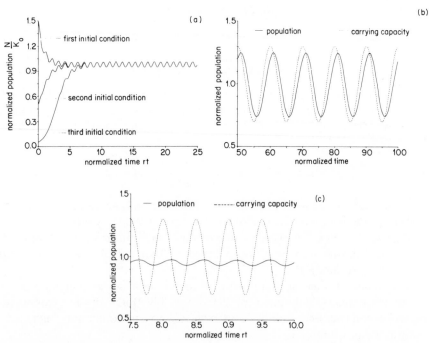

Fig. 2.6. General features of the response of a logistic population to a sinusoidally varying carrying capacity. (a) The system 'forgets' its initial condition. (b) The population size tracks slow variations in K. (c) Fast variations in carrying capacity ($\omega \gg r$) produce small population oscillations which lag the K variations by about $\frac{1}{4}$ cycle.

(b)   If the angular frequency of the oscillation is low compared to the inverse of the natural time scale ($\omega' \ll 1$, $\omega \ll r$) then the amplitude of the population oscillations, p, is almost equal to the amplitude of the carrying capacity variations, b, and the phase angle ε is very small. Thus the population 'tracks' oscillations in carrying capacity which have a period significantly greater than the characteristic response time of the system to a *single* perturbation (r^{-1}).

(c)   If the angular frequency is high ($\omega' \gg 1$, $\omega \gg r$) then the population cannot change fast enough to respond to the rapid changes in the environment and the population oscillations are much smaller than the carrying capacity variations ($p \ll b$) and lag behind them by about one quarter of a period ($\varepsilon \simeq \pi/2$).

That these effects, predicted by our approximate solution (2.5.29) do indeed occur in the system described by the logistic equation (2.5.17) is illustrated in Fig. 2.6.

The logistic example can also be used as a test of the robustness of the approximations made in the general analysis. As with the neighbourhood stability theory, it is clear that the analysis is strictly valid only for infinitesimally small fluctuations about the deterministic steady state. However, comparison of the results of the approximate analysis with exact results, obtained from numerical solution of equation (2.5.17) reveal that the approximate theory provides remarkably accurate estimates even of the amplitude of relatively large population oscillations. This is illustrated in Fig. 2.7.

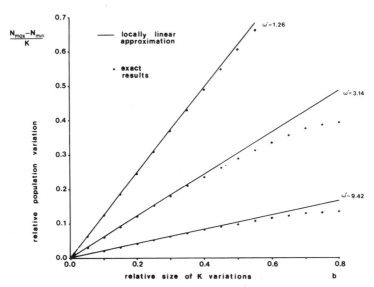

Fig. 2.7. Exact and approximate values of the variation induced in a logistic population by sinusoidal variations in carrying capacity.

2.6 MATHEMATICAL TECHNIQUES FOR ANALYSING DRIVEN SYSTEMS

A. Complex exponentials

In the course of calculations such as that set out in the previous section the analyst must dredge from his subconcious a number of exceedingly unmemorable trigonometrical identities. However, the same results can be obtained with noticeably less labour by the expedient of representing trigonometrical quantities by complex exponentials. We illustrate this by repeating the analysis of Section 2.5 in complex notation.

It is a standard result in the theory of complex numbers that if

$$i = \sqrt{-1}, \tag{2.6.1}$$

then for any angle θ

$$e^{i\theta} = \cos \theta + i \sin \theta \tag{2.6.2}$$

which in turn implies

$$\cos \theta = \tfrac{1}{2}[e^{i\theta} + e^{-i\theta}] . \tag{2.6.3}$$

The sinusoidal variation in carrying (equation (2.5.15)) which is the basis of the analysis of Section 2.5 can thus equally well be presented by

$$K(t) = K_0\left[1 + \frac{b}{2} \{e^{i\omega t} + e^{-i\omega t}\}\right], \tag{2.6.4}$$

in which case the locally linear approximation (equation (2.5.21)) to the scaled dynamic equation is replaced by

$$\frac{dn'}{dt'} = -n' + \frac{b}{2}e^{i\omega't'} + \frac{b}{2}e^{-i\omega't'}. \tag{2.6.5}$$

Since the persisting part of the solution of this equation (the particular integral) must be a sinusoid at the same frequency as, but out of phase with, the driving fluctuations it must be of the general form

$$n'(t') = pe^{i\omega't'} + qe^{-i\omega't'}, \tag{2.6.6}$$

where p and q are, in general, complex numbers. Substitution of this into the linearized dynamic equation (2.6.5) yields

$$\left(i\omega'p + p - \frac{b}{2}\right)e^{i\omega't'} = \left(i\omega'q - q + \frac{b}{2}\right)e^{-i\omega't'}. \tag{2.6.7}$$

Since equation (2.6.7) must be true at all times, which can only be so if both the terms in brackets are zero, this tells us at once that

$$p = \frac{b}{2(1 + i\omega')}, \qquad q = \frac{b}{2(1 - i\omega')}, \tag{2.6.8}$$

and hence by analogy with equation (2.5.29), that the general solution of equation (2.6.5) is

$$n'(t') = n'_0 e^{-t'} + \frac{b e^{i\omega' t'}}{2(1 + i\omega')} + \frac{b e^{-i\omega' t'}}{2(1 - i\omega')} . \qquad (2.6.9)$$

That this solution, the persisting part of which we obtain in only three lines of algebra, is indeed identical to equation (2.5.29) can easily be demonstrated by first substituting from equation (2.6.2) to yield

$$n'(t') = n'_0 e^{-t'} + \frac{b}{1 + \omega'^2} \cos \omega' t' + \frac{b\omega}{1 + \omega'^2} \sin \omega' t' \qquad (2.6.10)$$

and then using standard trigonometrical identities to show that this is equivalent to

$$n'(t') = n'_0 e^{-t'} + \frac{b}{\sqrt{(1 + \omega'^2)}} \cos(\omega' t' - \varepsilon) \qquad (2.6.11)$$

where ε is obtained from equation (2.5.26).

B. The transfer function

In Section 2.6A we considered a logistic population perturbed by a single sinusoidal variation in carrying capacity. We now analyse a somewhat more general version of the same problem in which the carrying-capacity variation can be represented as a sum of sinusoidal components at a variety of different frequencies, so that

$$K(t) = K_0 \left[1 + \sum_{j=1}^{M} b_j e^{i\omega_j t} \right], \qquad (2.6.12)$$

and hence the locally linear approximation to the scaled dynamic equation is

$$\frac{dn'}{dt'} = -n' + \sum_{j=1}^{M} b_j e^{i\omega_j' t'} \qquad (2.6.13)$$

Equation (2.6.13) can be solved by exactly the same technique we used in Section 2.6A. We recognize immediately that the complementary function (transient) must be $n_0 e^{-t'}$, where as before n'_0 is determined from the initial conditions, and we seek the persisting part of the solution (particular integral) by substitution of an appropriate trial solution. The obvious form of trial solution in this case is

$$n'(t') = \sum_{j=1}^{M} p_j e^{i\omega_j' t'}, \qquad (2.6.14)$$

and on substituting this back into equation (2.6.13) we find

$$\sum_{j=1}^{M} (i\omega_j' p_j + p_j - b_j) e^{i\omega_j' t'} = 0. \qquad (2.6.15)$$

Our trial function is a good solution of equation (2.6.13) if and only if equation (2.6.15) is true at all times, a condition which can only be fulfilled if all the p's have the same functional dependence on ω', namely

$$p_j = \frac{b_j}{1 + i\omega'_j}. \tag{2.6.16}$$

We emphasize the functional similarity between the members of the set of p_js by writing the general solution of equation (2.6.13) as

$$n'(t') = n'_0 e^{-t'} + \sum_{j=1}^{M} T(\omega'_j) b_j e^{i\omega'_j t'} \tag{2.6.17}$$

where

$$T(\omega'_j) \equiv \frac{1}{1 + i\omega'_j} \tag{2.6.18}$$

is called the *transfer function* of the system.

We observe from equation (2.6.17) that in this locally linear approximation the persisting behaviour is described by a *linear* combination of components at the frequencies present in the driving fluctuation. The reader may verify that the response *cannot* contain frequencies not present in the driving fluctuations by repeating our analysis using a trial solution which contains such additional components. It is an obvious corollary of this observation that we can obtain a locally linear estimate of the persisting response of the system to a complex input by considering its response to each individual component and then simply adding up the answers. This provides a very straightforward route to the treatment of complicated driving functions, since the response to sinusoidal components at differing frequencies is systematically related by the transfer function $T(\omega')$ which can be evaluated with minimal labour by simply considering the response to a single perturbation $e^{i\omega t}$.

Thus in the example of Section 2.6A we would evaluate $T(\omega')$ by starting from

$$\frac{dn'}{dt'} = -n' + b e^{i\omega' t'}, \tag{2.6.19}$$

substituting a trial solution

$$n' = p e^{i\omega' t'}, \tag{2.6.20}$$

and hence concluding that the system transfer function is

$$T(\omega') \equiv p/b = \frac{1}{1 + i\omega'}. \tag{2.6.21}$$

Examination of equation (2.6.5) then reveals a two-component driving function with angular frequencies ω', and $-\omega'$ enabling us to conclude immediately that

$$n'(t') = n'_0 e^{-t'} + T(\omega') \frac{b}{2} e^{i\omega' t'} + T(-\omega') \frac{b}{2} e^{-i\omega' t'} \tag{2.6.22}$$

so that, from equation (2.6.21)

$$n'(t') = n'_0 e^{-t'} + \frac{b}{2(1 + i\omega')} e^{i\omega't'} + \frac{b}{2(1 - i\omega')} e^{-i\omega't'}. \quad (2.6.23)$$

Although it is always possible to use the transfer function in this way to construct the explicit solution of a locally linear approximate dynamic equation, this is often not the most effective route to real insight. When one requires qualitative information about the general behaviour of a system it is often preferable to obtain it from a direct examination of the form of the transfer function, an undertaking which necessitates a very clear understanding of its meaning. It follows from our earlier discussion that the value of the transfer function (which is of course complex) at angular frequency ω entirely characterizes the relationship between the persisting component of the population (output) fluctuations at angular frequency ω and the component of the driving (input) fluctuations at the same frequency. The nature of this relationship is clarified if we write the component of the driving fluctuations at angular frequency ω as $Re\{Ae^{i\omega t}\} = A \cos \omega t$ and the appropriate component of the population fluctuations as $Re\{Be^{i(\omega t + \varepsilon)}\} = B \cos (\omega t + \varepsilon)$. We now see from equation (2.6.21) that

$$\frac{B}{A} = |T(\omega)| = [(Re\{T(\omega)\})^2 + (Im\{T(\omega)\})^2]^{1/2} \quad (2.6.24)$$

and

$$\varepsilon = \arg(T(\omega)) = \tan^{-1}\left[\frac{Im\{T(\omega)\}}{Re\{T(\omega)\}}\right] \quad (2.6.25)$$

where the notation $Re\{\ \}$ and $Im\{\ \}$ stands for 'real part of' and 'imaginary part of' respectively. Thus we conclude that the value of the transfer function at any frequency is a complex number whose modulus gives the ratio of the amplitudes of and whose argument gives the phase angle between, the components of populations and driving fluctuations at that frequency.

C. Fourier transforms

The reader must by now feel that we have devoted quite sufficient time to the analysis of purely sinusoidal disturbances, whose occurrence in nature is undoubtedly very infrequent, and we therefore turn finally to the question of disturbances of arbitrary shape. All our previous efforts are, however, by no means in vain, because the technique of *Fourier analysis* allows us to represent any function of time as a superposition of sinusoidal components. Thus in the linear approximation, where superposition of responses is also valid, an understanding of sinusoidal disturbances leads naturally to an understanding of more complex disturbances.

The analysis of the previous section is thus much more general than it might seem at first sight. It can be shown that any periodic disturbance with repeat period $T_0 = 2\pi/\omega_0$ can be written

$$x(t) = \sum_{q=-\infty}^{\infty} b_q e^{iq\omega_0 t}, \qquad \text{integer } q \qquad (2.6.26)$$

so that we have in effect already analysed the case of an arbitrary shaped (i.e. non-sinusoidal) periodic disturbance.

It thus remains only to extend our analysis to disturbances which are not constrained to any kind of periodicity. This we do by making use of the *Fourier transform*. We show in Appendix F that any function of time $x(t)$, which is known over the time interval $-T/2 \leqslant t \leqslant T/2$, can be rewritten

$$x(t) = \frac{1}{2\pi} \int_{-\infty}^{\infty} \tilde{x}(\omega) e^{i\omega t} \, d\omega, \qquad (2.6.27)$$

where $\tilde{x}(\omega)$, which is known as the Fourier transform of $x(t)$, is defined as

$$\tilde{x}(\omega) = \int_{-T/2}^{T/2} x(t) e^{-i\omega t} \, dt. \qquad (2.6.28)$$

The analogy between equations (2.6.27) and (2.6.26) is very clear, and it is therefore easy to see that in the case of an arbitrary disturbance $x(t)$, the 'amplitude of the component at angular frequency ω' is $(1/2\pi)\,\tilde{x}(\omega)d\omega$. Armed with this insight we return for the last time to our familiar logistic example and consider the case where

$$K(t) = K_0(1 + f(t)), \qquad (2.6.29)$$

$f(t)$ being an arbitrary function of time. The locally linear, approximate, scaled, dynamic equation is now

$$\frac{dn'}{dt'} = -n' + f'(t'), \qquad (2.6.30)$$

which we shall analyse by resolving $n'(t)$ and $f'(t')$ ($\equiv f(t'/r)$) into their respective components. We define $\tilde{f}'(\omega')$ as the Fourier Transform of $f'(t')$ and $\tilde{n}'(\omega')$ as the Fourier Transform of the *persisting* part of $n'(t')$, so that

$$f'(t') = \frac{1}{2\pi} \int_{-\infty}^{\infty} \tilde{f}'(\omega') e^{i\omega' t'} \, d\omega', \qquad (2.6.31)$$

and

$$n'(t') = n'_0 e^{-t'} + \frac{1}{2\pi} \int_{-\infty}^{\infty} \tilde{n}'(\omega') e^{i\omega' t'} \, d\omega'. \qquad (2.6.32)$$

However, we already know that in the linear approximation the persisting response of our system to each individual component of the driving fluctuations is given by the transfer function $T(\omega')$, which we originally defined (equation (2.6.21)) as the ratio of the complex amplitudes of the components of $n'(t')$ and $f'(t')$ at an angular frequency ω'. It thus seems natural to extend this definition of $T(\omega')$ to cover arbitrary rather than simply periodic forcing functions, and write $T(\omega')$ as the ratio of the *transforms* of $n'(t')$ and $f'(t')$

$$T(\omega') = \frac{\tilde{n}'(\omega')}{\tilde{f}'(\omega')}, \tag{2.6.33}$$

so that

$$n'(t') = n_0' e^{-t'} + \frac{1}{2\pi} \int_{-\infty}^{\infty} T(\omega') \tilde{f}'(\omega') e^{+i\omega't'} \, d\omega'. \tag{2.6.34}$$

It now remains to show formally that our redefined transfer function is precisely the same function we calculated so easily at the end of the last section. This we can do with the aid of a general property of the Fourier transform which we prove formally in Appendix F: namely that if $x(t)$ and $y(t)$ are two functions of time known at all times (i.e. $T = \infty$) and related by

$$y(t) = \frac{dx(t)}{dt}, \tag{2.6.35}$$

then their transforms are related by

$$\tilde{y}(\omega) = i\omega \tilde{x}(\omega). \tag{2.6.36}$$

If we Fourier transform both sides of equation (2.6.30) making use of this property, we find that the transform of the persisting part of $n'(t')$ (i.e. that part which remains significant as $T \to \infty$) is related to the transform of f' by

$$i\omega \tilde{n}'(\omega') = -\tilde{n}'(\omega') + \tilde{f}'(\omega'), \tag{2.6.37}$$

so that, referring back to our original calculation of $T(\omega')$, equation (2.6.18), we find

$$\frac{\tilde{n}'(\omega')}{\tilde{f}'(\omega')} = \frac{1}{1 + i\omega'} = T(\omega'). \tag{2.6.38}$$

Finally we note that although in this treatment of the use of Fourier transforms we have concentrated on calculating the persisting part of $n'(t')$, it is possible by the judicious use of δ-functions (see Appendix D) to use the same techniques to also obtain the transient solution. In our view, however, this introduces more mathematical complexity than is warranted by the possible gains and so we shall not proceed further along these lines.

2.7 DELAYED REGULATION

We mentioned in Section (2.2) that density-dependent factors may influence birth and death rates after a time delay. We now discuss three types of models which incorporate time delays, with the twin aims of presenting the mathematical procedures for handling delays, and obtaining some intuition concerning their effects.

We start in Section A by examining models incorporating delayed regulation of the *per capita* vital rates. With the exception of a few microbiological systems (e.g. the algae of Chapter 9), where such an assumption is defensible if not particularly plausible, there are few situations where this type of model can be convincingly justified; indeed many models of this type violate the fundamental principle that all population models should be based on plausible functional forms for the vital rates. However, the analysis of this case is particularly simple, the results are readily interpreted intuitively, and moreover much of the insight thus gained carries over to the general case (analysed fully in Section B) where there is delayed regulation of the population birth or death rates. In Section C the theory is generalized to cover models with 'distributed' delays, i.e. models in which the vital rates are regulated by a weighted average of previous population values.

A. Delayed regulation of the per capita vital rates

We consider a model in which density-dependent regulation of the per capita vital rates operates after a discrete, constant delay T_D. The population then obeys a *delay-differential equation* of the form

$$\frac{1}{N}\frac{dN}{dt} = g(N_D) \tag{2.7.1}$$

where $N_D(t) \equiv N(t - T_D)$. We assume that there is a single steady-state population size N^*, and we linearize equation (2.7.1) about this steady state. The resulting linear equation for n, the displacement of the population from its steady-state value is

$$\frac{dn}{dt} = -bn_D, \tag{2.7.2}$$

where

$$b \equiv -N^*\left(\frac{dg}{dN_D}\right)_{N_D=N^*}. \tag{2.7.3}$$

To investigate stability and the conditions for overdamping/underdamping we assume that equation (2.7.2) has a solution of the form

$$n(t) \propto e^{-\mu t}e^{i\omega t}. \tag{2.7.4}$$

There are in fact an infinite number of solutions of this form and as a result the analysis which follows is not mathematically rigorous. However, a rigorous analysis yields identical results to the present methods which are much easier to follow. Substituting the solution (2.7.4) back into (2.7.2) and equating real and imaginary parts yields two simultaneous equations for μ and ω:

$$\mu = be^{\mu T_D}\cos \omega T_D, \tag{2.7.5}$$

$$\omega = be^{\mu T_D}\sin \omega T_D. \tag{2.7.6}$$

The behaviour of the solutions of these equations for μ and ω is discussed in detail in the case study of Chapter 8 (Nicholson's blowflies) where we make use of the explicit results. For the present, however, it is sufficient to note that for the system to be *stable* and *overdamped*, there must be a (real) positive value of μ which satisfies equation (2.7.5) when $\omega = 0$, and it can be shown that this only happens if

$$0 \leqslant bT_D \leqslant e^{-1} = 0.368. \tag{2.7.7}$$

It can also be shown that the system is *stable* and *underdamped* if

$$e^{-1} < bT_D < \pi/2. \tag{2.7.8}$$

Hints on the derivation of these results are given in Problems 8 and 9.

When bT_D is slightly greater than $\pi/2$ the steady state is unstable, and after a perturbation, the population exhibits a series of divergent oscillations which if g is a decreasing function of N_D will normally lead to a limit cycle. The period (P) of the limit cycle is approximately that of the original divergent oscillations and can hence be estimated as

$$P \simeq 4T_D. \tag{2.7.9}$$

B. Delayed regulation of the population birth rate

By far the most plausible type of model incorporating time delays has a population birth rate which because of developmental delays depends on N_D and not on N. This assumption yields an equation of the form

$$\frac{dN}{dt} = B(N_D) - D(N), \tag{2.7.10}$$

which is obviously a special case of the more general equation

$$\frac{dN}{dt} = G(N, N_D), \tag{2.7.11}$$

where the population growth rate $G(= B - D)$ is an arbitrary function of N and N_D. Linearizing this equation about the steady state (N^*) leads to

$$\frac{dn}{dt} = -an - bn_D \tag{2.7.12}$$

where

$$a \equiv -\left(\frac{\partial G}{\partial N}\right)_{N=N_D=N^*}, \qquad b \equiv -\left(\frac{\partial G}{\partial N_D}\right)_{N=N_D=N^*}. \tag{2.7.13}$$

The stability and the conditions for overdamping/underdamping of equation (2.7.12) are analysed by the same method as in Section 2.7A and in place of

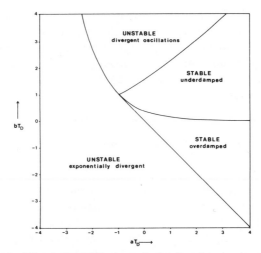

Fig. 2.8. Stability boundaries for the system
$$\dot{n} = - an - bn_D.$$

equations (2.7.5) and (2.7.6) we obtain the simultaneous equations

$$\mu = a + be^{\mu T_D} \cos \omega\, T_D, \qquad (2.7.14)$$

$$\omega = be^{\mu T_D} \sin \omega\, T_D. \qquad (2.7.15)$$

The nature of the solution(s) of these equations is determined by the values of the dimensionless quantities aT_D and bT_D and is illustrated in Fig. 2.8 for a range of values which includes all those likely to be of biological significance. Two main points emerge from the graph:

(a) If a and b are both positive, the time delay has a *destabilizing* effect. Increasing T_D (which corresponds to moving 'north-east' from the origin in a straight line) leads first to a regime of damped oscillations and possibly (depending on the ratio a/b) to a regime of instability and divergent oscillations. This is similar to the behaviour of the model analysed in Section 2.7A.

(b) If in the absence of a time delay the steady state would be unstable, (i.e. if $a + b < 0$) this situation is unchanged by the time delay. However, numerical calculations by Beddington, and May (1975) reveal that as T_D increases, the (negative) value of μ corresponding to the largest root of equations (2.7.14) and (2.7.15) increases in value, indicating that an increase in the delay slows down the divergence from the steady state. Thus in the vicinity of an unstable steady state, a delay may have a stabilizing effect.

C. Distributed delays

The previous two models involved the idealization of a fixed, discrete, time delay. In many situations we might expect birth rates to depend on a weighted average of previous populations which we write as

$$N_w(t) = \int_0^\infty w(u)N(t - u)du, \qquad (2.7.16)$$

where the weighting function $w(u)$ is assumed to be normalized, i.e.

$$\int_0^\infty w(u)du = 1. \qquad (2.7.17)$$

The models analysed in Sections 2.7A and 2.7B are special cases which arise if $w(u)$ has a (theoretically infinite) sharp spike at $u = T_D$. However, other forms of weighting function may arise in different applications—see Fig. 2.9.

If the population growth rate depends on N and N_w then the population will follow an equation of the form

$$\frac{dN}{dt} = G(N, N_w) \qquad (2.7.18)$$

and stability can be investigated in the standard manner. Linearizing about the steady state we obtain the equation

$$\frac{dn}{dt} = -an - bn_w \qquad (2.7.19)$$

with

$$a \equiv -\left(\frac{\partial G}{\partial N}\right)_{N=N_w=N^*}, \qquad b \equiv -\left(\frac{\partial G}{\partial N_w}\right)_{N=N_w=N^*}. \qquad (2.7.20)$$

As usual we assume a solution of the form

$$n(t) \propto e^{-\mu t}e^{i\omega t} \qquad (2.7.21)$$

and on substituting in equation (2.7.19) we obtain the simultaneous equations

$$\mu = a + b\int_0^\infty w(u)e^{\mu u} \cos \omega u \, du, \qquad (2.7.22)$$

$$\omega = b\int_0^\infty w(u)e^{\mu u} \sin \omega u \, du. \qquad (2.7.23)$$

The feasibility of extracting any information from these two equations is determined by the choice of weighting function $w(u)$. We know of no applications where there is accurate, experimentally-based, information available and the aim of modelling with distributed delays is usually to find out the effects of different *shapes* of weighting function. Common sense then dictates that we select functions which lead to simple mathematics, and it is therefore useful to note that with the functions (b)–(d) in Fig. 2.9 the integrals in equations (2.7.22) and (2.7.23) can be evaluated exactly, reducing these equations to algebraic equations.

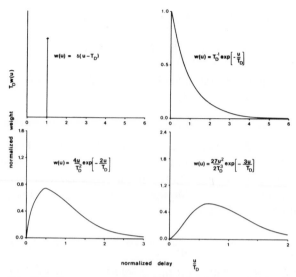

Fig. 2.9. Some examples of simple forms of 'distributed' delay; in each case the average delay is T_D.

Like so much prescriptive mathematics, the above argument looks somewhat imposing. To illustrate how simple the manipulations can become given a suitable choice of weighting function we consider an example in which $a = 0$, and $w(u)$ has the form of Fig. 2.9(b). Then from the combination of equations (2.7.22) and (2.7.23).

$$\mu - i\omega = \frac{b}{T_D}\int_0^\infty e^{-u/T_D}e^{\mu u}e^{-i\omega u}du$$

$$= b/(1 - \mu T_D + i\omega T_D). \qquad (2.7.24)$$

If we define $\lambda \equiv -\mu + i\omega$, then equation (2.7.24) implies

$$\lambda^2 T_D + \lambda + b = 0, \qquad (2.7.25)$$

where

$$\lambda \equiv -\mu + i\omega = (2T_D)^{-1}\{-1 \pm \sqrt{(1 - 4bT_D)}\}. \qquad (2.7.26)$$

Thus the system is stable provided $b > 0$, overdamped if in addition $4bT_D < 1$ and underdamped if $4bT_D > 1$. We can conclude that although an exponentially distributed time delay can induce damped oscillations about a steady-state value it cannot completely destabilize the steady state.

A similar analysis can be performed for the peaked delay distribution in Fig. 2.9(c). If a is still zero, then in place of the quadratic equation (2.7.25) we obtain the cubic

$$\tfrac{1}{4}\lambda^3 T_D{}^2 + \lambda^2 T_D + \lambda + b \qquad (2.7.27)$$

In Chapter 4 we shall quote conditions for the real part of all three roots of a polynomial to be negative; when applied to this equation these yield that for stability

$$0 < bT_D < 4. \tag{2.7.28}$$

The similarity between this result and the condition for stability in the model with a discrete delay is striking and suggests that the general observation, that delays in regulation can destabilize a stable steady state, is robust with respect to changes in the details concerning the distribution of the delay. Confirmation of this can be found by analysing case (d) in Fig. 2.9 but this is left as a problem for the reader.

The present analysis also provides some justification for our neglect of very large delays in the examples with discrete delays. For example we stated that the model of Section 2.7A had an instability when $rT_D > \pi/2$, but it can be shown that there is also a further stable region when

$$\frac{3\pi}{2} < rT_D < \frac{5\pi}{2} \tag{2.7.29}$$

However, this and other similar regions have no counterpart in the models with distributed delays which we have studied and we can conclude that it is a special mathematical feature associated with an assumption of a *very* narrow distribution of delays. In the absence of evidence for such a special feature we feel justified in neglecting its possible consequences.

2.8 NON-LINEAR EFFECTS

Although we shall frequently stress the power of locally linear approximations to non-linear models, it is important to be aware of some of the intrinsically non-linear phenomena that may arise even with the simple single-species models which are the subject of the present chapter. However, since non-linear effects only become significant in situations involving large population fluctuations they are likely to occur in contexts where the reliability of any particular model is in some doubt, and we must always attempt to distinguish those non-linear phenomena which mimic some effect in the real world from those which are noteworthy only for their mathematical fascination. With this in mind we investigate in turn non-linear effects in autonomous (i.e. undriven) systems and in systems driven by some environmental parameter.

A. Autonomous systems

In Section 1.7 we pointed out that where a neighbourhood stability analysis indicated divergent oscillations the non-linear terms which were neglected in the analysis could eventually stop the growth of the oscillations. The resulting *limit cycle* has both amplitude and frequency independent of initial conditions. Of the types of model considered in the present chapter only those with discrete generations and those involving time delays are candidates for limit cycles.

One of the best documented population models with a limit-cycle is the 'time-delayed logistic' model

$$\frac{dN(t)}{dt} = rN(t)\left[1 - \frac{N(t - T_D)}{K}\right].$$ (2.8.1)

which we used (with $r = 1$ and $T_D = 1.7$) to calculate the curve shown in Fig. 1.12. This model has a steady state $N = K$, which is locally unstable if $rT_D > \pi/2$, and in Table 2.1 we show the numerical results obtained by May (1974b) characterizing the limit cycles to which the divergent oscillations eventually lead. We have already shown (Section 2.7) that when rT_D is close to $\pi/2$ the divergent oscillations have a period of approximately $4T_D$ and it is clear from May's calculations that the limit cycle period is between $4T_D$ and $5T_D$ even for values of rT_D which produce very large amplitude limit cycles. This tends to confirm our earlier assertion (Section 1.6) that the locally linear estimate of the period of the divergent oscillations is a good first approximation for the limit cycle period.

Stable cyclic behaviour is also found with difference equations, and as an example we consider the 'logistic' difference equation (2.4.14)

$$N_t - N_{t-\tau} = r\tau N_{t-\tau}(1 - N_{t-\tau}/K).$$ (2.8.2)

Clearly the shortest possible cycle which this system could exhibit would have period 2τ, and to investigate whether such a cycle occurs we compare a plot of $N_{t+2\tau}$ against N_t constructed from equation (2.8.2) with the straight line $N_{t+2\tau} = N_t$. Where these two curves intersect there are population values which repeat at intervals of 2τ, so that a single intersection indicates a stable stationary state while multiple intersections indicate the existence of cycles. As we would expect from our previous analysis, when $r\tau < 2$ (Fig. 2.10(a)) this system shows only a single intersection, while if $r\tau > 2$ additional intersection points are found (see Fig. 2.10(b). When $r\tau$ is close to the critical value the

Table 2.1. Periods and ratios of maximum to minimum population of limit cycle solutions of the time-delayed logistic equation (2.8.1) (from May, 1974b).

rT_D	N_{max}/N_{min}	Period
1.6	2.56	$4.03\,T_D$
1.7	5.76	$4.09\,T_D$
1.8	11.6	$4.18\,T_D$
1.9	22.2	$4.29\,T_D$
2.0	42.3	$4.40\,T_D$
2.1	84.1	$4.54\,T_D$
2.2	178	$4.71\,T_D$
2.3	408	$4.90\,T_D$
2.4	1040	$5.11\,T_D$
2.5	2930	$5.36\,T_D$

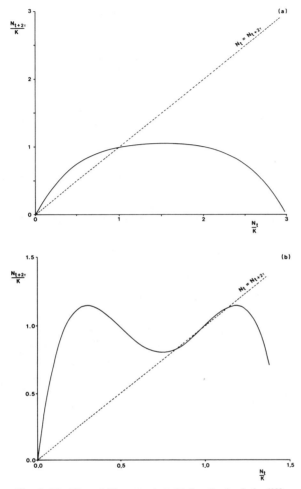

Fig. 2.10. Plot of $N_{t+2\tau}$ against N_t for the logistic difference equation. (a) $r\tau = 0.5$ (b) $r\tau = 2.1$.

cycle period is observed to be 2τ, but as $r\tau$ is increased further, cycles of period 4τ, 8τ, 16τ etc. are found and if $r\tau > 2.57$ the solutions of equation (2.8.2) are of a type known by mathematicians as *chaotic* (cf. Fig. 2.4(c)). The main properties of chaotic solutions are that *very* small changes in initial conditions can lead to very different population behaviour, and very small changes in r can lead to large changes in population trajectory from a particular initial condition.

Chaotic solutions in fact occur in many kinds of population dynamic equation, and it might appear that this is a major obstacle to population modelling, since in the chaotic regime prediction of future population requires both a perfect model and perfect data. However, the difficulty is a familiar one in physical systems with non-linear interactions and there are several well-known ways of avoiding it, all of which boil down to finding some property of the solution which, unlike its detailed trajectory, is well behaved and independent of initial conditions.

This is illustrated in Chapter 8 where we analyse a continuous-time insect-population model which produces chaotic solutions over part of its parameter space. The data with which the model is to be compared is subject to the usual (considerable) degree of experimental uncertainty and thus even in the region where the solutions are formally cyclic we concentrate on properties such as the limits of population excursion and the position of the dominant spectral peak, which are likely to be relatively insensitive to such uncertainty. In the chaotic regime we find that these features provide a well-behaved and initial-condition-independent characterization which moreover maps smoothly across the boundary into the cyclic regime.

In physical systems with non-linear interactions such findings are rather common, and since such few biologically-based examples as have been analysed seem also to conform to the same pattern it is to the statistical and spectral properties of the solution that we shall normally turn first in our search for a well-behaved characterization. However, some recent computations by Poole (1977) and by Smith and Mead (1980) suggest that this insight may allow us to proceed a little beyond simple characterization of solutions. It is found that the spectral properties of the solutions of non-linear difference equations in the chaotic regime are, in practice, likely to be indistinguishable from those obtained in the locally stable regime with a randomly fluctuating carrying capacity. As the mathematical techniques for analysing this latter case are well known (see Chapter 7) we may thus obtain at least a rough approximation to the spectral properties of the chaotic regime by analytic means.

B. Driven systems

In Sections 2.5 and 2.6 we analysed the effect of small fluctuations in an environmental parameter. We demonstrated that a small oscillation in one parameter of a model equation usually causes a similar small population oscillation of the same frequency, the amplitude and phase of this oscillation being easily calculable from the transfer function. If, however, the imposed oscillation is of large amplitude, or if the undriven system itself is limit cycling then non-linear effects may cause qualitative changes in the behaviour of the population. Two such effects may be of ecological significance, (a) subharmonic resonance, and (b) synchronization.

Subharmonic resonance occurs if a deterministically stable population, when driven by a large oscillation in an environmental parameter, oscillates at a frequency equal to a subharmonic of the driving frequency. By a subharmonic frequency we mean an integer fraction ($\frac{1}{2}$, $\frac{1}{3}$ etc.) of the driving frequency. Thus for instance the annual climatic cycle could produce population cycles with a period of several years. The effect may occur if in the absence of driving oscillations the population would be underdamped with the damped oscillations having a period close to the subharmonic frequency.

Synchronization occurs when a population which, in the absence of an environmental perturbation would execute a limit cycle, instead exhibits oscillations at the frequency of the driving perturbation. The importance of this effect in natural ecosystems was appreciated by Nicholson (1954) who asserted that 'any periodic change of climate tends to impose its period upon oscillations of internal origin or cause such oscillations to have a harmonic relation to periodic climatic change'.

We illustrate both these phenomena by examining the time-delayed logistic model (equation 2.8.1) with a sinusoidally varying carrying capacity

$$K(t) = K_0(1 + b \cos \omega t). \tag{2.8.3}$$

When scaled using $N' = N/K_0$, $t' = rt$, $\omega' = \omega/r$, the resulting dynamic equation becomes

$$\frac{dN'(t')}{dt'} = N'(t')\left[1 - \frac{N'(t' - rT_D)}{1 + b \cos \omega't'}\right]. \tag{2.8.4}$$

We first place the model in the stable underdamped regime by setting $rT_D = 1.4$. The scaled 'natural' frequency (i.e. the frequency of the damped oscillations which can be found numerically from equations (2.7.5) and (2.7.6)) is now 1.08 and we drive the carrying capacity at approximately twice this frequency by setting $\omega' = 2.39$. With small values of b the solution is a superposition of the transient damped oscillations and persistent oscillations at the driving frequency, an example being illustrated in Fig. 2.11. However if b is large enough the situation becomes complicated since the non-linear form

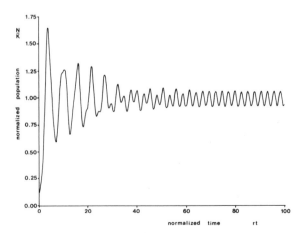

Fig. 2.11. Transient damped oscillations and persisting 'driven' oscillations in the time-delayed logistic with $rT_D = 1.4$, $\omega = 2.39\ r$, and $b = 0.2$.

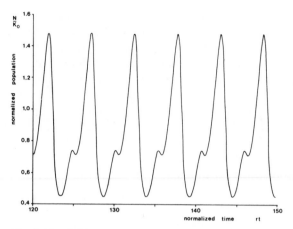

Fig. 2.12. Subharmonic resonance in the time-delayed logistic with $r\tau_D = 1.4$, $\omega = 2.39r$, $b = 0.6$. The period of the population oscillations is twice that of the driving oscillations.

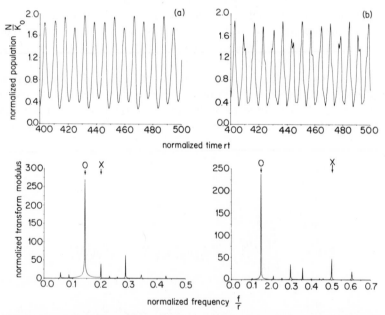

Fig. 2.13. Population plots and the modulus of their Fourier transforms for limit cycling systems with an oscillating carrying capacity but with *no* synchronization of the limit cycle to this driving oscillation. In both Fourier Transform plots the abscissa is normalized frequency $f/r = \omega'/2\pi$, the limit cycle frequency is marked ○ and the driving frequency is marked ×. The absence of synchronization is due in (a) to the small amplitude of the driving oscillation ($b = 0.1$) and in (b) to the high driving frequency ($\omega' = 3.14$) to which the system cannot synchronize in spite of a large amplitude driver ($b = 0.5$).

of equation (2.8.4) causes the rate of population recovery after an upswing and downswing to be respectively faster and slower than is predicted by the linear theory. Thus if the population at some instant is much lower than K_0, then it cannot recover to K_0 before the cyclic fluctuation in K starts pulling it down again. Consequently oscillations with a period equal to the driving frequency cannot be sustained, and the population cycles at a lower frequency—in this case half the driving frequency, as we illustrate in Fig. 2.12.

To illustrate synchronization we place the model in the locally unstable regime ($rT_D = 1.7$), so that it exhibits a small amplitude limit cycle (see Table 2.1) with $N_{max}/N_{min} = 5.76$ and $\omega' = 0.904$ (period $4.09\,T_D$). Numerical studies now reveal the following points.

(a) If the amplitude of the driving oscillations is small then the oscillations in K have very little effect on the limit cycle except when the driving frequency is harmonically related to the limit-cycle frequency. When b in equation (2.8.3) is large, the limit cycle is still robust against oscillations in K provided the driving frequency is not close to the limit-cycle frequency or one of its subharmonics. These points are illustrated in Fig. 2.13.

(b) When the limit-cycle frequency is close to the driving frequency or one of its subharmonics synchronization may occur. After a complex period of

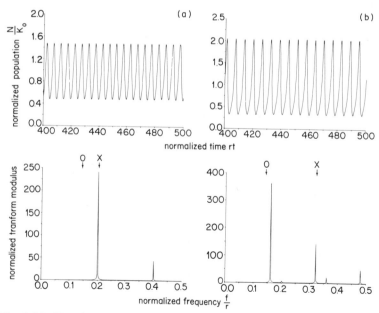

Fig. 2.14. Population plots and the modulus of their Fourier transforms for synchronization of a limit cycle to (a) the driving frequency, and (b) a subharmonic of the driving frequency. In the plots of the Fourier transforms $\bigcirc$ denotes the limit cycle frequency while $\times$ denotes the driving frequency.

transient behaviour the population oscillates at the driving frequency or a subharmonic, and the limit cycle disappears completely from the Fourier spectrum. Synchronization to both the fundamental and subharmonic frequencies is illustrated in Fig. 2.14

2.9 COMPARISON OF DYNAMICAL PROPERTIES OF MODELS AND REAL POPULATIONS

In this chapter we have reviewed several types of single-species model paying particular attention to steady states and their stability. Although any systematic review of field or laboratory data is beyond the scope of the present work, it is necessary to demonstrate which of the dynamical attributes of the models have counterparts in the real world or, failing that, in the laboratory.

A. Laboratory populations

There are countless examples of stable, overdamped, populations, the yeast population in Fig. 1.3 or the algal batch culture in Fig. 9.1 being typical examples. Obvious examples of stable, underdamped populations are less common, probably because overdamping seems to be the rule and underdamping the exception in natural populations, but also because as we demonstrate in Chapter 7 even a small amount of environmental or demographic stochasticity causes an underdamped system to fluctuate quasi-cyclically. There are, however, a fair number of laboratory populations (e.g. Nicholson's blowflies in Fig. 8.1) which exhibit persistent oscillations which may be of limit-cycle type.

The techniques developed in this chapter relate qualitative aspects of the dynamics of a population to a small number of parameters whose values are not normally known. However, there is evidence of two kinds which supports the contention that the nature of the dynamical behaviour can be influenced by a relatively small number of parameters:

(a) experiments on different strains of a particular organism kept under identical conditions;
(b) experiments in which populations of a particular organism are studied at different temperatures.

A spectacular example of the first kind of experiment which has been quoted by many authors is Fujii's (1967, 1968) and Utida's (1967) study of three different strains of the stored-product beetle *Callosobruchus*, of which one is overdamped, one underdamped, and one cycling—see Fig. 2.15. May (1976b, 1976c), interprets these differences as being due to increases in the product $r\tau$ where r is the intrinsic growth rate and τ is the interval between generations. This interpretation is plausible provided λ in equations (2.4.9) and (2.4.11) is proportional to r, as for example it is in a logistic model.

Examples of the second kind of experiment include Pratt's (1943) classic

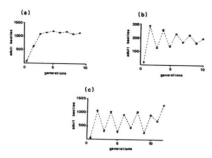

Fig. 2.15. Population dynamics of laboratory cultures of *Callosobruchus*. (a) *C. chinensis* (after Fujii, 1968). (b) *C. maculatus* (after Utida, 1967). (c) *C. maculatus* (after Fujii, 1967). (Taken from Hassell, Lawton, and May, 1976; reproduced by permission of Blackwell Scientific Publications Limited.)

experiments on the water flea *Daphnia magna* in which the population appeared to be stable and overdamped at 18 °C and to be cycling at 25 °C. Experiments of Beddington (1974) on the Collembola *Folsomia candida* showed the opposite effect, a steady state which at 16 °C is stable and over-damped, at 10 °C becomes stable and underdamped. As these experiments involved populations with overlapping generations it seems natural to inter-pret the results in terms of a time delay, the effect of temperature being to change the product λT_D derived from equations (2.7.1) and (2.7.11). How the product is affected by temperature depends on the physiology of the particu-lar organisms.

B. Natural populations

Because of environmental fluctuations, the only generally applicable method of determining unambiguously whether a natural population is overdamped or underdamped is to construct the ACF which for an overdamped popu-lation is non-oscillatory (e.g. Fig. 1.6(d)) and for an underdamped population exhibits damped oscillations (e.g. Fig. 1.6(c)). Unfortunately determination of the ACF from a time series of population values is statistically unreliable unless the run of population data is very long. This is of course simply an example of the general principle that 'non-parametric' or 'model-free' statisti-cal analysis requires immense quantities of data.

We know of only a few cases where a population has been subjected to a large single, perturbation and its subsequent response observed. Bigger (1976 and private communication) has found series of damped oscillations in the numbers of cocoa trees in a plantation in Ghana containing the mealybug *Phenococus hargreavesi* after the end of each year's dry season while other mealybug populations in the same plantation showed no oscillations. Hurd and Wolf (1974) and Barrett (1968) have studied artificial perturbations of grassland ecosystems through respectively nutrient enrichment and insecticide applications but did not publish data on population of single species, concentrating instead on entire trophic levels.

However, another way of obtaining insight on whether a natural population is overdamped or underdamped without previously obtaining vast quantities of census data is to fit a much smaller amount of data to a model which can exhibit all the types of dynamical behaviour of interest. This type of investigation is by no means foolproof since it only predicts the nature of the dynamics provided all significant factors are incorporated in the model. Thus it is possible to 'fit' good data on a population to a single-species model, conclude that the population should be stable and overdamped, and find that in practice predator–prey interactions (which were 'averaged out' in the model) cause oscillations. Notwithstanding this possibility we believe that this type of analysis can yield useful *prima facie* evidence on the qualitative dynamics of any particular species.

Hassell, Lawton, and May (1976) performed an analysis of this type for twenty-four natural insect populations which were fitted to a difference equation model that in our notation takes the form

$$N_{t+\tau} = (r + 1)N_t(1 + aN_t)^{-\beta}, \qquad (2.9.1)$$

where r, a, β are parameters. The stability boundaries for this model depend only on r and β and in Fig. 2.16 we reproduce their graph of these boundaries. As a test of the validity of the procedure they applied the same procedures to the *Callosobruchus* populations shown in Fig. 2.15. Cases (a) and (b) come out as expected in respectively the overdamped and underdamped regions. With case (c) the uncertainty in β is sufficiently great for either a stable two-point limit cycle or very lightly damped oscillations to be possible. This again is constant with observation.

The procedure used by Hassell, Lawton, and May is, of course, always susceptible to the danger that the model used is structurally inappropriate to the system under examination; a possibility which is well illustrated by two of the points in Fig. 2.16. The point labelled 1 in the diagram refers to the larch bud moth *Zeiraphera diniana* (Gn) which is placed well into the overdamped region. However, field observations (Baltensweiler, 1968) show that under certain circumstances this species exhibits well-defined population oscillations, and although the mechanism underlying this phenomenon is still the subject of debate it certainly lies among the factors ignored by or averaged out of the model. A similar, if less dramatic, example is provided by the point labelled 'blowflies', which places Nicholson's blowfly cultures firmly in the chaos region. Although our detailed study in Chapter 8 shows that this conclusion is not wholly inappropriate it also shows that a number of essential features of the data can only be explained by a model which allows for the possibility of overlapping generations.

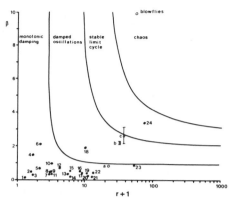

Fig. 2.16. Stability boundaries for the system $N_{t+\tau} = (r + 1)(N_T(1 + aN_t)^{-\beta}$ in terms of the maximum growth rate r and the density dependence parameter β. The solid circles show the position with respect to these boundaries of the various natural populations listed in Table 1 of Hassell, Lawton, and May (1976) (reproduced by permission of Blackwell Scientific Publications Limited). The open circles refer to the laboratory populations shown in Fig. 2.15 and to the blowfly populations discussed in Chapter 8.

Despite these two failures, which are more fully discussed in the original paper, we share the authors' belief that the majority of the populations examined are at least approximately described by equation (2.9.1) and hence that the overall conclusions of the work are valid. The most striking of these is the strong suggestion that deterministic stability is the rule rather than the exception, at least with insect populations, and moreover that overdamping rather than underdamping is to be expected. This is very reassuring to us, as the linear analysis which we have advocated in this chapter and which we shall develop in the next five chapters is based on a presumption of deterministic stability.

It remains to discuss the non-linear effects discussed in Section 2.8 all of which involve cycling populations. Populations which fluctuate in a cyclic manner with a period different from obvious environmental drivers are relatively rare, and even then the oscillations may well be the response of an underdamped system to environmental noise. We in fact know of no natural populations which are indisputably limit cycling, though it is possible that some of the famous (or notorious) cycles in mammalian populations (e.g. Canadian lynx, several vole species) may be of this type. There are, furthermore, possible evolutionary reasons for believing that limit cycles should be rare. Selective pressures on individuals which increase the intrinsic growth rate r of a species are likely to increase the magnitude of the product $\lambda\tau$ in

56

equation (2.4.12) or, for a species with overlapping generations, the product bT_D in equations (2.7.7) and (2.7.8). We shall see later that as $\lambda\tau$ or bT_D approaches the value for marginal stability the effect of environmental fluctuations on the population is grossly magnified and extinction becomes likely. Thus group selective pressures are likely to stop any species evolving through individual selection a value of r which would cause its population to execute limit cycles. This argument is of course only valid in the absence of large-scale environmental changes and a species which has evolved in one environment may well show population cycles when introduced to a new environment. The argument is furthermore clearly simplistic—it has no relevance to prey-predator or host-parasite oscillations, to local oscillations in regions of marginal habitat or to local or global oscillations in patchy environments. Yet taken with the apparent absence of limit cycles in nature it suggests that, despite their mathematical elegance, limit cycles are of limited ecological significance.

The non-linear effects which potentially occur in driven systems are also in our opinion relatively unimportant for modelling. One possible example of subharmonic resonance occurs in populations of the coffee leaf miner *Leucoptera caffeina* (Washb.) which were studied by Bigger, and Tapley (1969). As is shown in Fig. 2.17 there is a clear 2-year periodicity superimposed on the annual fluctuations, the resulting pattern being similar to our example in Fig. 2.12. However, we mentioned that subharmonic resonance effects are likely in practice to be indistinguishable from long transients and it is thus perhaps significant that this population was part of a community recovering from a period of extensive use of DDT.

Examples of synchronization of a limit cycle to an external driver are obviously hard to find since it is very difficult to establish whether the population would limit cycling in the absence of the driving oscillations. Fitting life-history data to a specific model such as that of Hassell, Lawton, and May would be a possible strategy but we know of no case where this programme has been carried out and has indicated synchronization of a limit cycle.

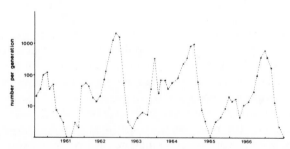

Fig. 2.17. Population of the leaf miner *Leucoptera Coffeina* (Washb.) (After Bigger, and Tapley, 1969; reproduced by permission of the Commonwealth Agricultural Bureaux.)

SOURCES AND SUGGESTED FURTHER READING

General: There have been many reviews of single species population models. We found that of May (1976b) particularly useful.

Difference Equations: We drew heavily from the work of May (1974c, 1975, 1976a); also May, Conway, Hassell and Southwood (1974) and Varley, Gradwell, and Hassell (1973). In May (1976a), May and Oster (1976), Fisher and Goh (1977), Allwright (1978) and Boyarsky (1980), there are discussions of the pattern of cyclic behaviour and 'chaos' in non-linear difference equations.

Differential Equations: Sanchez (1968) is an excellent introduction to the stability theory in this chapter and the next. (The reader should not be discouraged by Chapter 1 which is much more demanding than the rest!). Other useful references are Piaggio (1952, especially Chapter 3) and Morris (1974) which is written at a more elementary level than the previous texts.

Dimensional Analysis: Pankhurst (1964) covers scaling in physical systems and includes a discussion of Buckingham's Theorem for which the original reference is Buckingham (1914). A more sophisticated treatment is provided by Langhaar (1951).

Driven Systems: The theory in Sections 2.5 and 2.6 is elaborated in countless texts on control theory, instrumentation, and signal processing, often under the title linear response theory. Readable examples include Doebelin (1962) and Betts (1970). However, the essential mathematics is adequately covered by Morris (1974) in the book already discussed. Fourier analysis is treated in more detail (with references) in Appendix F. Our discussion of non-linear effects in driven systems follows closely Nisbet and Gurney (1976); further discussion of the 'driven logistic' is given by Coleman (1979), Coleman, Hsieh, and Knowles (1979) and Boyce and Daley (1980).

Time delays: A comprehensive mathematical text is Bellman and Cooke (1963) and a more recent text involving applications to population dynamics is Cushing (1977). Most of the ecological interpretation of time delay models has been covered by May (1973a, 1974b, 1979), Beddington and May (1975), Brauer and Sanchez (1975), Brauer (1977), Gurney, Blythe, and Nisbet (1980). The linearized analysis of our general model with discrete delay (equation (2.7.11)) seems first to have been investigated by Hayes (1950) and is also covered in detail by Maynard Smith (1974, pp. 43–46). Models with distributed delays (especially those with the forms in Fig. 2.9) are the main topic in MacDonald (1978). There has been a fair amount of mathematical research on the existence and stability of limit cycles (e.g. Kaplan and Yorke, 1975, 1977 and much of Cushing's book), but we know of little rigorous material yielding insight on the onset of chaos in delay-differential equation models.

PROBLEMS

(Those marked * are mathematically more demanding than the others.)

1. (May, Conway, Hassell, and Southwood, 1974). The following difference equations have been used by various authors to represent the population dynamics of a single species:

    (a) $N_{t+1} = \lambda N_t^{-(1+b)}$
    (b) $N_{t+1} = \lambda N_t \exp(-\alpha N_t)$
    (c) $N_{t+1} = N_t\{1 + r(1 - N_t/K)\}$

    For each case calculate the steady-state population N^*, the conditions on the model parameters for stability and the conditions for over/under-damping.

2. (Moran, 1953). The population of the Canadian lynx has been modelled by an equation which, in the absence of demographic or environmental stochasticity, would take the form

    $$(y_t - m) = \alpha(y_{t-1} - m) + \beta(y_{t-2} - m)$$

    where t is measured in years, $y = \log_{10} N_0$, $m = 2.90$, $\alpha = 1.41$, $\beta = -0.7734$. Show that the population is deterministically stable but underdamped.

3. (Goel, Maitra, and Montroll, 1971). The Gompertz differential equation for population growth is

    $$\frac{dN}{dt} = -\alpha N \ln(N/K)$$

    (a) By linearizing about the steady state $N^* = K$, show that the steady state is locally stable provided $\alpha > 0$.
    (b) By substituting $y = \ln(N/K)$ in the equation, show that the *exact* solution is

    $$N(t) = K\left(\frac{N_0}{K}\right)^x, \qquad (x = e^{-\alpha t})$$

    where N_0 is the population at time $t = 0$. Hence show that the population is globally stable if $\alpha > 0$.

4.* (Brauer and Sanchez, 1975). Suppose that a population which follows the logistic equation is harvested at a constant rate (i.e. a fixed number of individuals E is removed from the population each year). The population dynamics is then given by the differential equation

    $$\frac{dN}{dt} = rN(1 - N/K) - E$$

    (a) Show that if $E < \frac{1}{4}rK$; then there are two possible steady state populations, the larger one being locally stable and the lower one locally unstable.

(b) Show that if $E > \frac{1}{4}rK$, then the population becomes extinct in a finite time and obtain an *approximate* expression for the extinction time.

(c) The model was applied to a population of sandhill cranes which were being hunted. The parameters were estimated as $r = 9.9 \times 10^2$ year^{-1}, $K = 2.0 \times 10^5$. Estimate the rate of extinction if the annual crop were 6000. Repeat the calculation for an annual crop of 12,000.

(d) Suppose harvesting involved removal of a constant *fraction* of the population each year. The harvesting term in the differential equation would now be EN instead of E. How would the results of parts (a) and (b) be affected?

5. (Ludwig, Jones, and Holling, 1978). Populations of the North American spruce budworm were modelled by assuming that:

(i) in the absence of predation the population would follow the logistic equation,

(ii) the population was subject to predation by birds. The resulting equation was

$$\frac{dN}{dt} = f(N) - g(N)$$

where $f(N) = rN\left(1 - \frac{N}{K}\right)$

$$g(N) = \frac{\beta N^2}{\alpha^2 + N^2}.$$

(a) Recast the equation in terms of the scaled variables

$$N' = \alpha^{-1}N, \qquad t' = \alpha^{-1}\beta t$$

and hence show that the behaviour of the system is controlled by the dimensionless groups of parameters

$$R = \beta^{-1}\alpha r, \qquad Q = \alpha^{-1}K$$

(b) By sketching the graphs of $f(N)$ and $g(N)$ (or their counterparts in scaled variables) against N(or N') show that the system has either one stable non-zero steady state or three steady states of which two are stable and one unstable.

(c)* By varying the control parameters R and Q, it is possible to cause the unstable steady state to coalesce with one of the stable steady states. Show that this happens on the curve given parametrically by

$$R = \frac{2N'^3}{(1 + N'^2)^2}; \quad Q = \frac{2N'^3}{(N'^2 - 1)}$$

(d)* The above authors argue that changes in the environment cause R and Q to change *slowly* relative to changes in N. Use the result of (c) to show that such slow changes can cause very rapid changes (outbreaks or collapses) in budworm populations.

6. Show that if a population follows the Gompertz equation (given in Problem 3) and if the carrying capacity K varies as

$$K(t) = K_0(1 + b \cos \omega t)$$

then eventually the population will exhibit oscillations of amplitude

$$\frac{\alpha b K_0}{\sqrt{(\alpha^2 + \omega^2)}}$$

and which lag the driving oscillations by an angle of ϕ with

$$\tan \phi = \omega/\alpha$$

7. (Brauer, 1977). Suppose a population obeying the time-delayed logistic equation is harvested at a constant rate E. Instead of the equation in Problem 4 we obtain

$$\frac{dN(t)}{dt} = rN(t)\{1 - N(t - T_D)/K\} - E .$$

Show that if this equation is linearized about a steady state N^*, then an equation of the form (2.7.12) is obtained. In the light of this result discuss whether harvesting has a stabilizing or a destabilizing effect on such a population.

8.* (Proof of Equation (2.7.7)). For a system to be stable and overdamped there must be a solution of equation (2.7.5) with $\omega = 0$, $\mu > 0$.

(a) Show that this implies

$$\ln(\mu/b) = (\mu/b)(bT_D).$$

(b) Show graphically that this equation only has a positive solution for μ/b provided

$$bT_D < \max_{\mu > 0} \left(\frac{\ln(\mu/b)}{(\mu/b)}\right)$$

(c) By evaluating the maximum on the right-hand side of the above inequality show that for the system to be stable and overdamped

$$bT_D \leq e^{-1} = 0.368$$

9.* (Proof of equation (2.7.8)). The transition from stability to instability occurs if equation (2.7.5) has a solution with $\mu = 0$.

(a) Show that this implies $\omega T_D = (n + \frac{1}{2})\pi/2$ where n is an integer.

(b) Take $n = 1$ and show using equation (2.7.6) that $\omega = b$, and thus that at the point of marginal stability

$$bT_D = \pi/2$$

Chapter 3

Single-Species Models with Age Structure

3.1 INTRODUCTION

Chapter 2 was concerned with models in which birth and death rates depend only on total population and not on the ages of the individuals who make up that population. The validity of this idealization is obviously questionable unless the distribution of ages within the population remains reasonably constant, and in this chapter we therefore study models which take explicit account of population age structure. We concentrate on those features emphasised in Chapter 2—steady states, stability and the effects of 'external' environmental fluctuations—and again base our analysis on techniques involving local linearization. Our reason for devoting a separate chapter to these models is that their analysis involves more complicated algebra than that required for most other single species models. We make little later use of this algebra and the reader who is uninterested in mathematical detail may safely omit many of the more intimidating sections. This applies particularly to Sections 3.3 and 3.4, although here we have stated the main results in words as well as in equations and the 'flavour' of the work can be captured without too much heavy calculation. Perhaps the most important general conclusion to emerge is that although age structure effects frequently influence the quantitative aspects of the population dynamics they are rather seldom responsible for qualitative changes in dynamic behaviour. This provides a measure of justification for our neglect of age-structure in subsequent chapters.

3.2 POPULATION MODELS INVOLVING AGE STRUCTURE

The literature on age-dependent population dynamics is made unusually difficult to follow by the existence of several different, but closely related formulations of the fundamental equations. In this section we develop basic results for the cases of discrete and continuous age classes in such a way as to emphasize the mathematical links between the two formulations. We then show how the theory can be elaborated to take account of the dependence of birth and death rates on factors other than chronological age.

A. Continuous time

To model the effects of age structure in a way appropriate to a continuous time formulation we define an *age distribution* $f(a, t)$, by letting $f(a, t)$ da be the number of individuals whose ages, at time t, lie between a and $a + $ da. During a very small time interval dt, chosen for convenience equal to da, the age distribution can change for only two reasons:

(a)   individuals aged between a and $a + $ dt mature to an older age class or die,
(b)   individuals aged between $a - $ dt and a who survive, enter the age class a to $a + $ dt.

Thus if $\gamma(a)$ dt is the average fraction of individuals aged a who die during a time interval dt, then for all age classes other than $a = 0$,

$$f(a, t + \mathrm{d}t) = \{1 - \gamma(a - \mathrm{d}t)\mathrm{d}t\}f(a - \mathrm{d}t, t). \qquad (3.2.1)$$

Since dt is small we can now evaluate $f(a, t + \mathrm{d}t)$, $f(a - \mathrm{d}t, t)$, and $\gamma(a - \mathrm{d}t)$ by a Taylor expansion neglecting terms of order dt^2 or higher. After a few lines of algebra we then obtain the partial differential equation sometimes known as the *von Foerster equation*,

$$\frac{\partial f}{\partial t} + \frac{\partial f}{\partial a} + \gamma(a)f = 0. \qquad (3.2.2)$$

It is relatively simple to show that this equation (3.2.2) has the formal solution

$$f(a, t) = f(a - t, 0)\exp\left[-\int_0^t \gamma(a - t + x)\,\mathrm{d}x\right] \quad \text{if} \quad t \leqslant a, \quad (3.2.3\mathrm{a})$$

and

$$f(a, t) = f(0, t - a)\exp\left[-\int_0^a \gamma(x)\,\mathrm{d}x\right] \quad \text{if} \quad t \geqslant a. \qquad (3.2.3\mathrm{b})$$

The first of these solutions (for $t \leqslant a$) represents the dying off of the population present at $t = 0$. The second (for $t \geqslant a$) is of purely academic interest unless we can find some means of calculating $f(0, t - a)$, the number of newborn ($a = 0$) individuals present at time $t - a$. To this end we make the simplifying assumption that the population sex ratio remains constant and hence define an age-specific birth rate $\beta(a)$ by letting $\beta(a)$ da be the average number of offspring produced per unit time by an individual aged between a and $a + $ da.

In this case, at any time t

$$f(0, t) = \int_0^\infty \beta(a)f(a, t)\, da. \tag{3.2.4}$$

This equation, usually called the *renewal condition*, can now be used in conjunction with equation (3.2.3a) or (3.2.3b) to calculate the age distribution at any time t, provided that we are given the initial age distribution at time $t = 0$.

Although the most systematic way to model age-structured population dynamics is by describing changes in the absolute population of a given age class, this quantity is often rather hard to measure experimentally. In the field it is frequently more convenient to make separate estimates of the total population and of the proportion of that population falling into any given age class. Fortunately both these quantities are easily obtainable from the basic age distribution $f(a, t)$. The total population $N(t)$ is simply

$$N(t) = \int_0^\infty f(a, t)\, da, \tag{3.2.5}$$

and if we define $F(a, t)da$ as the proportion of the population falling into age class a to $a + da$ then clearly the *normalized age distribution* $F(a, t)$ is given by

$$F(a, t) = \frac{f(a, t)}{N(t)} \tag{3.2.6}$$

In the model described by equations (3.2.2) and (3.2.4) the *per capita* birth and death rates are independent of total population size. We might thus in general expect that, after any transients have died away the normalized age distribution (i.e. the proportion of the population in any given age class) will achieve a stationary form $F^*(a)$ and hence the total population $N(t)$ will grow or decay exponentially. In this case it is appropriate to investigate simultaneous solutions of equations (3.2.2) and (3.2.4) of the form

$$f(a, t) \propto F^*(a)e^{\lambda t} \tag{3.2.7}$$

where, by definition,

$$\int_0^\infty F^*(a)\, da = 1. \tag{3.2.8}$$

On substituting this form into equation (3.2.2) and solving the resulting ordinary differential equation we find that if we define

$$\pi(a) \equiv \exp\left[-\int_0^a \gamma(x)\, dx \right], \tag{3.2.9}$$

then

$$F^*(a) = F^*(0)e^{-\lambda a}\pi(a). \tag{3.2.10}$$

When this latter expression is substituted into the renewal condition (3.2.4) we obtain

$$F^*(0) = F^*(0) \int_0^\infty e^{-\lambda a} \beta(a)\pi(a) \, \mathrm{d}a, \qquad (3.2.11)$$

and thus show that if equation (3.2.7) is to be a simultaneous solution of equations (3.2.2) and (3.2.4) then λ must be a root of

$$\int_0^\infty e^{-\lambda a} \beta(a)\pi(a) \, \mathrm{d}a = 1. \qquad (3.2.12)$$

It can be shown (see Pollard, 1973) that this equation has exactly one real root, λ^*, which has a value greater than that of the real part of any of the complex roots. Thus eventually the population must grow or decay exponentially with a time constant $(\lambda^*)^{-1}$. Clearly the nature of its ultimate fate will be determined by the sign of λ^*, and we see from equation (3.2.12) that λ^* must be negative and hence that the population must ultimately decay to extinction if

$$\int_0^\infty \beta(a)\pi(a) \, \mathrm{d}a < 1. \qquad (3.2.13)$$

Conversely λ^* will be positive and the population will ultimately grow without limit if the inequality is reversed. This result becomes self-evident as soon as we realize that $\pi(a)$ is just the probability that a newly recruited individual will survive to age a; so that the integral in equation (3.2.13) simply represents the total number of offspring produced, on average, by an individual during its lifetime.

B. Discrete time

Another representation of age-structure dynamics (normally attributed to Leslie) is obtained by working with discrete age-classes. Suppose there are $m + 1$ age classes numbered $0, 1, 2, \ldots m$; each covering an age interval τ. If $f_{i,t}$ denotes the number of individuals in age class i at time t and P_i denotes the fraction of the population in this age class that survives to enter age class $i + 1$, then clearly

$$f_{i,t+\tau} = P_{i-1} f_{i-1,t} \qquad (3.2.14)$$

which is essentially equation (3.2.1) recast in new notation. To obtain a discrete analogue of the renewal condition (3.2.4) we again assume that the population has a constant sex-ratio and define an age-specific fertility β_i as the average number of offspring born in time interval τ to an individual in age class i. We thus find

$$f_{0,t+\tau} = \sum_{i=0}^{m} \beta_i f_{i,t} \qquad (3.2.15)$$

The combination of equations (3.2.14) and (3.2.15) may be written more elegantly using matrix notation (see Appendix M) as

$$\mathbf{f}_{t+\tau} = \mathbf{A}\mathbf{f}_t \qquad (3.2.16)$$

where

$$\mathbf{f}_t \equiv \begin{bmatrix} f_{0,t} \\ f_{1,t} \\ f_{2,t} \\ \cdot \\ \cdot \\ \cdot \\ f_{m,t} \end{bmatrix} \quad \text{and} \quad \mathbf{A} \equiv \begin{bmatrix} \beta_0 & \beta_1 & \beta_2 & \cdots & & \beta_m \\ P_0 & 0 & 0 & \cdots & & 0 \\ 0 & P_1 & 0 & \cdots & & 0 \\ \cdot & & & & & \\ \cdot & & & & & \\ 0 & 0 & 0 & \cdots & P_{m-1} & 0 \end{bmatrix}. \qquad (3.2.17)$$

It is evident that if we know the population in each age class at any one time ($t = 0$) we can predict these populations at any later time by repeated applications of equation (3.2.16), so that

$$\mathbf{f}_t = \mathbf{A}^k \mathbf{f}_0, \quad \text{where} \quad t = k\tau. \qquad (3.2.18)$$

As in the continuous case, comparison of the results of this procedure with experimental observations may well be facilitated by noting that the total population at time t is

$$N_t = \sum_{i=0}^{m} f_{i,t} \qquad (3.2.19)$$

and defining a normalized discrete-age distribution

$$F_{i,t} \equiv f_{i,t}/N_t \qquad (3.2.20)$$

which represents the proportion of the population in age class i at time t.

In this discrete model, as with its continuous analogue, we have assumed birth and death rates to be independent of total population size and hence we expect that eventually the population will achieve a stable normalized age distribution, $\mathbf{F}^*$, and grow or decay exponentially. We investigate this possibility by assuming a population vector of the general form

$$\mathbf{f}_t \propto F^* e^{\lambda t} \quad \text{where} \quad \sum_{i=0}^{m} F_i^* = 1 \qquad (3.2.21)$$

which, on substitution in equation (3.2.16) yields

$$\mathbf{A}\mathbf{F}^* = e^{\lambda \tau}\mathbf{F}^*. \qquad (3.2.22)$$

Thus $e^{\lambda \tau}$ and $\mathbf{F}^*$ are respectively an 'eigenvalue' and the corresponding 'eigenvector' of the matrix $\mathbf{A}$. Eigenvalues and eigenvectors of a matrix are defined in Appendix M, but the reader who is unfamiliar with matrix theory is advised to postpone serious study of matrices until Chapter 4 where matrix theory plays a more significant role in the exposition than at present. It is, however, a standard result that if

$$y = e^{\lambda \tau} \tag{3.2.23}$$

then (see Appendix M) y must be a solution of the characteristic equation of $\mathbf{A}$ which can be shown to take the form

$$y^{m+1} = \sum_{i=0}^{m} \beta_i \pi_i y^{m-i}, \tag{3.2.24}$$

where

$$\pi_i \equiv \prod_{j=0}^{i-1} P_j, \tag{3.2.25}$$

is the fraction of individuals entering the population at age zero who survive to enter age class i. On dividing throughout equation (3.2.24) by y^{m+1} and substituting from equation (3.2.23) which defines y, we finally see that λ must be a root of

$$\sum_{i=0}^{m} \beta_i \pi_i e^{-(i+1)\lambda \tau} = 1, \tag{3.2.26}$$

which is manifestly the discrete analogue of equation (3.2.12).

As in the continuous case it can be shown that there is only one real root, λ^*, of equation (3.2.26) and that the real parts of all the complex roots are less than λ^*. Thus the population ultimately grows or declines as $e^{\lambda^* t}$, with decline if

$$\sum_{i=0}^{m} \beta_i \pi_i < 1 \tag{3.2.27}$$

and growth if this inequality is reversed. It can also be shown that the stationary normalized age distribution which accompanies this exponential growth or decay has the form

$$F_j^* \propto e^{-j\lambda \tau} \pi_j \tag{3.2.28}$$

which is clearly the analogue of equation (3.2.10).

C. Elaborations of the basic model

As we have presented them, the above models are applicable only to cases where *per capita* birth and death rates depend solely on age and not on time, external environmental factors, population density, sex ratio, or individual physiological factors such as size or weight. We deal in detail with the extension of the model to the case of density dependent population growth in both constant and variable environments in Section 3.3 and 3.4. In this section we outline several other possible extensions of the basic formalism, not with any aim at exhaustive cover but in the hope of taking the reader to the stage where he can easily tackle further modifications himself. We confine our

68

attention to the continuous time formalism which is more amenable to elaboration than its discrete counterpart.

The first extension we consider is the case where birth and death rates depend on both age and a single physiological factor which, to be specific, we take to be mass. We denote by $f(a, m, t)\, \mathrm{d}a\, \mathrm{d}m$ the number of individuals who, at time t, have ages in the range a to $a + \mathrm{d}a$ and masses in the range m to $m + \mathrm{d}m$. We introduce a new function $g(a, m, t)$ which represents the growth rate of an individual of mass m and age a at time t, and note that

$$g(a, m, t) \equiv \frac{\mathrm{d}m}{\mathrm{d}t} = \left(\frac{\partial m}{\partial t}\right)_a + \left(\frac{\partial m}{\partial a}\right)_t. \tag{3.2.29}$$

Here $(\partial m/\partial t)_a$ represents the change in mass of an individual aged a due to external variations (represented by the explicit dependence of g on time) while $(\partial m/\partial a)_t$ represents the normal growth of an individual due to ageing.

The development of the population is conveniently visualized with the aid of the schematic representation of Fig. 3.1. Each individual in the population can be represented by a dot on the a–m plane and the number of dots in the area labelled t is simply the number of individuals with ages and masses respectively in the ranges a to $a + \mathrm{d}a$ and m to $m + \mathrm{d}m$. The population of the area labelled $t + \Delta t$ is just the population which was in the rectangle labelled t at time t less those individuals who have died in the time interval Δt. Thus if A_t and $A_{t+\Delta t}$ are the areas in the a–m plane labelled t and $t + \Delta t$ respectively in Fig. 3.1 then

$$f(t + \Delta t, a + \Delta a, m + \Delta m)A_{t+\Delta t} = f(a, m, t)[1 - \gamma(a, m, t)\Delta t]A_t. \tag{3.2.30}$$

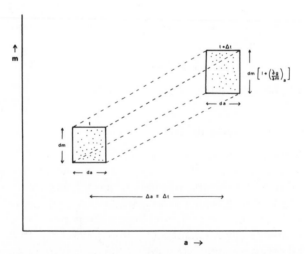

Fig. 3.1. Schematic representation of the development of a population whose members are characterized by age (a) and mass (m).

But if we set

$$A_t = da \; dm \tag{3.2.31}$$

then to first order in Δt

$$A_{t+\Delta t} = da \; dm \left[1 + \left(\frac{\partial g}{\partial m} \right)_a \right]. \tag{3.2.32}$$

On substituting these expressions in the continuity equation (3.2.30) and discarding all but first order terms in small quantities we obtain

$$\frac{\partial f}{\partial t} + \frac{\partial f}{\partial a} + g \frac{\partial f}{\partial m} + f \frac{\partial g}{\partial m} + \gamma f = 0 \tag{3.2.33}$$

which can be re-written more compactly as

$$\frac{\partial f}{\partial t} + \frac{\partial f}{\partial a} + \frac{\partial}{\partial m} \{ gf \} + \gamma f = 0. \tag{3.2.34}$$

This result obviously generalizes to the case where a set of M quantities $\{ m_i \}$ all influence the growth and reproduction of an individual. If

$$g_i \equiv \frac{dm_i}{dt} \tag{3.2.35}$$

then equation (3.2.34) becomes

$$\frac{\partial f}{\partial t} + \frac{\partial f}{\partial a} + \sum_{i=1}^{M} \frac{\partial}{\partial m_i} \{ g_i f \} + \gamma f = 0. \tag{3.2.36}$$

We obtain a complete specification of the population dynamics by combining equation (3.2.34) or (3.2.36) with the appropriate renewal condition, which in the case of a single physiological variable is

$$f(0, m, t) = \int_0^\infty \int_0^\infty \beta(a, m', m, t) f(a, m', t) \, dm' \, da \tag{3.2.37}$$

where $\beta(a, m', m, t) \, dt$ is the number of offspring of mass m born during time increment t to $t + dt$ to an individual of mass m' and age a.

A second important extension of the basic model involves organisms which reproduce by binary fission. Suppose that during time interval t to $t + dt$ a fraction $b(a, m, t) \, dt$ of cells aged a with mass m divide into two identical neonates of age a and mass $m/2$. In this case the original cells appear to die and the term γf in equation (3.2.33) is replaced by $[\gamma + b]f$, so that

$$\frac{\partial f}{\partial t} + \frac{\partial f}{\partial a} + \frac{\partial}{\partial m} (gf) + \{ \gamma + b \} f = 0, \tag{3.2.38}$$

although in many microbiological applications (e.g. the algae in Chapter 9) the rate of natural cell death $\gamma(a, m, t)$ is small and may be neglected in modelling.

For a complete specification of the dynamics of a population which reproduces by binary fission we also need a renewal condition. Clearly we can in principle use the appropriate general form set out in equation (3.2.37), but a considerable simplification can be effected if we assume that the binary fission of an organism of mass m always produces exactly two neonates of mass $m/2$. In this case we can recast (3.2.37) as

$$f(0, m, t) = 2\left\{2\int_0^\infty b(a, 2m, t)f(a, 2m, t)\,\mathrm{d}a\right\}. \qquad (3.2.39)$$

The first of the two leading factors of 2 in this expression simply represents the fact that each fission produces two neonates, but the second is somewhat more subtle and arises because parents whose sizes span the range m to $m + \mathrm{d}m$ produce offspring whose size range $(m/2$ to $(m + \mathrm{d}m)/2)$ is only half as large.

Countless further variations on the basic continuous time model are possible but no new mathematical ideas are involved. For an extensive review we refer the reader to Streifer (1974).

3.3 DENSITY-DEPENDENT POPULATION DYNAMICS IN AN UNCHANGING ENVIRONMENT

In the previous section we analysed an age-structured population model in which the per capita birth and death rates depended *only* on age, and found that ultimately the total population always either decayed exponentially to extinction or grew exponentially without limit. Since rather few real populations actually behave in either of these ways we now seek to extend the repertoire of our model by incorporating into it density-dependent regulatory effects.

A. Continuous time

We postulate that both the *per capita* death rate γ and the *per capita* birth rate β are functions of age and total population

$$N(t) = \int_0^\infty f(a, t)\,\mathrm{d}a. \qquad (3.3.1)$$

Recruitment to the population (equation (3.2.4)) thus depends on its current total size since

$$f(0, t) = \int_0^\infty \beta(a, N)f(a, t)\,\mathrm{d}a \qquad (3.3.2)$$

and changes in the age distribution due to death and ageing (equation (3.2.2)) are also influenced by total population through the continuity equation

$$\frac{\partial f}{\partial t} + \frac{\partial f}{\partial a} + \gamma(a, N)f = 0. \qquad (3.3.3)$$

As usual the first stage of our analysis is to seek a stationary-state age distribution, $f^*(a)$, which is a simultaneous solution of the dynamic equations (3.3.2) and (3.3.3). We first note from the continuity equation (3.3.3) that if the steady-state total population is N^*, then

$$f^*(a) = f^*(0)\pi(a, N^*) \qquad (3.3.4)$$

where, by analogy with equation (3.2.9)

$$\pi(a, N^*) \equiv \exp\left\{-\int_0^a \gamma(x, N^*)\, dx\right\} \qquad (3.3.5)$$

is the probability that, at the steady state, a newly recruited individual will survive to age a. Substituting this form back into the renewal condition (3.3.2) now shows us that the steady-state population N^* must satisfy

$$\int_0^\infty \beta(a, N^*)\pi(a, N^*)\, da = 1; \qquad (3.3.6)$$

a relationship which is made more meaningful by noting that the integral simply represents the average number of offspring born to a single individual when the population is stationary at N^*. Finally, for completeness, we note that equation (3.3.4) is only consistent with equation (3.3.1) if

$$f^*(0) = \frac{N^*}{\displaystyle\int_0^\infty \pi(a, N^*)\, da}. \qquad (3.3.7)$$

We now investigate small deviations from the steady state by defining

$$\xi(a, t) \equiv f(a, t) - f^*(a), \qquad (3.3.8)$$

$$n(t) \equiv N(t) - N^* = \int_0^\infty \xi(a, t)\, da, \qquad (3.3.9)$$

and hence showing after some lengthy, but routine, manipulations of equations (3.3.2) and (3.3.3) that to a first approximation

$$\frac{\partial \xi}{\partial t} + \frac{\partial \xi}{\partial a} + \gamma^*(a)\xi + f^*(a)g(a)n = 0, \qquad (3.3.10)$$

$$\xi(0, t) = \int_0^\infty [\beta^*(a) - \kappa]\xi(a, t)\, da, \qquad (3.3.11)$$

where

$$g(a) = \left[\frac{\partial}{\partial N}\gamma(a, N)\right]_{N=N^*} \qquad (3.3.12)$$

$$\kappa = -\int_0^\infty f^*(a)\left[\frac{\partial}{\partial N}\beta(a, N)\right]_{N=N^*} da \qquad (3.3.13)$$

and $\gamma^*(a)$, $\beta^*(a)$, are shorthand notation for $\gamma(a, N^*)$, and $\beta(a, N^*)$, respectively.

We now investigate the stability of the steady state against small, single perturbations by assuming a simultaneous solution of equations (3.3.10) and (3.3.11) of the form

$$\xi(a, t) = L(a)e^{\lambda t} \qquad (3.3.14)$$

where $L(a)$ is an arbitrary function of age and λ is a (complex) constant. For this form of solution to satisfy equation (3.3.10) $L(a)$ must obey

$$\frac{dL(a)}{da} + L(a)\{\gamma^*(a) + \lambda\} + f^*(a)g(a)\int_0^\infty L(x)\,dx = 0, \qquad (3.3.15)$$

from which it can be shown with yet more manipulation that $L(a)$ must be of the form

$$L(a) = L(0)\pi^*(a)\{e^{-\lambda a} - \rho_\lambda \theta_\lambda(a)\}, \qquad (3.3.16)$$

where

$$\rho_\lambda = \frac{f^*(0)\int_0^\infty \pi^*(x)e^{-\lambda x}\,dx}{1 + f^*(0)\int_0^\infty \pi^*(x)\theta_\lambda(x)\,dx} \qquad (3.3.17)$$

$$\theta_\lambda(a) = \int_0^a g(x)e^{-\lambda(a-x)}\,dx. \qquad (3.3.18)$$

and $\pi^*(a)$ is shorthand for $\pi(a, N^*)$.

We now make use of the linearized renewal condition (3.3.11) which, on substituting for $\xi(a, t)$ using equation (3.3.14) and then in turn for $L(a)$ using equation (3.3.16) gives

$$L(0) = L(0)\int_0^\infty [\beta^*(a) - \kappa]\pi^*(a)[e^{-\lambda a} - \rho_\lambda \theta_\lambda(a)]\,da. \qquad (3.3.19)$$

On multiplying out the right-hand side of this equation, and simplifying with the aid of equations (3.3.6) and (3.3.17), we finally obtain

$$\kappa\rho_\lambda = f^*(0)\int_0^\infty \pi^*(a)\beta^*(a)[e^{-\lambda a} - \rho_\lambda \theta_\lambda(a) - 1]\,da, \qquad (3.3.20)$$

a result first derived in a slightly different form by Gurtin and MacCamy (1974). For neighbourhood stability all solutions of the linearized dynamic equations (3.3.10) and (3.3.11) must decay exponentially to zero, which is guaranteed provided that all values of λ which satisfy equation (3.3.20) have negative real parts.

As it stands this stability analysis is of little real interest since equation (3.3.20) is far too complicated to admit of ready interpretation. However, from it we can derive two results of major significance for strategic modelling:

(a) If the death rate is independent of total population then a necessary and sufficient condition for neighbourhood stability is $\kappa > 0$. Since from equation (3.3.13), κ is a weighted average of $[-\partial\beta/\partial N]$ over the stationary population the requirement that κ be positive simply says that on average, increasing the population must decrease the overall birth rate.

(b) If the death rate depends only on the total population and not on age then sufficient conditions for neighbourhood stability are

$$\kappa \geqslant 0 \qquad (3.3.21)$$

$$\left[\frac{\mathrm{d}\gamma(N)}{\mathrm{d}N}\right]_{N=N^*} \geqslant 0 \qquad (3.3.22)$$

with equality permitted in at most only one of these inequalities. We have already discussed the first condition, while the second is merely a requirement that increasing the total population shall increase the per capita death rate.

The proof of (a) is straightforward. If the death rate, γ, is independent of population then $g(a) = 0$ and equations (3.3.10) and (3.3.11) are identical in form to the linear equations (3.2.2) and (3.2.4) which describe the density independent case, except that the 'birth rate' is reduced by an amount κ below the value $\beta^*(a)$ which corresponds to a stationary population. Thus, provided κ is positive, $\xi(a, t)$ must ultimately decay exponentially and the stationary state is locally stable.

The proof of (b) is more technically involved, and the reader uninterested in it may jump to the final paragraph of this section. We proceed by first setting $\lambda = -\mu + i\omega$ and then showing that provided γ is independent of a and both inequalities (3.3.21) and (3.3.22) hold, then μ must be positive so guaranteeing the local stability of the steady state. If the death rate is independent of age and has a value γ^* at the steady state then from equation (3.3.12) we see that $g(a)$ must also be age independent and will thus have a fixed value, say g^*, at the steady state. In this case the functions θ_λ and ρ_λ defined by equations (3.3.17) and (3.3.18) must take the following rather simple forms

$$\theta_\lambda(a) = \frac{g^*}{\mu - i\omega}[e^{(\mu - i\omega)a} - 1], \qquad (3.3.23)$$

$$\rho_\lambda = \frac{f^*(0)\gamma^*}{(g^*f^*(0) + \gamma^{*2} - \mu\gamma^*) + i\omega\gamma^*}. \qquad (3.3.24)$$

Substituting for $\theta_\lambda(a)$ in the stability equation (3.3.20) now yields

$$\frac{\kappa\rho_\lambda}{[g^*\rho_\lambda/(\mu - i\omega)] - 1} = f^*(0)\int_0^\infty \pi^*(a)\beta^*(a)[1 - e^{(\mu - i\omega)a}]\,\mathrm{d}a. \qquad (3.3.25)$$

If we write the real and imaginary parts of ρ_λ as ρ' and ρ'' respectively, then equality of the real parts of both sides of equation (3.3.25) requires

$$\frac{\kappa[g^*\mu(\rho'^2 + \rho''^2) - \rho'(\mu^2 + \omega^2)]}{(g^*\rho' - \mu)^2 + (g^*\rho'' + \omega)^2} = f^*(0)\int_0^\infty \pi^*(a)\beta^*(a)(1 - e^{\mu a}\cos\omega a)\,da.$$

$$(3.3.26)$$

Now suppose that this equation has a solution with $\mu < 0$, corresponding to an unstable steady state. The restrictions (equations (3.3.21) and (3.3.22)) on the density dependence of the birth and death rates imply that the constants κ and g^* are both positive, and hence that if $\mu < 0$ then the right hand side of equation (3.3.26) must be positive. But, from equation (3.3.24) if $\mu < 0$ then $\rho' > 0$ and hence the left hand side of equation (3.3.26) must be negative. Thus, since the assumption that $\mu < 0$ leads to a clear contradiction, there can be no solutions of equation (3.3.26) which correspond to unstable steady states ($\mu < 0$). Hence under the restrictions of (b) above all steady states must be locally stable.

These results are of considerable significance as they suggest that, at least in qualitative 'strategic' studies directed to the elucidation of general criteria for stability, it will frequently be safe to neglect age-structure effects. However, two caveats must accompany this assertion. First, our analysis of (b) assumes an age-independent death rate, and until some mathematically adept worker has established the effects of relaxing this assumption there remains the possibility that density dependent mortality strongly confined to certain age-groups might have a destabilizing effect. Secondly, even when destabilization does not occur, age-structure effects may be responsible for a change from overdamping to underdamping and hence (see Chapter 7) in a variable environment may cause 'quasi-cyclic' fluctuations. We develop this latter point further in Section 3.5.

B. Discrete time

In the discrete-time description of density-dependent population growth the elements of the Leslie matrix **A** (equation (3.2.17)) become functions of the total population N_t given by equation (3.2.19). If this system has a steady state then $\lambda = 0$ must be a root of equation (3.2.22), and thus from equation (3.2.25) the steady-state population N^* must be given by

$$\sum_{i=0}^m \beta_i(N^*)\pi_i(N^*) = 1, \qquad (3.3.27)$$

which is clearly the exact discrete analogue of equation (3.3.6). From equation (3.2.28) we see that if $\lambda = 0$ the steady state age distribution f_j^*, which is then simply proportional to the steady state normalized age distribution F_i^*, must be

$$f_j^* \propto \pi_j(N^*) \qquad (3.3.28)$$

We again consider small deviations from the steady state by setting

$$\xi_t \equiv \mathbf{f}_t - \mathbf{f}^*; \qquad n_t \equiv N_t - N^*, \tag{3.3.29}$$

and find that, to first order in ξ_t and n_t

$$\xi_{t+\tau} = \mathbf{A}(N^*)\xi_t + \frac{d\mathbf{A}}{dN}\mathbf{f}^* n_t \tag{3.3.30}$$

which, on rearranging and making use of the fact that $n_t = \sum_{i=0}^{m} \xi_{i,t}$ yields

$$\xi_{t+\tau} = \mathbf{B}\xi_t, \tag{3.3.31}$$

where the matrix B is defined by

$$B_{ij} = A_{ij}(N^*) + \sum_{k=1}^{m} \left(\frac{dA_{ik}}{dN}\right)_{N=N^*} f_k^*. \tag{3.3.32}$$

It now follows from an argument identical to that developed in Section 3.2B for the simple Leslie matrix, that the perturbation $\xi_{i,t}$ will either grow or decay exponentially depending on the magnitude of the eigenvalues of the matrix $\mathbf{B}$. Hence the condition for local stability is that all the eigenvalues of $\mathbf{B}$ have a modulus strictly less than unity.

This criterion for local stability is the discrete analogue of equation (3.3.20). However, because of the possibility in discrete time models of a population overcompensating for any perturbations, the simple sufficient conditions for stability (involving the density dependence of birth and death rates) which we evolved for continuous time models do not generalize to the discrete case. Thus in the analysis of any particular model there is no alternative to a complete investigation of the eigenvalues of $\mathbf{B}$. An example of such an investigation is given in Problem 7.

3.4 THE EFFECTS OF A VARIABLE ENVIRONMENT

In Sections 2.5 and 2.6 we introduced the use of transfer functions to describe the effect of environmental fluctuations on a population described by a simple differential or difference equation model. This technique is readily generalized to models with age structure, although because of the crudeness of discrete-time representations of environmental variability we shall confine our attention to the continuous time formulation.

In order to incorporate environmental variability into our model we assume that the age-specific density dependent birth and death rates of the previous section now depend also on parameters $\phi_1(t)$ and $\phi_2(t)$ which represent external environmental factors, and write

$$\beta = \beta(a, N, \phi_1(t)), \qquad \gamma = \gamma(a, N, \phi_2(t)). \tag{3.4.1}$$

We consider only birth and death rate functions whose density dependence would lead to a steady-state age distribution $f^*(a)$ and a stationary population N^* in an environment where ϕ_1 and ϕ_2 had fixed values ϕ_1^* and ϕ_2^* respectively. We describe small fluctuations about this steady state by setting

$$\xi(a, t) \equiv f(a, t) - f^*(a), \qquad n(t) \equiv N(t) - N^*,$$
$$e_1(t) \equiv \phi_1(t) - \phi_1^*, \qquad e_2(t) \equiv \phi_2(t) - \phi_2^*, \qquad (3.4.2)$$

and find that to first order in these small quantities

$$\frac{\partial \xi}{\partial t} + \frac{\partial \xi}{\partial a} + \gamma^*(a)\xi + f^*(a)g(a)n(t) + f^*(a)r(a)e_2(t) = 0, \qquad (3.4.3)$$

and

$$\xi(0, t) = Se_1(t) + \int_0^\infty [\beta^*(a) - \kappa]\xi(a, t)\, da \qquad (3.4.4)$$

where

$$r(a) \equiv \left[\frac{\partial}{\partial \phi_2} \gamma(a, N^*, \phi_2) \right]_{\phi_2 = \phi_2^*}, \qquad (3.4.5)$$

$$S \equiv \int_0^\infty f^*(a) \left[\frac{\partial}{\partial \phi_1} \beta(a, N^*, \phi_1) \right]_{\phi_1 = \phi_1^*} da, \qquad (3.4.6)$$

and all other quantities have been defined in Section 3.3. To solve the linearized dynamic equations (3.4.3) and (3.4.4) we first define $\tilde{\xi}(a, \omega), \tilde{n}(\omega), \tilde{e}_1(\omega)$ and $\tilde{e}_2(\omega)$ as the Fourier transforms with respect to time of $\xi(a, t), n(t), e_1(t)$ and $e_2(t)$ respectively. We then see that these transforms are related by

$$\frac{\partial}{\partial a} \tilde{\xi} + (\gamma^*(a) + i\omega)\tilde{\xi}(\omega) + f^*(a)g(a)\tilde{n}(\omega) + f^*(a)r(a)\tilde{e}_2(\omega) = 0 \qquad (3.4.7)$$

and

$$\tilde{\xi}(0, \omega) = S\tilde{e}_1(\omega) + \int_0^\infty [\beta^*(a) - \kappa]\tilde{\xi}(a, \omega)\, da. \qquad (3.4.8)$$

Equation (3.4.7) can now, with some considerable labour, be solved for $\tilde{\xi}(a, \omega)$. However, as we make no further use of the techniques employed we refer the interested reader to the appendix of Gurney and Nisbet (1980) and simply quote the result, which is

$$\tilde{\xi}(a, \omega) = \tilde{\xi}(0, \omega)\pi^*(a)[e^{-i\omega a} - \rho_0(\omega)\theta_0(a, \omega)]$$
$$+ f^*(a)[Y(\omega)\theta_0(a, \omega) - \Phi(a, \omega)]\tilde{e}_2(\omega) \qquad (3.4.9)$$

where

$$\Phi(a, \omega) \equiv \int_0^\infty e^{i\omega(x-a)}r(x)\, dx \qquad (3.4.10)$$

$$Y(\omega) \equiv \frac{f^*(0) \int_0^\infty \pi^*(x)\Phi(x, \omega)\, dx}{1 + f^*(0) \int_0^\infty \pi^*(x)\theta_0(x, \omega)\, dx} \qquad (3.4.11)$$

and where for the present special case of $\lambda = 0 + i\omega$ we have rewritten $\rho_{0+i\omega}$ and $\theta_{0+i\omega}(a)$ as defined in equations (3.3.17) and (3.3.18) as $\rho_0(\omega)$ and $\theta_0(a, \omega)$ respectively.

We require a simultaneous solution of the pair of transformed dynamic equations (3.4.7 and 3.4.8). Equation (3.4.9) is a solution of the transformed continuity equation (3.4.7) but is not yet also a solution of the transformed renewal condition (3.4.8). By substituting it into equation (3.4.8) we now see that equation (3.4.9) is the required simultaneous solution if

$$\tilde{\xi}(0, \omega) = \frac{S\tilde{e}_1(\omega) + \left[\int_0^\infty \{\beta^*(a) - \kappa\} Z(a, \omega)\, da \right] \tilde{e}_2(\omega)}{1 - \int_0^\infty \pi^*(a)\{\beta^*(a) - \kappa\}\{e^{-i\omega a} - \rho_0(\omega)\theta_0(a, \omega)\}\, da} \qquad (3.4.12)$$

where

$$Z(a, \omega) \equiv f^*(a)[Y(\omega)\theta_0(a, \omega) - \Phi(a, \omega)] \qquad (3.4.13)$$

Thus finally we see that for the deterministically stable system we have considered, the Fourier transform of the fluctuations in the age distribution function may be related to the transforms of the driving environmental fluctuations through a pair of age-dependent transfer functions $T_1(a, \omega)$ and $T_2(a, \omega)$ thus

$$\tilde{\xi}(a, \omega) = T_1(a, \omega)\tilde{e}_1(\omega) + T_2(a, \omega)\tilde{e}_2(\omega), \qquad (3.4.14)$$

where

$$T_1(a, \omega) = \frac{S\pi^*(a)[e^{-i\omega a} - \rho_0(\omega)\theta_0(a, \omega)]}{1 - \int_0^\infty \pi^*(a)[\beta^*(a) - \kappa][e^{-i\omega a} - \rho_0(\omega)\theta_0(a, \omega)]\, da}, \qquad (3.4.15)$$

and

$$T_2(a, \omega) = Z(a, \omega) + \frac{T_1(a, \omega)}{S} \int_0^\infty [\beta^*(x) - \kappa] Z(x, \omega)\, dx. \qquad (3.4.16)$$

Information about the fluctuations in total population is now easily obtainable by integration of equation (3.4.14) over all ages, from which it follows that the Fourier transform of the fluctuations in total population is related to the Fourier transform of the environmental variations which cause them by

$$\tilde{n}(\omega) = P_1(\omega)\tilde{e}_1(\omega) + P_2(\omega)\tilde{e}_2(\omega) \qquad (3.4.17)$$

where the 'population transfer functions' are defined as

$$P_1(\omega) \equiv \int_0^\infty T_1(a, \omega) \, \mathrm{d}a, \qquad P_2(\omega) \equiv \int_0^\infty T_2(a, \omega) \, \mathrm{d}a. \qquad (3.4.18)$$

Although the algebra involved in their derivation is tedious the interpretation of these transfer functions is no different from that of the simpler transfer function of Section 2.6. If the driving fluctuation, say $e_1(t)$, is sinusoidal then $|P_1(\omega)|$ is the ratio of the amplitudes of the population oscillations to that of the driving oscillations, while $\arg\{P_1(\omega)\}$ is the phase difference between them. If the sinusoidal driving fluctuation were $e_2(t)$ then $P_2(\omega)$ would bear an exactly similar interpretation.

3.5   OSCILLATIONS DUE TO AGE-STRUCTURE EFFECTS

We have established that, except with combined age and population dependent mortality where our analysis is incomplete, the incorporation of age-structure effects into a population model is unlikely to lead to the destabilization of a stationary state. However, nothing in our analysis precludes the occurrence of damped oscillations which may be of significance for two reasons. First, if some external environmental quantity exhibits periodic variations (e.g. annual climatic changes), and if the frequency of these external fluctuations is close to that of the damped population oscillations which would arise after a single perturbation, the effect of the external oscillations is strongly amplified and large population oscillations may result from small driving oscillations. Mathematically this 'resonance' can be detected by the existence of a peak in the graphs of the modulus of the transfer functions $P_1(\omega)$ and $P_2(\omega)$ against angular frequency (ω). Secondly, if the population fluctuations are very lightly damped then, even if the environmental fluctuations are non-cyclic in character, regular 'bursts' of oscillations—the quasicycles defined in Chapter 1—may be observed.

It is easy to construct examples of population models in which underdamping and resonance can occur as a result of age structure effects (see, for example, Problem 5), but few of these examples correspond to plausible life histories. One mechanism which can lead to this type of resonance arises in a population whose members pass through an immature, infertile phase before breeding, resonance occurring when the frequency of the driving oscillation is equal to, or to an integral multiple of, the reciprocal of the duration of the infertile phase. We devote the remainder of this section to an analysis of one such model.

We retain the notation of Section 3.4 and assume a population- and age-dependent birth rate of the form

$$\beta(a, N, \phi_1) = \begin{cases} B\alpha^{-1}\phi_1 \exp[-N/N_0] & \text{if } a_0 \leq a \leq a + \alpha, \\ 0 & \text{otherwise,} \end{cases} \qquad (3.5.1)$$

and a death rate independent of both age and population of the form

$$\gamma(a, N, \phi_2) = q\phi_2, \tag{3.5.2}$$

where B, α, N_0, and q are constants. We have parameterized these functions so that with no loss of generality we may assume $\phi_1^* = \phi_2^* = 1$ and we incorporate the effect of environmental variability by setting

$$\phi_1(t) = 1 + e_1(t), \qquad \phi_2(t) = 1 + e_2(t) \tag{3.5.3}$$

It is straightforward to calculate the steady-state population and age distribution using equations (3.3.4), (3.3.6) and (3.3.7), the results being

$$N^* = N_0 \ln\left[Be^{-qa_0}\left(\frac{1 - e^{-q\alpha}}{q\alpha}\right)\right], \tag{3.5.4}$$

and

$$f^*(a) = qN^*e^{-qa}. \tag{3.5.5}$$

After an intimidating quantity of algebra (the main steps of which are outlined in Gurney and Nisbet (1980)) the population transfer functions can be calculated analytically as

$$P_1(\omega) = \frac{N^*}{1 + \dfrac{N^*}{N_0} - \left[\dfrac{1 - e^{-(q+i\omega)\alpha}}{1 - e^{-q\alpha}}\right]e^{-i\omega a_0} + \dfrac{i\omega}{q}}, \tag{3.5.6}$$

$$P_2(\omega) = \frac{qN^*}{(q + i\omega)} \frac{1 + \left[1 - \dfrac{iq}{\omega}\right]\left[1 - \left\{\dfrac{1 - e^{-(q+i\omega)\alpha}}{1 - e^{-q\alpha}}\right\}e^{-i\omega a_0}\right] + \dfrac{i\omega}{q}}{1 + \dfrac{N^*}{N_0} - \left[\dfrac{1 - e^{-(q+i\omega)\alpha}}{1 - e^{-q\alpha}}\right]e^{-i\omega a_0} + \dfrac{i\omega}{q}} \tag{3.5.7}$$

These functions are alarmingly complicated, and we have, therefore, illustrated some of the various effects which can occur by displaying the transfer functions as explicit functions of frequency ($\omega/2\pi$) for various specific combinations of model parameters. Our primary interest is in the presence of sharp peaks in the transfer function modulus and it turns out that these can arise under two distinctly different conditions.

(a) If the total length of the reproductive cycle ($a_0 + \alpha$) is short compared with the average lifetime q^{-1} then there is a broad resonance in both $P_1(\omega)$ and $P_2(\omega)$.

(b) If the fertile age range α is much shorter than the maturation time a_0 then there is a sharp resonance in $P_1(\omega)$ at a frequency close to a_0^{-1} and a very weak resonance in $P_2(\omega)$ at the same frequency.

The 'long lifetime' (type a) resonance, illustrated in Fig. 3.2, is clearly of little significance since it requires an entirely implausible life history com-

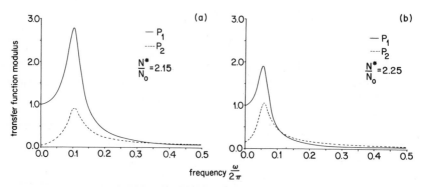

Fig. 3.2 Low frequency resonance induced by very small average death rate. $B = 10$, $\alpha = 1.0$, $q = 0.1$. (a) System with no juvenile infertility $a_0 = 0$. (b) System with juvenile infertility $a_0 = 1.0$.

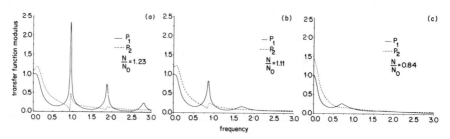

Fig. 3.3. Resonance induced by narrow fertile age range: effect of variations in fertile age range for model parameters $B = 10$, $a_0 = 1.0$, $q = 1.0$. (a) $\alpha = 0.15$. (b) $\alpha = 0.4$. (c) $\alpha = 1.0$.

posed of a short fertile phase (with or without a preceding immature period) followed by a long period of senile infertility. Careful analysis of the type (b) resonance arising from the presence of a juvenile infertile period and illustrated in Fig. 3.3 reveals that it is only sharp enough to be observable if the reproductively active phase (α) is much shorter than the period of juvenile infertility (a_0). Clearly a long maturing period followed by a short burst of intense reproductive effort is not a plausible life history for any vertebrate species, and thus resonances due to single species age-structure effects are very unlikely to be observed in vertebrate populations. However, some insects (for example the Ephemeroptera) do indeed have life cycles of precisely this kind, are therefore potentially likely to show either quasi-cyclic fluctuations driven by external noise, or a strongly amplified response to external oscillations at an appropriate frequency.

SOURCES AND SUGGESTED FURTHER READING

Models with no density dependence: The basic continuous time formalism is due to Sharpe, and Lotka (1911), although the PDE on which we based our approach appears to date from von Foerster (1959). A mathematically heavy but detailed exposition which includes a wide variety of variants on the basic formalism (e.g. two-sex models, stochastic extensions) is given in the book by Pollard (1973). Kyner and Sanchez (1978) have constructed an algorithm for obtaining the asymptotic growth rate (λ) from equation (3.2.12). The discrete time formalism is normally attributed to Leslie (1945) although Pollard (1973) reports previous papers with essentially the same model by Bernardelli (1941) and Lewis (1942). A wide range of variants on the basic Leslie model are discussed by Usher (1972). Pielou (1969), and Charlesworth (1980) give lucid introductions to both the discrete and continuous representations while the inter-relations between the different approaches are clearly explained by Goodman (1967). Streifer (1974) gives a wide-ranging review of many of the extensions of the basic continuous-time model.

Models with Density Dependence: Many complicated simulations with non-linear vital rates are reviewed by Streifer (1974). However, the key paper on age- and density-dependent population dynamics appears to be that of Gurtin and MacCamy (1974) who rigorously established our equation (3.3.20) as the condition for local stability. From this result the effects on stability of various forms of vital rates have been investigated by Gurtin and MacCamy (1978, 1979) and by Gurney and Nisbet (1980) (on which Section 3.3A is based). The special case where density dependence is restricted to the birth rate has been investigated in detail by Rorres (1976, 1979a, 1979b) and Coleman (1978). Coffman and Coleman (1978, 1979) have studied the case of a population where fertility and mortality at a particular age depend on the number of individuals of that age in the population. Discrete time models with density dependence have been studied by many workers starting with Leslie (1948); our treatment is based on Beddington (1974). Also instructive in this context is de Angelis (1975). The construction of discrete life tables for insect populations and their relevance to population modelling is treated by Varley, Gradwell, and Hassell (1973).

Variable Environment: Papers on age- and density-dependent population dynamics in a variable environment include those of Oster and Takahashi (1974), Coleman and Coffman (1979), Gurney and Nisbet (1980), and Coleman and Hsieh (1979).

PROBLEMS

(Those marked * are mathematically more demanding than the others.)

1. (Williamson, 1972). For some fish populations, once the fish reach an 'adult' state at which they are big enough to be caught there is a constant probability of survival from year to year. Such a population can be modelled as containing newborns, immatures and adults, and its growth without

harvesting is described by the 'Leslie-like' matrix

$$\begin{bmatrix} 0 & 0 & \beta \\ P_n & 0 & 0 \\ 0 & P_i & P_a \end{bmatrix}$$

where β is the average fertility of the adult and P_n, P_i, P_a are the survival probabilities from year to year of respectively newborns, immatures and adults. If a constant fraction f of the adult stock is harvested each year calculate the new Leslie-like matrix and hence calculate the maximum harvesting rate f_{max} at which the stock can be maintained.

2. A population has a constant *per capita* death rate γ and an age-dependent, but population-independent per capita birth rate of the form

$$\beta(a) = \beta_0 a e^{-\alpha a}$$

Show that the population grows exponentially if $(\gamma + \alpha)^2 < \beta_0$ and decays exponentially if $(\gamma + \alpha)^2 > \beta_0$.

3.* (Vansickle, 1977). Suppose m represents the 'physiological age' (i.e. some measure of maturity or physiological development) of individuals in a population and

$$g(m, t) = \frac{dm}{dt}.$$

Let the *per capita* birth rate depend on m and not on a, but assume all neonates have physiological age zero. Then if $f(m, t)dm$ is the number of individuals at time t with physiological age between m and $m + dm$,

$$f(0, t) = \int_0^\infty \beta(m, t) f(m, t) \, dm.$$

Let γ be the per capita death rate of individuals of physiological age m and let

$$\tau(m) = \int_0^m \frac{dz}{g(z)},$$

$$l(m) = \exp\left[-\int_0^m \frac{\gamma(z)}{g(z)} \, dz\right].$$

Show that the population eventually grows or decays exponentially as $e^{\lambda t}$ where (cf. equation (3.2.12))

$$1 = \int_0^\infty \exp\{-\lambda \tau(m)\} \frac{\beta(m) l(m)}{g(m)} \, dm.$$

4. (Pollard, 1973; May, 1976d). A population with density-independent birth and death rates has achieved a stable age distribution and is growing

exponentially at a rate λ, i.e.

$$\int_0^\infty e^{-\lambda a}\beta(a)\pi(a)\,\mathrm{d}a = 1 \tag{A}$$

Define the *mean generation time T* by

$$T \equiv \frac{\displaystyle\int_0^\infty a\beta(a)\pi(a)\,\mathrm{d}a}{\displaystyle\int_0^\infty \beta(a)\pi(a)\,\mathrm{d}a} \tag{B}$$

and let R be the average number of offspring produced by a single individual, i.e.

$$R = \int_0^\infty \beta(a)\pi(a)\,\mathrm{d}a. \tag{C}$$

(a) By expanding the exponential in equation (A) show that if the population is growing slowly, i.e. $\lambda T \ll 1$, then

$$\lambda \simeq \frac{(R-1)}{T}$$

(b*) If the function $\beta(a)\pi(a)$ can be approximated by a normal distribution with standard deviation σ, i.e.

$$\beta(a)\pi(a) = \frac{R}{\sqrt{(2\pi)}\sigma} \exp \frac{(a-T)^2}{2\sigma^2}$$

with $\sigma \ll T$, show that

$$\lambda \simeq T^{-1} \ln R.$$

(c) Usher (1972) proposes that in the 1930s a Leslie matrix for the blue whale *Balaenoptera musculus* was

$$A = \begin{bmatrix} 0 & 0 & 0.19 & 0.44 & 0.50 & 0.50 & 0.45 \\ 0.57 & 0 & 0 & 0 & 0 & 0 & 0 \\ 0 & 0.87 & 0 & 0 & 0 & 0 & 0 \\ 0 & 0 & 0.87 & 0 & 0 & 0 & 0 \\ 0 & 0 & 0 & 0.87 & 0 & 0 & 0 \\ 0 & 0 & 0 & 0 & 0.87 & 0 & 0 \\ 0 & 0 & 0 & 0 & 0 & 0.87 & 0.80 \end{bmatrix}$$

whose maximum eigenvalue is 1.0986. Write down discrete analogues for equation (B) and (C), calculate T and R, and hence test the accuracy of the above formulae for λ.

5.* (Gurtin and MacCamy, 1974). Suppose we have a *per capita* birth rate of the form

$$\beta(a, N) = \beta_0(N)e^{-\alpha a},$$

and a per capita death rate $\gamma(N)$ which depends only on N.

(a) Show that if there is a stationary state N^*, then

$$\beta_0(N^*) = \gamma(N^*) + \alpha$$

and that this stationary population is locally stable if

$$\frac{dR(N)}{dN} < 0,$$

where

$$R(N) \equiv \int_0^\infty \beta(a, N)\pi(a, N)\, da.$$

(b) Show that if $\beta_0(N)$ is independent of N, then the system is over-damped, but if $\gamma(N)$ is constant and the population is regulated purely through the birth rate, then the system may be overdamped or underdamped.

6.* (Usher, 1972; Beddington, 1974). A simple model with three age classes in which the sole effect of crowding is a reduction in the probability of survival of juveniles has Leslie matrix

$$\begin{bmatrix} 0 & 9 & 12 \\ S & 0 & 0 \\ 0 & \tfrac{1}{2} & 0 \end{bmatrix}$$

where $S = \tfrac{1}{3}[1 + \exp\{N/A - C\}]^{-1}$ (A, C constant)

(a) Show that the steady state population N^* is given by

$$N^* = A(\ln 4 + C)$$

(b) Show that the stability matrix B in equation (3.3.32) is

$$\begin{bmatrix} 0 & 9 & 12 \\ \tfrac{1}{15}-\theta & -\theta & -\theta \\ 0 & \tfrac{1}{2} & 0 \end{bmatrix}$$

where $\theta = 8(\ln 4 + C)/165$.

(c) Using the Routh–Hurrwitz criteria (introduced in Chapter 4) show that the steady state can become unstable (with divergent oscillations) if C is sufficiently large.

7.* To see that the oscillations in problem 6 are related to the discrete-time formulation we consider a continuous-time model in which the sole density-dependent factor is the mortality of newborns. Let

$$\gamma(a, N) = g(N)\delta_{\text{Dirac}}(a) + \mu$$

where $\delta_{\text{Dirac}}(a)$ is the 'Dirac δ-function' discussed in Appendix D and $g(N) > 0$ for all N. Show that if a stationary state exists, then it is stable for the following birth rates.

(a) $\beta(a) = \beta_0 e^{-\alpha a}$

(b) $\beta(a) = \beta_0 a\, e^{-\alpha a}$

$$\left[\text{Hint: For (a) define } B = \int_0^\infty \beta(a) f(a, t)\, \mathrm{d}a \text{ and obtain a pair of differential equations in } N \text{ and } B. \right.$$

$$\left. \text{For (b) define } D = \int_0^\infty \beta_0 e^{-\alpha a} f(a, t)\, \mathrm{d}a \text{ and obtain three simultaneous differential equations in } N, B, D. \right]$$

Chapter 4

Models of Interacting Species

4.1 INTRODUCTION

In Chapter 2 we studied simple differential and difference equation models of a single species population. We then investigated the effects of such complicating factors as a variable environment, time delays, and age structure. The result was a bewildering variety of possible types of dynamical behaviour and we therefore attempted to assess the relative ecological importance of different dynamic regimes. The principal conclusion was that in natural populations deterministic stability was to be expected, with overdamping more probable than underdamping.

We now extend our analysis to cover the case of interacting species and it is obvious that this extension could lead to an even greater variety of possible dynamic regimes. For example, a lifetime could easily be devoted to the study of three-species differential equation models without exhausting the questions of mathematical interest. We must, therefore, be highly selective in the questions we pose, and in this chapter we attempt to present the discussion of many-species models primarily in terms of concepts whose importance has already been established in the single-species case. Thus we start with a formal analysis of steady states, local and global stability, effects of a varying environment, and limit cycles. As with the single-species models the techniques based on local linearization are systematic and in principle straightforward (although they may be algebraically somewhat tedious), while no similar systematic approach to non-linear phenomena exists. We therefore consider the question of how necessary is non-linear analysis of many-species systems. We conclude that subject to certain restrictions, whose interpretation we discuss later, the linear techniques are of use in a much wider range of situations than those for which they were originally derived.

Much of the mathematics involved in the analysis of many-species models becomes very cumbersome unless we use matrix formalism and the principal results we require are summarized in Appendix M. However, many workers will only wish to use the methods in this chapter on two-species models for which matrix formalism has few advantages. We have, therefore, treated the theory of two-species models separately from, and in advance of, the general case of M-species models. As a result the uninterested reader may safely omit the more general formalism while the reader tackling the general case is strongly advised to interpret any intimidating expressions by identifying their two-species counterparts.

4.2   NEIGHBOURHOOD STABILITY ANALYSIS

A. Differential equation model of two interacting species

We consider an idealized system consisting of two interacting species and denote by $N_1(t)$, $N_2(t)$ the populations of the two species at time t. We assume initially that the environment is unchanging (though this assumption is relaxed later) and also neglect the effects of time delays or age structure. The populations then follow differential equations of the form

$$\dot{N}_1 = G_1(N_1, N_2), \tag{4.2.1}$$

$$\dot{N}_2 = G_2(N_1, N_2), \tag{4.2.2}$$

where $\dot{}$ denotes d/dt. We assume that the equations have a steady state solution (N_1^*, N_2^*) which satisfies

$$G_1(N_1^*, N_2^*) = 0, \qquad G_2(N_1^*, N_2^*) = 0, \tag{4.2.3}$$

and in which both the individual populations (N_1^* and N_2^*) are positive.

The neighbourhood stability analysis of the two-species model defined by equations (4.2.1) and (4.2.2) is similar in spirit to that for single-species models. Our interest is again in small fluctuations from the steady state, so we define

$$n_1 \equiv N_1 - N_1^*, \qquad n_2 \equiv N_2 - N_2^*, \tag{4.2.4}$$

and hence on expanding $G_1(N_1, N_2)$ about the steady state, obtain

$$G_1(N_1, N_2) = G_1(N_1^*, N_2^*) + \left(\frac{\partial G}{\partial N_1}\right)^* n_1 + \left(\frac{\partial G}{\partial N_2}\right)^* n_2 + 0(n^2), \tag{4.2.5}$$

where the star on a partial derivative indicates that it is evaluated with both populations at their steady-state values. The notation $0(n^2)$ represents terms 'of order n^2 or higher', i.e. terms involving products of two or more n's. A similar equation can be written for $G_2(N_1, N_2)$. Equation (4.2.5) is simply the two-species analogue of equations (2.4.5) and (2.4.6), and we obtain the analogue of the linear differential equation (2.4.8) by noting from the steady-state condition (equation (4.2.3)) that $G_1(N_1^*, N_2^*)$ and $G_2(N_1^*, N_2^*)$ are both zero and that near the steady-state terms of order n^2 should be negligible compared to terms of order n. Thus to a good approximation

$$\dot{n}_1 = A_{11}n_1 + A_{12}n_2, \tag{4.2.6}$$

$$\dot{n}_2 = A_{21}n_1 + A_{22}n_2, \tag{4.2.7}$$

where

$$A_{ij} = \left(\frac{\partial G_i}{\partial N_j}\right)^*, \quad \begin{matrix} i = 1, 2. \\ j = 1, 2. \end{matrix} \tag{4.2.8}$$

The four coefficients A_{ij} are constants and so we now have a pair of simultaneous *linear* differential equations which we solve by continuing to exploit the analogy with the single species case and initially assuming solutions of the form

$$n_1 = u_1 e^{\lambda t}, \quad n_2 = u_2 e^{\lambda t}, \tag{4.2.9}$$

where u_1 and u_2 are constants. Substituting these solutions in the differential equations (4.2.6) and (4.2.7) and rearranging the terms yields

$$(A_{11} - \lambda)u_1 + A_{12} u_2 = 0, \tag{4.2.10}$$

$$A_{21}u_1 + (A_{22} - \lambda) u_2 = 0. \tag{4.2.11}$$

These equations each yield a *different* expression for the ratio u_1/u_2, namely

$$\frac{u_1}{u_2} = -\frac{A_{12}}{A_{11} - \lambda},$$

and $\qquad\qquad\qquad\qquad\qquad\qquad\qquad\qquad\qquad\qquad\qquad$ (4.2.12)

$$\frac{u_1}{u_2} = -\frac{A_{22} - \lambda}{A_{21}},$$

but since they represent a single quantity these expressions must clearly be equal

$$\frac{A_{12}}{A_{11} - \lambda} = \frac{A_{22} - \lambda}{A_{21}}, \tag{4.2.13}$$

so that we can calculate λ in terms of the coefficients A_{ij} from

$$\lambda^2 + a_1\lambda + a_2 = 0, \tag{4.2.14}$$

with

$$\begin{aligned} a_1 &= -(A_{11} + A_{22}), \\ a_2 &= A_{11}A_{22} - A_{12}A_{21}. \end{aligned} \tag{4.2.15}$$

Equation (4.2.14) is a quadratic equation whose two roots (λ_1 and λ_2) are

$$\begin{aligned} \lambda_1 &= \tfrac{1}{2}[-a_1 + \sqrt{(a_1^2 - 4a_2)}], \\ \lambda_2 &= \tfrac{1}{2}[-a_1 - \sqrt{(a_1^2 - 4a_2)}]. \end{aligned} \tag{4.2.16}$$

Thus (unless λ_1 and λ_2 are equal) we have found two independent solutions of the differential equations. However, it is a standard mathematical result that the most general possible solution of a pair of simultaneous, linear first-order differential equations is a sum of exactly two independent solutions. Thus we have found the most general possible solution of the differential equations which must be of the form

$$n_1 = u_{11}e^{\lambda_1 t} + u_{12}e^{\lambda_2 t}, \tag{4.2.17}$$

$$n_2 = u_{21}e^{\lambda_1 t} + u_{22}e^{\lambda_2 t}, \tag{4.2.18}$$

where the constants u_{ij} can be determined (by a procedure of no relevance in the present context) from a knowledge of the population perturbations at some particular time (usually taken to be $t = 0$). The case where λ_1 and λ_2 are equal is seldom of practical interest in modelling since an infinitesimal change in one of the A_{ij}s will normally remove the problem. However, for completeness we note that in the case of equal roots the general solution is of the form

$$n_1 = u_{11}e^{\lambda t} + u_{12}t\, e^{\lambda t}, \tag{4.2.19}$$

(with a similar expression for n_2) whose behaviour at large values of t is dominated by the exponential terms.

For *local stability* of the steady state we require that all small perturbations shall ultimately decay to zero, and from the solutions (4.2.17) and (4.2.18) (or in the special case (4.2.19)), it is clear that this is guaranteed if either:

(a) λ_1 and λ_2 are both real and negative, or
(b) λ_1 and λ_2 are complex but have negative real parts.

In the first case the population ultimately approaches the steady state exponentially (though it may 'overshoot' once) and the system is *overdamped*. In the second, the roots are of the form

$$\lambda = -\mu \pm i\omega \tag{4.2.20}$$

where

$$\mu = \tfrac{1}{2}a_1, \qquad \omega = \tfrac{1}{2}\sqrt{(4a_2 - a_1^2)}, \tag{4.2.21}$$

and when the constants u_{11}, u_{12} are evaluated they turn out to be complex conjugates of each other. Thus n_1 is of the form

$$n_1 = v_{11}e^{-\mu t} \cos \omega t + v_{12}e^{-\mu t} \sin \omega t, \tag{4.2.22}$$

when v_{11}, v_{12} are real constants. The return to the steady state now involves a series of damped oscillations, and the system is *underdamped*. Examples of both overdamped and underdamped behaviour are shown in Fig. 4.1.

In many applications (particularly in strategic modelling) the explicit expressions for n_1 and n_2 are of little or no interest and it is very useful to note that we can check on stability *without evaluating* the roots λ_1 and λ_2 since from (4.2.16) we can see that necessary and sufficient conditions for the roots to be negative or to have negative real parts are

$$a_1 > 0,$$
$$a_2 > 0. \tag{4.2.23}$$

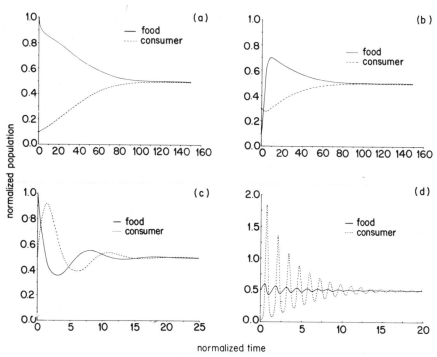

Fig. 4.1 Return of a two-species predator–prey system to a stable equilibrium. (a) Overdamped—first initial condition. (b) Overdamped—second initial condition. (c) Marginally underdamped. (d) Considerably underdamped.

The reader familiar with matrix theory may prefer to define a matrix

$$\mathbf{A} \equiv \begin{bmatrix} A_{11} & A_{12} \\ A_{21} & A_{22} \end{bmatrix} \tag{4.2.24}$$

and note from equation (4.2.15) that the stability conditions can be written in the form

$$a_1 = -\text{trace } \mathbf{A} > 0,$$
$$a_2 = \det \mathbf{A} > 0. \tag{4.2.25}$$

where the *trace* of a matrix is simply the sum of the elements in the principal diagonal (top left—bottom right) and the *determinant* is a more complicated function of the matrix elements defined and discussed in Appendix M.

B. Differential equation model of *M* interacting species

We now generalize the theory of the previous section to the case of *M* species. Here the population dynamics are specified by a set of differential equations of the form

$$\dot{N}_1 = G_1(N_1, N_2 \ \ldots \ N_M),$$
$$\dot{N}_1 = G_2(N_1, N_2 \ \ldots \ N_M),$$
$$\vdots$$
$$\dot{N}_M = G_M(N_1, N_2 \ \ldots \ N_M). \tag{4.2.26}$$

which can be written more concisely using matrix notation if we define the column vectors

$$\mathbf{N} \equiv \begin{bmatrix} N_1 \\ N_2 \\ \vdots \\ N_M \end{bmatrix} \quad \text{and} \quad \mathbf{G} \equiv \begin{bmatrix} G_1 \\ G_2 \\ \vdots \\ G_M \end{bmatrix} \tag{4.2.27}$$

in terms of which we have

$$\dot{\mathbf{N}} = \mathbf{G}(\mathbf{N}). \tag{4.2.28}$$

At a steady state

$$G_i(N_1^*, N_2^*, \ldots N_M^*) = 0, \qquad \text{for } i = 1, 2 \ldots M, \tag{4.2.29}$$

or more concisely

$$\mathbf{G}(\mathbf{N}^*) = 0. \tag{4.2.30}$$

The linear differential equations obeyed by the perturbations $n_i (= N_i - N_i^*)$ of the individual populations from their steady state values are derived exactly as with the two-species case with the result

$$\dot{n}_i = \sum_{j=1}^{M} A_{ij} n_j, \qquad i = 1, 2 \ldots M. \tag{4.2.31}$$

where

$$A_{ij} \equiv \left(\frac{\partial G_i}{\partial N_j} \right)^* \tag{4.2.32}$$

Equation (4.2.31) represents a set of simultaneous, linear differential equations which can also be written more concisely using matrix notation. If

$$\mathbf{n} \equiv \begin{bmatrix} n_1 \\ n_2 \\ \vdots \\ n_M \end{bmatrix} \quad \mathbf{A} \equiv \begin{bmatrix} A_{11} & A_{12} & \cdots & A_{1M} \\ \vdots & \vdots & & \vdots \\ \vdots & \vdots & & \vdots \\ A_{M1} & A_{M2} & \cdots & A_{MM} \end{bmatrix} \tag{4.2.33}$$

then using the rules for matrix multiplication (see Appendix M)

$$\dot{\mathbf{n}} = \mathbf{An}. \tag{4.2.34}$$

We investigate the solution of equation (4.2.34) by our well-tried method of assuming a solution of the form

$$\mathbf{n} = \mathbf{n}_0 e^{\lambda t} \tag{4.2.35}$$

where $\mathbf{n}_0$ is the column vector containing the perturbation of each population at time $t = 0$. Substituting this assumed form in the differential equations yields

$$\lambda \mathbf{n}_0 e^{\lambda t} = \mathbf{A} \mathbf{n}_0 e^{\lambda t}, \tag{4.2.36}$$

which, since $e^{\lambda t}$ is never identically zero, reduces to

$$(\mathbf{A} - \lambda \mathbf{I})\mathbf{n}_0 = \mathbf{0} \tag{4.2.37}$$

where $\mathbf{I}$ is the $M \times M$ unit matrix and $\mathbf{0}$ is a column vector of zeros. It is a standard mathematical result that this equation only possesses a non-trivial solution (i.e. a solution with $\mathbf{n}_0$ not identically zero) if

$$\det (\mathbf{A} - \lambda \mathbf{I}) = 0 \tag{4.2.38}$$

where 'det' denotes the determinant of the matrix which is evaluated using rules given in Appendix M. In this case the determinant is a polynomial of degree M in λ and equation (4.2.38) thus has exactly M roots. It follows that provided the roots are all distinct there are exactly M possible independent solutions of the form in equation (4.2.35). However, it is also a standard mathematical result that the most general solution of a set of M simultaneous, linear first-order differential equations is a sum of exactly M independent solutions. Thus if the roots of equation (4.2.38), which are known as eigenvalues of the matrix $\mathbf{A}$, are distinct, then *the most general possible solution of the linear differential equation (4.2.34) is a sum of solutions each proportional to $e^{\lambda_j t}$ where the various λ_j's are all eigenvalues of* $\mathbf{A}$. The case where the eigenvalues are not all distinct is seldom of practical interest in modelling since an infinitesimal change in one of the matrix elements will normally remove the problem. However, in this case the occurrence of k equal roots (λ) of equation (4.2.38) merely leads to k solutions of the form

$$n_j = (\text{polynomial in } t) \times e^{\lambda t}, \tag{4.2.39}$$

whose behaviour at large values of t is dominated by the exponential term.

For local stability of the steady state we require that all small perturbations will ultimately decay to zero, and it is now obvious that this is guaranteed *provided all the eigenvalues of* $\mathbf{A}$, which we write as

$$\lambda_j \equiv -\mu_j + i\omega_j, \qquad (\mu_j, \omega_j \text{ real}) \tag{4.2.40}$$

have negative real parts ($\mu_j > 0$ for all j). If *any* eigenvalue of $\mathbf{A}$ has a positive real part ($\mu_j < 0$ for some j), the steady state is unstable. However, the con-

Table 4.1. The Routh–Hurwitz stability criteria (from May, 1974b).

Number of species M	Stability criteria
2	$a_1 > 0; a_2 > 0$
3	$a_1 > 0; a_3 > 0; a_1a_2 > a_3$
4	$a_1 > 0; a_3 > 0; a_4 > 0$
	$a_1a_2a_3 > a_3^2 + a_1^2a_4$
5	$a_i > 0$ for all i; $a_1a_2a_3 > a_3^2 + a_1^2a_4$
	$(a_1a_4 - a_5)(a_1a_2a_3 - a_3^2 - a_1^2a_4) > a_5(a_1a_2 - a_3)^2 + a_1a_5^2$

cepts of over- and under-damping, which we have deliberately defined in terms of oscillatory or non-oscillatory approach to equilibrium, become somewhat impractical to apply to systems with more than two species. It is certainly true that if all the eigenvalues of **A** are real and negative ($\omega = 0$, $\mu > 0$) the system is overdamped and the approach to equilibrium involves at most a finite number of overshoots and no true oscillations. However, if one pair of eigenvalues (say $\lambda_r = -\mu_1 + i\omega$, $\lambda_s = -\mu_1 - i\omega$) is complex, then depending on the relative magnitudes of μ_1 and the other μ_j's (and also weakly on the initial conditions) the approach to a steady state may or may not appear oscillatory.

The eigenvalues of an $M \times M$ matrix are the roots of an Mth degree polynomial and hence (except when $M = 1$ or 2) cannot be conveniently evaluated analytically. However, there are some very useful mathematical theorems which provide necessary and sufficient conditions for all the eigenvalues of a matrix to have negative real parts, without involving explicit calculation of the eigenvalues. The eigenvalues of **A** are the roots of equation (4.2.38) which we can write explicitly in the form

$$\lambda^M + a_1\lambda^{M-1} + \ldots + a_M = 0 \qquad (4.2.41)$$

where a recipe for the coefficients a_i in terms of the original matrix elements is given in Appendix M. The stability conditions (known as the Routh–Hurrwitz criteria) now involve only these coefficients but in their general form they are not particularly enlightening. The particular results for $M \le 5$ are listed in Table 4.1. It can easily be seen that by the time we reach $M = 5$ the number of inequalities is increasing rapidly and we cannot dissent from May's (1974b) observation that 'no-one in their right mind is going to use these criteria on $M > 5$'. However, with small numbers of species the inequalities are readily evaluated and they constitute one of the most powerful and widely used theoretical tools in deterministic population modelling.

C. Difference equation model of M interacting species

Except in certain host-parasitoid models it is highly unlikely that the discrete generations of interacting species will be identical in length and the bulk of this chapter is therefore concerned with differential equation models. However, it is worth while to indicate briefly how the results of the differential equation analysis are modified when we consider difference equations since, as well as being applicable to those situations where we model a system by difference equations, the results are applicable to situations where we *approximate* differential equations by difference equations, for example in the time-series analysis of census data.

The difference equation model is of the form (analogous to equation (2.2.3))

$$\Delta N_i \equiv N_i(t) - N_i(t - \tau) = \tau G_i(N_1, N_2, \ldots, N_M), \qquad i = 1, 2, \ldots, M.$$

$$(4.2.42)$$

the right-hand expression of course being evaluated at time $t - \tau$. Obviously the differential equations (4.2.26) are the result of taking the limit $\tau \to 0$ in this expression.

Neighbourhood stability analysis for the system is performed in exactly the same way as for the differential equations. We first linearize about the steady state, with the result (analogous to equation (4.2.31))

$$n_i(t) - n_i(t - \tau) = \tau \sum_{j=1}^{M} A_{ij} n_j(t - \tau), \qquad i = 1, \ldots M. \quad (4.2.43)$$

When we assume a solution of these equations of the form

$$\mathbf{n}(t) = \mathbf{n}_0 e^{\lambda t}, \qquad (4.2.44)$$

then in place of equation (4.2.37) we obtain

$$[\mathbf{A} - \tau^{-1}(e^{\lambda \tau} - 1)\mathbf{I}]\mathbf{n}_0 = 0. \qquad (4.2.45)$$

(The reader should check that this reduces to equation (4.2.37) in the limit of small τ by expanding the exponential to first order in τ). Thus if we define

$$z \equiv \tau^{-1}(e^{\lambda \tau} - 1), \qquad (4.2.46)$$

then z is an eigenvalue of $\mathbf{A}$. The equation defining z can be rearranged to give

$$\lambda = \tau^{-1} \ln(1 + z\tau), \qquad (4.2.47)$$

and for neighbourhood stability we require that the real part of λ is negative. The real part of the logarithm of a complex number is equal to the logarithm of its modulus (see, for example, Copson, 1962, p. 47) and hence for stability we require

$$Re\{\lambda\} = \tau^{-1} \ln |1 + z\tau| < 0 \qquad (4.2.48)$$

This in turn implies

$$|1 + z\tau| < 1 \qquad (4.2.49)$$

i.e.

$$|\tau^{-1} + z| < \tau^{-1} \qquad (4.2.50)$$

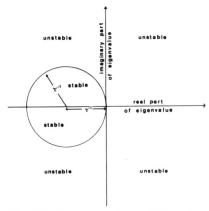

Fig. 4.2 Domain of stability for M-species difference equation model.

and thus for stability the eigenvalues of $\mathbf{A}$ must lie in a circle in the complex plane, centre τ^{-1}, and radius τ^{-1} as shown in Fig. 4.2. May (1974b), pp. 219–20, quotes some useful algebraic short cuts in testing these inequalities for two- and three-species models.

4.3 'DRIVEN' SYSTEMS

In Chapter 2 we demonstrated for single-species models a linear analysis of the effect of fluctuating environmental parameters, emphasizing the role of transfer functions which relate the Fourier transforms of the driving fluctuations and the population fluctuations. We now generalize this analysis first to two-species and then to many-species models.

A. Two-species differential equation models

We consider the effects of a single time-dependent parameter $\phi(t)$ whose mean value over a long period of time is ϕ^*. To emphasize this parameter we write the differential equations as

$$\dot{N}_1 = G_1(N_1, N_2, \phi(t)), \tag{4.3.1}$$

$$\dot{N}_2 = G_2(N_1, N_2, \phi(t)). \tag{4.3.2}$$

Provided a steady-state solution of these equations (with $\phi(t)$ held constant at ϕ^*) is deterministically stable, small fluctuations in ϕ about its mean value cause small population fluctuations. If (cf. equation (2.5.2)) we define

$$f(t) \equiv \phi(t) - \phi^*, \tag{4.3.3}$$

then on expanding G_1 and G_2 about the steady state and dropping terms of second or higher order in n and ϕ, we obtain

$$\dot{n}_1 = G_1(N_1^*, N_2^*, \phi^*) + \left(\frac{\partial G_1}{\partial N_1}\right)^* n_1 + \left(\frac{\partial G_1}{\partial N_2}\right)^* n_2 + \left(\frac{\partial G_1}{\partial \phi}\right)^* f(t) + 0(n^2),$$

(4.3.4)

where the * on a partial derivative indicates that it is evaluated at the steady state with $\phi = \phi^*$. Recognizing that $G_1(N_1^*, N_2^*, \phi^*) = 0$ and assuming that all fluctuating quantities are small enable us to simplify equation (4.3.4) to

$$\dot{n}_1 = A_{11}n_1 + A_{12}n_2 + \alpha_1 f(t),$$

(4.3.5)

where A_{11} and A_{12} were defined in Section (4.2A) and

$$\alpha_i \equiv \left(\frac{\partial G_i}{\partial \phi}\right)^*, \qquad \text{for } i = 1, 2.$$

(4.3.6)

A similar equation, namely

$$\dot{n}_2 = A_{21}n_1 + A_{22}n_2 + \alpha_2 f(t),$$

(4.3.7)

holds for the second species.

As in the single-species case the full mathematical solution of equations (4.3.5) and (4.3.7) is the sum of a transient, initial-condition dependent, 'complementary function' and a persisting 'particular integral' which is independent of initial conditions. Where our prime interest is in the persisting fluctuations it is convenient to use Fourier transforms to convert our two simultaneous *differential* equations into two simultaneous *algebraic* equations. Fourier transformation of equations (4.3.5) and (4.3.7) yields (on using equation (F32))

$$i\omega \tilde{n}_1(\omega) = A_{11}\tilde{n}_1(\omega) + A_{12}\tilde{n}_2(\omega) + \alpha_1\tilde{\phi}(\omega),$$

(4.3.8)

$$i\omega \tilde{n}_2(\omega) = A_{21}\tilde{n}_1(\omega) + A_{22}\tilde{n}_2(\omega) + \alpha_2\tilde{\phi}(\omega).$$

(4.3.9)

Solving these two equations involves only routine, if tedious, elementary algebra with the result that the relationship between the Fourier transforms of the population fluctuations and of the driving environmental fluctuations is of the form

$$\tilde{n}_1(\omega) = T_1(\omega)\tilde{\phi}(\omega),$$

$$\tilde{n}_2(\omega) = T_2(\omega)\tilde{\phi}(\omega),$$

the transfer functions $T_1(\omega)$ and $T_2(\omega)$ being given by

$$T_1(\omega) = \frac{A_{12}\alpha_2 - A_{22}\alpha_1 + i\omega\alpha_1}{(\omega_0^2 - \omega^2) + i\omega\beta},$$

(4.3.11)

$$T_2(\omega) = \frac{A_{21}\alpha_1 - A_{11}\alpha_2 + i\omega\alpha_2}{(\omega_0^2 - \omega^2) + i\omega\beta},$$

(4.3.12)

where the quantities

$$\beta \equiv -(A_{11} + A_{22}),$$
$$\omega_0^2 \equiv A_{11}A_{22} - A_{12}A_{21}$$

(4.3.13)

are both guaranteed positive provided that the original steady state was stable.

In the case where the input fluctuations in $\phi(t)$ are sinusoidal, the moduli of the transfer functions $T_1(\omega)$ and $T_2(\omega)$ simply represent the ratios of the amplitudes of the oscillations in the two populations to the amplitude of the oscillations in ϕ. These moduli can take several very characteristic forms, which we illustrate in Fig. 4.3.

If $\beta \ll \omega_0$ then by noticing that β and ω_0^2, although so named for ease of future interpretation, are in fact identical to the a_1 and a_2 of equation (4.2.15), we see at once from equation (4.2.16) that in the absence of any driving fluctuations the system would be significantly *underdamped* and would exhibit a transient consisting of decaying oscillations with an angular frequency close to ω_0. In this case the modulus of the transfer function always takes on the characteristic shape shown in Fig. 4.3(a), with a single sharp

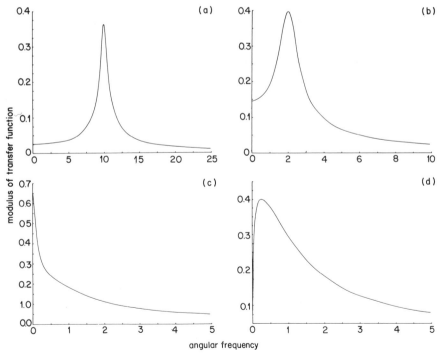

Fig. 4.3. Typical transfer functions for a two-species system. (a) Considerably underdamped: $\beta \ll \omega_0$. (b) Marginally underdamped: $\beta \lesssim 2\omega_0$. (c) Overdamped, $\beta \gg \omega_0$: normal case. (d) Overdamped, $\beta \gg \omega_0$: special case with zero response at low frequencies.

maximum centred on an angular frequency close to the 'natural frequency' ω_0. It is thus clear that the response of such a population to any sinusoidal driving oscillation will be particularly pronounced if the driving frequency is close to the natural frequency of the system. Where the driving fluctuations are not oscillatory, we saw in Section 2.6 that they may still be represented (using a Fourier series) as a sum of sinusoidal components. In this case any Fourier components of the driving fluctuations with frequencies close to the natural frequency are strongly amplified and dominate the Fourier representation of the population fluctuations which as a result appear quasi-cyclic. These effects are mathematically similar to resonance in physical systems where large oscillations can be generated by external oscillations of either single frequency (e.g. breaking glass by a sound of a particular pitch) or of a wide spectrum of frequencies (e.g. the destruction of the Tacoma Narrows Bridge by wind in 1940). However, the analogy with resonance in physical systems should not be over-emphasized, as the 'resonances' presently under discussion differ in many other aspects from physical resonances, probably the most important being that energy transfer is of no significance in the present context.

In the second case of interest ($\beta \gg \omega_0$), where the undriven behaviour of the system would be heavily overdamped, the transfer function modulus takes on one of the two characteristic forms shown in Figs. 4.3(c) and 4.3(d). The behaviour represented by Fig. 4.3(c) is essentially similar to the single species case of Section 2.5; the population tracks external fluctuations with angular frequencies less than β but cannot respond fast enough to follow more rapid oscillations. The function displayed in Fig. 4.3(d) characterizes a system whose high-frequency behaviour is essentially the same as that of Fig. 4.3(c) but which in addition responds only weakly to low frequency disturbances. Since there is, of necessity, a maximum in such a transfer function it might be supposed that this type of system might also exhibit quasi-cyclic fluctuations in certain circumstances. However, in Chapter 7 we shall see that this does not in fact happen.

Lastly we consider the case of weak resonance ($\beta \lesssim 2\omega_0$) shown in Fig. 4.3(b). Mathematically the system is underdamped if $\beta < 2\omega_0$ but substantially smaller values of β are required before either damped oscillations in a static environment or quasi-cycles in a fluctuating environment become significant (as population data is normally too imprecise for tiny oscillations to be observable). A useful measure of whether a system is significantly underdamped, and thus of whether resonance effects might be observable in practice, is the *coherence* number n_c which we define to be the number of cycles over which a population exhibiting damped oscillations in a static environment has the amplitude of those cycles reduced by a factor e^{-1} ($\approx 37\%$). In the present two-species systems the coherence number has a value

$$n_c = \frac{1}{\pi} \sqrt{\left(\frac{\omega_0^2}{\beta^2} - \frac{1}{4} \right)}, \qquad (4.3.14)$$

which reduces to $n_c \simeq \omega_0/(\pi\beta)$ if β is small. We discuss quasi-cycles in more detail in Chapter 7, but for the present a satisfactory rule of thumb is that significant resonance is only observed if $n_c \geq 1$.

B. Many-species differential equation models

We now generalize the concepts introduced in the previous section to the case of M interacting species. Using the vector notation introduced in the previous section we write the differential equations in the concise form

$$\dot{\mathbf{N}} = \mathbf{G}(\mathbf{N}, \phi(t)). \qquad (4.3.15)$$

If $\mathbf{N}^*$ denotes the vector of steady state populations when ϕ is held at a constant value ϕ^*, and

$$f(t) = \phi(t) - \phi^*, \qquad (4.3.16)$$

then for small fluctuations about the steady state

$$\dot{\mathbf{n}} = \mathbf{A}\,\mathbf{n} + \boldsymbol{\alpha} f(t), \qquad (4.3.17)$$

where $\mathbf{n}$ and $\mathbf{A}$ have already been defined in Section 4.2, and

$$\boldsymbol{\alpha} \equiv \begin{bmatrix} \left(\dfrac{\partial G_1}{\partial \phi}\right)^* \\[2ex] \left(\dfrac{\partial G_2}{\partial \phi}\right)^* \\[2ex] \vdots \\[2ex] \left(\dfrac{\partial G_M}{\partial \phi}\right)^* \end{bmatrix} \qquad (4.3.18)$$

To investigate the persisting fluctuations caused by the external variable ϕ we Fourier transform equation (4.3.17), yielding

$$i\omega\tilde{\mathbf{n}}(\omega) = \mathbf{A}\tilde{\mathbf{n}}(\omega) + \boldsymbol{\alpha}\tilde{f}(\omega) \qquad (4.3.19)$$

and hence

$$\tilde{\mathbf{n}}(\omega) = (i\omega\mathbf{I} - \mathbf{A})^{-1}\boldsymbol{\alpha}\tilde{f}(\omega) \qquad (4.3.20)$$

Evaluation of this expression is, for any particular model, a routine, if tiresome, exercise in matrix algebra. However, the result is always a relationship between the Fourier transform of the driving function $\tilde{f}(\omega)$ and any one of the population fluctuations ($\tilde{n}_i(\omega)$) of the by now familar form

$$\tilde{n}_i(\omega) = T_i(\omega)\tilde{f}(\omega), \qquad (4.3.21)$$

where the transfer function $T_i(\omega)$ is calculable from the recipe in equation (4.3.20).

C. Many-species difference equation models

Locally linear techniques for calculating the effects of environmental fluctuations can also be applied to difference equation models with the result

$$\tilde{\mathbf{n}}(\omega) = [\tau^{-1}(e^{i\omega\tau} - 1)\mathbf{I} - \mathbf{A}]^{-1}\alpha\tilde{f}(\omega) \qquad (4.3.22)$$

It is hard to imagine this expression ever being used with $M > 2$, and for the special case of $M = 2$ it reduces to

$$\tilde{n}_1(\omega) = \left[\frac{A_{12}\alpha_2 - A_{22}\alpha_1 + \tau^{-1}(e^{i\omega\tau} - 1)\alpha_1}{(\omega_0^2 - \omega^2) + \tau^{-1}(e^{i\omega\tau} - 1)\beta}\right]\tilde{f}(\omega), \qquad (4.3.23)$$

$$\tilde{n}_2(\omega) = \left[\frac{A_{21}\alpha_1 - A_{11}\alpha_2 + \tau^{-1}(e^{i\omega\tau} - 1)\alpha_2}{(\omega_0^2 - \omega^2) + \tau^{-1}(e^{i\omega\tau} - 1)\beta}\right]\tilde{f}(\omega). \qquad (4.3.24)$$

4.4 NON-LINEAR PHENOMENA

A. Global stability analysis

The neighbourhood stability analysis of Section 4.2 is, strictly speaking, only applicable to infinitesimally small fluctuations from the steady state. To check stability with respect to larger perturbations from the steady state we have in practice normally found it necessary to resort to the consideration of circumstantial evidence consisting of an analytic demonstration of local stability plus a number of numerical checks involving larger fluctuations. However, there is one technique—the use of Lyapunov functions—which can occasionally be used in rigorous analytic proofs of global stability.

The idea underlying Lyapunov stability theory is to construct a mathematical function which plays the same role as does energy in physical systems. This role is commonly illustrated by considering a marble in a bowl (see, for example, Gilpin, 1974); there is a steady state at the bottom of the bowl and because of friction the marble steadily loses energy until it settles at that steady state. The energy function in this situation possesses two key properties:

(a) If we measure potential energy relative to the steady state at the bottom of the bowl, *the total energy (kinetic plus potential) of the marble is always positive except at the steady state where it is zero.*
(b) Since energy is constantly being dissipated as heat (due to the friction between the marble and the bowl) *the total energy of the marble is always decreasing except at the steady state where it is zero.*

Since the dynamics of a marble in a bowl are described by simple differential equations we might hope to exploit the above idea in stability analysis of non-physical systems also modelled by differential equations and it can be proved that global stability of a system obeying the differential equations

(4.2.26) is guaranteed if we can find any function $L(\mathbf{N})$ with the properties;

(a) $L(\mathbf{N}^*) = 0$ (4.4.1)

(b) $L(\mathbf{N}) > 0$ for all $N \neq N^*$.   (4.4.2)

(c) $dL/dt \leqslant 0$ with equality only if $\mathbf{N} = \mathbf{N}^*$ (4.4.3)

The function L with these properties is known as a *Lyapunov function*.

Lyapunov functions can also be used in studies of difference equation models with the obvious modification that condition (c) is replaced by

(c) $L(\mathbf{N}(t + \tau)) - L(\mathbf{N}(t)) \leqslant 0$ with equality only if $\mathbf{N} = \mathbf{N}^*$,   (4.4.4)

but we know of no population models where this modification has proved useful and Beddington, Free, and Lawton (1976) report failures with the technique in some quite simple prey-predator models.

Unfortunately, in population biology there is no universal principle to guide us in choosing Lyapunov functions in the way the energy principle can be used in physical systems. Furthermore, in those situations where Lyapunov functions have been successfully constructed for population equations their interpretation has frequently been obscure. These two observations are not unrelated and to us indicate that the usefulness of this technique for demonstrating global stability in ecological systems is limited.

B. Limit cycles

We saw in Chapter 2 that a single-species differential equation model with no time delay could not exhibit limit cycles. A steady state in such a model is either stable and overdamped or unstable with perturbations growing exponentially; neither convergent nor divergent oscillations can occur. With two-species models oscillations can occur even in the absence of delay, and divergent oscillations are likely to grow into limit cycles.

There is a useful graphical representation of two-species oscillating systems known as the *phase diagram*, in which we plot the development with time of the two populations as a single trajectory on a graph with axes N_1 and N_2. An example is shown in Fig. 4.4 and it is clear that a limit cycle corresponds to a closed loop in the phase diagram. Furthermore it can be shown that the closed loop representing a stable limit cycle always contains within it an unstable steady state from whose vicinity trajectories diverge towards the limit cycle. This feature is very useful in practice, as a necessary condition for a limit cycle in a two-species system is thus the existence of an unstable steady state, a property that can be established by routine neighbourhood stability analysis.

More rigorously it can be shown that, subject to a few formal mathematical conditions, a two-species non-linear differential equation model in which one or both of the population growth rates G_i depends on a parameter ϕ, and in which increasing ϕ past a critical value ϕ_c changes the sign of the real part of a pair of complex eigenvalues of the stability matrix, exhibits a limit cycle, at

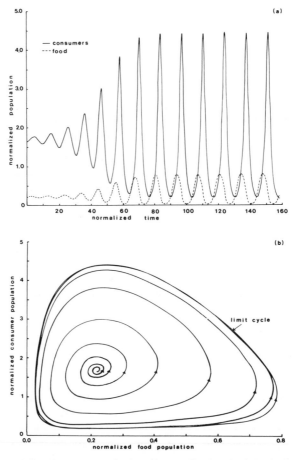

Fig. 4.4. An example of a limit cycle in a two-species
model. (a) Time domain plot. (b) Phase diagram.

least for some small range of values of ϕ near ϕ_c. Unfortunately this limit
cycle can be of two types;

(a) an unstable limit cycle on the 'stable side' of the critical value ϕ_c from
     which trajectories spiral inwards (corresponding to 'subcritical Hopf
     bifurcation'),

(b) a stable limit cycle towards which trajectories spiral outwards from the
     vicinity of the steady state (corresponding to 'supercritical Hopf bifurca-
     tion').

Only stable limit cycles are of any ecological interest but the mathematical
tests for distinguishing (a) and (b) (see, for example, MacDonald (1978) and
references therein) are most intimidating. However, for the purposes of prac-

tical modelling, a single well-chosen numerical integration of the differential equations on the unstable side of the critical point is sufficient to distinguish the two cases. A further mathematical weakness of the above result is that we have in general no quantitative specification of the size of the region near ϕ_c for which the theorem is valid; again a few judiciously chosen numerical integrations of the differential equations appear to be the obvious remedy.

The difficulty in formulating usable general criteria for the existence of limit cycles in two-species models is the need to define conditions which, irrespective of the initial populations, rigorously preclude extinction or unbounded growth of either species. However, for one special type of two-species model (predator–prey) it is possible to write down some rather general and ecologically interpretable conditions which guarantee *either* a single, globally stable steady state *or* a stable limit cycle. The best known set of conditions was derived by Kolmogorov and more recently popularized by May (1972), but successively less restrictive sets of conditions have since been published by Bulmer (1976) and Brauer (1979). If we write the predator–prey equation in the form

$$\dot{F} = FP(F, C) \qquad\qquad (4.4.5)$$
$$\dot{C} = CQ(F, C) \qquad\qquad (4.4.6)$$

where F ('food') denotes the prey population and C ('consumer') the predator population, then *sufficient* conditions which guarantee a stable steady or a stable limit cycle are that for all $F > 0$, $C > 0$:

(a) $\partial P/\partial C < 0$ and $\partial Q/\partial F > 0$ (condition ensuring a predator–prey type of interaction between F and C),
(b) $\partial Q/\partial C \leqslant 0$ (the consumer per capita growth rate is either density independent or decreases with increasing consumer population).
(c) *either* there exists a positive constant K (the carrying capacity of the prey population in the absence of predators) such that $P(K, 0) = 0$.
     or $FP(F, C)$ and $C^*(F)$ (defined as the value of C which for a particular F makes $Q(F, C) = 0$) both remain bounded above as $F \to \infty$,
(d) there exists a positive constant J (the minimum prey population necessary for growth of a small predator population) such that $Q(J, 0) = 0$.

This result (which we call the Kolmogorov–Brauer theorem) has been generalized by Brauer (1979) to cover populations with dynamics given by the predator–prey equations (4.4.5) and (4.4.6) but with one or both population harvested at a constant rate. He was able to show that in such cases extinction is possible in a finite time.

To summarise, with two-species models the Hopf bifurcation theorem suggests we should look for limit cycles near unstable spiral points in the phase plane but, except for certain predator–prey models to which the Kolmogorov–Brauer theorem is applicable, further investigation of limit cycles is most conveniently pursued numerically.

C. Other non-linear exotica

With many-species non-linear difference equations, and with differential equations involving three or more species, an almost endless miscellany of strange types of dynamical behaviour can occur. As with single-species models we may find a transition from cyclic behaviour to chaotic behaviour but now chaos can arise even in differential equation models. Other fascinating mathematical phenomena can occur even with quite simple three-species models but the possibility of recognizing them in the field or even in the laboratory is small, and we do not discuss them further. However, it is important to be aware of the existence of these effects, if only as a deterrent against placing over much credibility in any unexpected behaviour exhibited by complicated non-linear computer models.

4.5 LINEAR VERSUS NON-LINEAR MATHEMATICS

A. General comments

The principal theme of this book is the utility of linear mathematics in the analysis of intrinsically non-linear problems. Our experience with many-species models is that there are two major contexts in which linear techniques yield reliable information on much larger population fluctuations than those for which they can rigorously be proved valid.

First, for most many-species models with a single, feasible, steady state, local stability seems to imply global stability. (We define as 'feasible' a steady state in which all $N_i^* \geq 0$, the importance of the possibility of equality being well illustrated by Problem 8.) We know of only one realistic situation in which this generalization is invalid namely the case of models where 'deterministic' extinction of one or more species may occur within a finite time (e.g. models with constant-rate harvesting).

Secondly, the linear theory of the response of deterministically stable systems to environmental fluctuations is very robust and transfer functions can be used to make reasonable estimates of the size of even rather large population fluctuations.

Both these points are best demonstrated by considering an example. We have chosen a slight modification of the famous (or notorious) Lotka–Volterra equations which purport to describe the interaction between prey and predator populations. It is perhaps worth emphasizing that our present concern is *not* the probity of the equations as a representation of real predator–prey interactions but with the mathematical techniques used in their analysis. Because some non-linear analysis of these equations is possible, they provide an excellent testing ground for our assertion of the power of linear techniques.

B. An illustrative example

We consider the population of a prey species (here denoted by F for 'food') and a predator species (denoted by C for 'consumer'). We assume that in the absence of predation the prey would obey the logistic equation and that the rate of cropping the prey is proportional to the product of the prey and predator populations. The result is a slight modification of the Lotka–Volterra equations

$$\dot{F} = rF(1 - F/K) - \theta FC, \tag{4.5.1}$$

$$\dot{C} = \gamma CF - \varepsilon C. \tag{4.5.2}$$

These equations contain five positive parameters (r, K, θ, γ, ε) but according to the argument of Section 2.3 we should be able to reduce this number by working with dimensionless quantities. As the method of scaling is a frequent source of confusion, and as serious interpretational errors due to carelessness with scaling are not uncommon even in the published literature, we give a systematic, if slightly tedious account of the method. We define dimensionless variables

$$F' \equiv F/F_0; \qquad C' \equiv C/C_0; \, t' \equiv t/t_0, \tag{4.5.3}$$

where F_0, C_0, t_0 are constants (as yet undefined) with the units of F, C, t, respectively. In terms of the new variables the differential equations become

$$\frac{dF'}{dt'} = rt_0 F'\left(1 - \frac{F_0 F'}{K}\right) - \theta t_0 C_0 F' C' \tag{4.5.4}$$

$$\frac{dC'}{dt'} = \gamma F_0 t_0 C' F' - \varepsilon t_0 C' \tag{4.5.5}$$

The trick is now to *choose* values for the constants F_0, C_0, t_0 that will reduce these equations to as simple a form as possible. Thus for instance if we choose

$$F_0 = K; \qquad C_0 = \theta^{-1}\gamma K; \qquad t_0 = r^{-1}, \tag{4.5.6}$$

equations (4.5.4) and (4.5.5) reduce to a form involving only two parameters, namely

$$\frac{dF'}{dt'} = F'(1 - F') - aF'C', \tag{4.5.7}$$

$$\frac{dC'}{dt'} = aC'F' - bC', \tag{4.5.8}$$

where

$$a \equiv r^{-1}\gamma K; \qquad b \equiv r^{-1}\varepsilon. \tag{4.5.9}$$

The scaled equations (4.5.7) and (4.5.8) have steady state solutions

$$F'^* = \frac{b}{a},$$

$$C'^* = \frac{a - b}{a^2}. \tag{4.5.10}$$

We linearize about this steady state by setting

$$f' = F' - F^*,$$
$$c' = C' - C^*,$$

(4.5.11)

and find that to first order (cf. equations (4.2.6) and (4.2.7))

$$\frac{\mathrm{d}f'}{\mathrm{d}t'} = -\frac{b}{a} f' - bc',$$

(4.5.12)

$$\frac{\mathrm{d}c'}{\mathrm{d}t'} = \left(1 - \frac{b}{a}\right) f'$$

(4.5.13)

We can now evaluate the neighbourhood stability of this system with the aid of equation (4.2.15), from which we find

$$a_1 = b/a$$
$$a_2 = b\left(1 - \frac{b}{a}\right),$$

(4.5.14)

and equation (4.2.23) which tells us that the stability of the system is guaranteed providing a_1 and a_2 are both positive. The constants a and b are both positive by definition, and thus if F'^* and C'^* are both to be positive (which they must be if we are to interpret them as populations) we must have $a > b$. This in turn ensures a_1 and a_2 are positive and guarantees the stability of the system. Thus we see that in this model all feasible (i.e. positive) steady states are locally stable.

We can further see from equation (4.2.16) that both values of the constant λ will be real and the return to equilibrium over-damped (non-oscillating), provided that

$$a_1^2 > 4a_2,$$

(4.5.15)

i.e.

$$b > \frac{4a^2}{1 + 4a}.$$

(4.5.16)

We have chosen this 'damped' Lotka–Volterra model as our illustrative example because it is one of the few two-species models for which we know of a Lyapunov function. Guided by the well-known properties of the undamped Lotka–Volterra model (the limiting case of the present model as $K \to \infty$), Goel, Maitra, and Montroll (1971) established that a possible Liapunov function for this model is

$$L(F', C') = C' - C'^* - C'^* \ln\left(\frac{C'}{C'^*}\right) + F' - F'^* - F'^* \ln\left(\frac{F'}{F'^*}\right)$$

(4.5.17)

We confine our comments on this form to a reiteration of the view (cf. Section 4.4) that the interpretation of Lyapunov functions in population biology is frequently obscure.

It is obvious that L is zero at the steady state $(F' = F'^*)$ and $(C' = C'^*)$, and it is a routine but uninstructive exercise to show that for all other positive populations L is positive; the key to this proof being the mathematical result that for any positive number x

$$\ln x < x - 1. \tag{4.5.18}$$

Equally routine and equally uninstructive is the evaluation of dL/dt. After some regrouping of terms it can be shown that

$$\frac{dL}{dt} = -(F' - F'^*)^2 \leqslant 0 \text{ with equality only when } F' = F'^* \tag{4.5.19}$$

Thus provided the steady state populations are positive, the Lyapunov function $L(C', F')$ satisfies the global stability conditions (equations (4.4.1)–(4.4.3)), and we have established that in this model the conditions for neighbourhood stability are sufficient for global stability.

We now demonstrate the calculation of the transfer functions relating population fluctuations to fluctuations in some external driving function. There are numerous traps for the unwary in attempting to insert external fluctuations directly into sets of scaled equations, and we therefore return to our original (unscaled) dynamic equations (4.5.1) and (4.5.2) before attempting any modifications. We assume that environmental fluctuations are reflected in a time varying carrying capacity, and hence set

$$K(t) = K^* + k(t) \tag{4.5.19}$$

Our original choice of scale factors (equation 4.5.6) is now clearly inappropriate since two of them include the carrying capacity K, which is now a function of time. We can, however, retain the spirit of our original scaling by choosing scale factors identical to equation (4.5.6) except that the instantaneous value of the carrying capacity is replaced by its average value K^*, so that

$$\frac{dF'}{dt'} = F'\left(1 - \frac{F'}{(1 + (k'(t')/K^*))}\right) - aF'C' \tag{4.5.20}$$

$$\frac{dC'}{dt'} = aC'F' - bC' \tag{4.5.21}$$

where $a = r^{-1}\gamma K^*$, $b = r^{-1}\varepsilon$ and $k'(t') = k(t'/r)$. Clearly in the absence of fluctuations $(k(t) = 0)$ this set of equations reduces to our original scaled equations (4.5.7) and (4.5.8) and thus the deterministic stationary state F^*, C^* is still given by equation (4.5.10). On linearizing about this stationary state we now find that to first order

$$\frac{df'}{dt'} = -\frac{b}{a} f' - bc' + \frac{b^2}{a^2 K^*} k' \tag{4.5.22}$$

$$\frac{dc'}{dt'} = \left(1 - \frac{b}{a}\right) f'. \tag{4.5.23}$$

These equations are clearly a special case of the general linear dynamic equations for a two-species system (equations (4.3.5) and (4.3.7)). We can thus obtain the transfer functions relating the fluctuations in food and consumer populations to the driving fluctuations in carrying capacity by direct substitution in equations (4.3.11), (4.3.12), and (4.3.13). Performing this substitution, and tidying up the algebra a little we find that

$$\tilde{f}(\omega') = T_f(\omega')\tilde{k}'(\omega'), \qquad \tilde{c}'(\omega') = T_c(\omega')\tilde{k}'(\omega'), \qquad (4.5.24)$$

with the transfer functions given by

$$T_f(\omega') = \frac{(b^2/aK^*)i\omega'}{b(1 - (b/a)) - \omega'^2 + i\omega'(b/a)}, \qquad (4.5.25)$$

$$T_c(\omega') = \frac{(b^2/a^2K^*)(1 - (b/a))}{b(1 - (b/a)) - \omega'^2 + i\omega'(b/a)}, \qquad (4.5.26)$$

where ω' $(\equiv \omega/r)$ represents a scaled angular frequency.

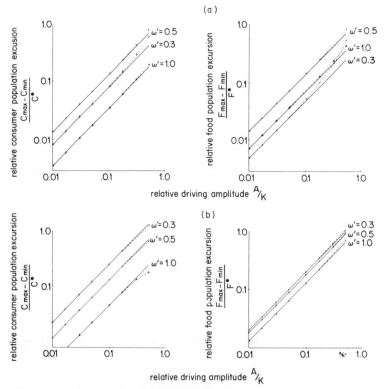

Fig. 4.5. A comparison of the locally linear approximation (——) with exact numerical results (×, ●, ▲) for the damped Lotka–Volterra model. The consumer population results are shown on the left and the food population results on the right. (a) An underdamped case. (b) An overdamped case.

We test the robustness of this approximation by setting

$$k'(t') = A \cos \omega' t' \qquad (4.5.27)$$

and then comparing (see Fig. 4.5) the exact values for the amplitude of the population oscillations which we obtain by examining numerical integrations of equations (4.5.20) and (4.5.21), with estimates of these amplitudes calculated from equations (4.5.25) and (4.5.26).

In all the cases we have examined except one it is clear that provided the total population excursion is less than about 30 per cent of the mean population then the locally linear estimates of the amplitude of the population oscillations will be indistinguishable from the exact results in the presence of any realistic degree of sampling error. However, for the underdamped system (whose natural angular frequency is $\omega' = 0.61$) a driving frequency of $\omega' = 0.3$ produces results showing a serious discrepancy between exact and approximate results for excursions as low as 10 per cent of the mean. Closer examination of the numerical results in this case immediately disclosed that this was caused by the appearance of subharmonic resonance (see Section 2.8b).

Thus our test results confirm the general robustness of locally linear approximations, but also serve to emphasize the necessity of using judiciously chosen numerical integrations to check for the appearance of genuinely non-linear phenomena.

4.6 IMPORTANT SPECIAL CLASSES OF MULTI-SPECIES MODEL

This book is primarily concerned with *how* to analyse models of fluctuating populations, and we therefore make no attempt to construct an exhaustive catalogue, far less an assessment, of the rapidly growing collection of multi-species models which can be found in the literature. However, the formulation and preliminary general analysis of any model is a vitally important part of any theoretical investigation, and in this section (by way of examples) we discuss this part of the process for two commonly encountered classes of population model. We pay particular attention to those general insights which may be gained as to the behaviour of the whole class of models rather than examine in detail the behaviour of any single member of the class.

A. Two-species predator-prey models

The most easily interpreted predator–prey models, and hence those which have the greatest predictive ability, are constructed from individual components which are directly measurable in the laboratory or in the field, namely the intrinsic growth rate of the prey and the functional and numerical responses of the predator. We assume that, in the absence of predation the per capita growth rate of the prey species depends only on the instantaneous prey population $F(t)$, and hence we write the *prey intrinsic growth rate* as $r(F)$.

If we further assume that the rate at which an individual predator consumes food (its *functional response*) depends only on the instanteous populations of prey and predators ($F(t)$ and $C(t)$ respectively) and we write this functional response as $I(F, C)$ then we see at once that the prey population obeys the simple differential equation

$$\dot{F} = Fr(F) - CI(F, C). \tag{4.6.1}$$

An additional assumption that all predators have the same per unit time maintenance and replacement cost, R, and that any food obtained in excess of this basic requirement is devoted to extra reproductive effort, now enables us to write the dynamics of the predator population as

$$\dot{C} = Cg(u). \tag{4.6.2}$$

Here the function $g(u)$ which describes the efficiency with which extra food is turned into extra predators is often called the predators' *numerical response*, and the excess food consumption rate u is given by

$$u = I(F, C) - R. \tag{4.6.3}$$

Although the model described by equations (4.6.1) to (4.6.3) is by no means the most general two-species predator–prey model one can formulate, it is still much too general to be the subject of much useful analysis. We therefore restrict its range of applicability in the hope of thereby increasing its predictive powers.

For some predators, particularly the invertebrates (see for example Beddington, Hassell, and Lawton, 1976) there is good experimental evidence that the numerical response function is a simple linear relationship

$$g(u) = \varepsilon u \tag{4.6.4}$$

and we thus first restrict our model to those predators whose conversion efficiency ε is a constant. The addition of a second restriction—that our model is only to apply to those situations where the amount of food taken by an individual predator is not influenced by competition from fellow predators—now enables us to write our dynamic equations in the very simple form

$$\dot{F} = Fr(F) - CI(F), \tag{4.6.5}$$

$$\dot{C} = \varepsilon C[I(F) - R]. \tag{4.6.6}$$

One final addition to the information at our disposal will enable us to gain considerable insight from these equations without the need to specify the functions r and I in detail. Holling (1965) has suggested that where there is no intra-specific competition there are only three plausible forms for the functional response $I(F)$ which we illustrate in Fig. 4.6.

We note at once from this figure that all these different functional forms have the common feature that $I(F)$ is a monotonical increasing function of F. Indeed this is not in the least surprising since if dI/dF were anywhere negative it would indicate the existence of circumstances in which an *increase* in supply brought about a *decrease* in consumption. Provided that $\mathrm{d}I/\mathrm{d}F$ is everywhere positive then we see at once from equation (4.6.6) that there can be at most one value of the prey population F^*, such that

$$I(F^*) = R \qquad (4.6.7)$$

and the predator population is held stationary ($\dot{C} = 0$). Conversely we see from equation (4.6.5) that with the prey population set at F^* there can be at most one value of the consumer population

$$C^* = \frac{F^* r(F^*)}{R} \qquad (4.6.8)$$

at which the intrinsic growth rate of the prey population and the predation load upon it exactly balance. Thus we see that, irrespective of the details of the functional forms of $r(F)$ and $I(F)$ our model can exhibit only one non-trivial stationary state.

Having ruled out the possibility of multiple stationary states, we now test the single non-trivial stationary state for local stability by the straightforward application of the techniques described in Section 4.2. From equation (4.2.15) we see that for a stationary state to be locally stable we require that the two quantities

$$a_1 = -r(F^*) - F^* \left(\frac{\mathrm{d}r}{\mathrm{d}F}\right)^* + C^* \left(\frac{\mathrm{d}I}{\mathrm{d}F}\right)^*, \qquad (4.6.9)$$

and

$$a_2 = \varepsilon R C^* \left(\frac{\mathrm{d}I}{\mathrm{d}F}\right)^*, \qquad (4.6.10)$$

shall both be positive. Now we see at once from Fig. 4.6 that for all plausible forms of $I(F)$, $\mathrm{d}I/\mathrm{d}F$ (and hence a_2) is always positive. The stability of the steady state thus clearly depends upon the sign of a_1, which we cannot determine until we know the specific functional forms of the response functions r and I.

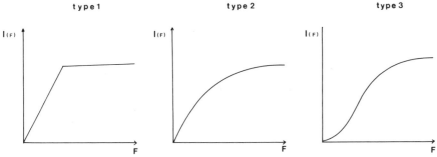

Fig. 4.6. Holling's classification of predator functional response.

Normally one cannot proceed much beyond this point until the response functions are specified in detail. However, for this particular model we can make use of the Kolmogorov–Brauer theorem (see Section 4.4.B). It turns out that provided $r(F)$ is a monotonically increasing function of F, our model satisfies all the Kolonogorov–Brauer criteria, and thus we can conclude that in this case our model must have either:

(a)   no steady state,
(b)   a single globally stable steady state,
(c)   a single stable limit cycle.

Because of the happy accident that it satisifies all the requirements of the Kolmogorov–Brauer theorem this rather simple predator–prey model has yielded its qualitative dynamics in their entirety to a routine application of the techniques described in this chapter. However, when one relaxes the rather restrictive assumptions we have made along the way and injects a greater degree of realism one begins to encounter a wide range of perfectly sensible population models from which routine non-linear analysis reveals almost nothing. In such circumstances the complete global dynamics can still be inferred (although without rigorous formal proof) by a judicious combination of routine locally linear analysis and numerical integration of carefully chosen special cases.

B. Models of interspecific competition

A second type of many-species model for which local linearization leads to simplification involves a number of species confined to two trophic levels. Suppose we have a community of M consumer species which compete for P different resources. We represent the population dynamics by the set of differential equations

$$\dot{F}_i = F_i \pi_i(\{F_j\}, \{C_j\}); \qquad i = 1, 2, \ldots P, \qquad (4.6.11)$$

$$\dot{C}_i = C_i g_i(\{F_j\}, \{C_j\}); \qquad i = 1, 2, \ldots M, \qquad (4.6.12)$$

where $\{F_j\}, \{C_j\}$ denote respectively the sets of resource and consumer populations, and π_i, g_j are respectively the specific growth rates of resource species i and consumer species j. We assume the system has a single steady state and we consider small fluctuations about this steady state. Setting

$$f_i = F_i - F_i^*, \qquad c_i = C_i - C_i^*, \qquad (4.6.13)$$

and linearizing about the steady state we obtain

$$\dot{f}_i = \sum_{j=1}^{P} \gamma_{ij} f_j + \sum_{j=1}^{M} h_{ij} c_j, \qquad (4.6.14)$$

$$\dot{c}_i = \sum_{j=1}^{P} g_{ij} f_j + \sum_{j=1}^{M} \beta_{ij} c_j, \qquad (4.6.15)$$

where

$$\gamma_{ij} = F_i^* \left(\frac{\partial \pi_i}{\partial F_j}\right)^*, \qquad h_{ij} = F_i^* \left(\frac{\partial \pi_i}{\partial C_j}\right)^*, \qquad (4.6.16)$$

$$g_{ij} = C_i^* \left(\frac{\partial g_i}{\partial F_j}\right)^*, \qquad \beta_{ij} = C_i^* \left(\frac{\partial g_i}{\partial C_j}\right)^*, \qquad (4.6.17)$$

In work on interspecific competition it is often assumed that the recovery rate of the resource population is very large and thus that very soon after any perturbation we may assume $\dot{f}_i = 0$ in equation (4.6.14). This assumption yields a set of P linear algebraic equations which can be solved for the P unknown f_is. Substituting these into equation (4.6.15) then yields a set of M simultaneous differential equations involving only the fluctuations in the consumer populations. In the special case where there is no significant competition among the resource species this procedure is very straightforward since then the only non-zero γ_{ij} have $i = j$ and so

$$f_i = -\gamma_{ii}^{-1} \sum_{j=1}^{M} h_{ij} c_j, \qquad i = 1, 2, \ldots P. \qquad (4.6.18)$$

Provided the only way in which the consumers compete is via the resources being modelled, then we may also assume that β_{ij} is zero unless $i = j$. If we further assume that there is no intraspecific competition among the consumers then clearly β_{ij} is zero even if $i = j$. Equations (4.6.15) and (4.6.18) then yield

$$\dot{c}_i = - \sum_{j=1}^{M} \alpha_{ij} c_j \qquad (4.6.19)$$

where the α_{ij}, known as *competition coefficients* are given by

$$\alpha_{ij} = \sum_{k=1}^{P} \gamma_{kk}^{-1} g_{ik} h_{kj} \qquad (4.6.20)$$

A very simple example which illustrates the principle involved in this competition approximation is given in Problem 5. It is worth noting that the procedure for defining competition coefficients depends (in our formulation) on linearization, but not on any assumed form for the predator–prey interaction terms. Considerable ambiguity can arise (see, for example DeBenedictis, 1977) if we attempt to extend the competition approximation to the nonlinear regime but in view of the general crudeness of the approximation, detailed investigation of these problems seem more likely to yield mathematical entertainment than ecological insight. However, notwithstanding these weaknesses, competition equations derived in this way have proved a simple and fruitful starting point for the interpretation of competing laboratory populations, and competition coefficients are used in field investigations as a quantitative measure of the extent of interspecific competition.

We conclude our discussion of competition equations by noting that the approximations introduced in their derivation are only valid if there is a clear separation of time scales between the rates of recovery of resources in the absence of predation and the rates of any changes in consumer populations. This is well illustrated in some computations by Pettipher (1981) who tested the accuracy of the competition approximation in a four species model with two consumers competing for two resources. The model was one which has been extensively used in theoretical studies of the 'ecological niche'; it was assumed that with no predation the prey would grow logistically and that the predator–prey interaction was of Lotka–Volterra type. The resulting dynamic equations take the form of equations (4.6.11) and (4.6.12) with the specific growth rates π_i and g_i given by

$$\pi_i = r_i(1 - F_i/K_i) - \sum_{j=1}^{2} a_{ij}C_j, \tag{4.6.21}$$

$$g_i = B_i\left[\sum_{j=1}^{2} a_{ij}b_j F_j - R_i\right]. \tag{4.6.22}$$

For simplicity, Pettipher assumed equality of the intrinsic growth rates ($r_1 = r_2 = r$) and carrying capacities ($K_1 = K_2 = K$) of the prey species, of consumer maintenance and replacement coats per unit time ($R_1 = R_2 = R$), and of food conversion efficiencies ($b_1 = b_2 = b$). He defined parameters $V = bK$ (the food value to consumers of the total resource carrying capacity) and $A = \sum_{j=1}^{2}a_{ij}$ (proportional to the fraction of the prey taken per unit time per predator and assumed independent of i). Scaling the equations with

$$C' \equiv r^{-1}AC_i, \qquad F' \equiv K^{-1}F_i, \qquad t' \equiv tBR, \tag{4.6.23}$$

and defining

$$E \equiv R^{-1}AV, \qquad H \equiv r(BR)^{-1}, \tag{4.6.24}$$

yielded

$$\dot{C}'_i = C'_i\left[E\sum_{j=1}^{2} P_{ij}F'_j - 1\right], \tag{4.6.25}$$

$$\dot{F}'_i + HF'_i\left[1 - F'_i - \sum_{j=1}^{2} P_{ij}C'_j\right], \tag{4.6.26}$$

where

$$P_{ij} = P_{ji} = a_{ij}\left/\sum_{j=1}^{2} a_{ij}\right.. \tag{4.6.27}$$

In this model the parameters r^{-1} and $(BR)^{-1}$ are measures of the time required for significant changes in the prey and predator populations respectively. Pettipher's investigations (which are illustrated in Fig. 4.7) show that the competition approximation to the consumer population fluctuations is

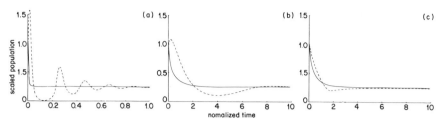

Fig. 4.7. Exact calculations (– – – –) of the return of Pettipher's (1981) competition model to a stable equilibrium, compared with the competition approximation (——). (a) H = 0.2, (b) H = 2. (c) H = 50.

only in acceptable agreement with exact calculations when $H = (BR)^{-1}/r^{-1}$ is very large. This confirms our intuitive expectation that the competition approximation is only likely to be reliable if the prey population can achieve its equilibrium size in a time short compared to that required for significant changes in the predator population.

SOURCES AND SUGGESTED FURTHER READING

Stability theory: Sanchez (1968) covers readably and thoroughly both local and global stability theory for systems of differential equations. For an approach to local stability based on Laplace transforms see Morris (1974). There are many mathematical texts giving more rigorous treatment of systems of differential equations, notable examples known to use including Minorsky (1962), Nemytskii and Stepanov (1960). We have not found the specialist literature on Lyapunov functions particularly useful but have on occasions referred to La Salle and Lefchetz (1961) and Barrett and Storey (1970). The ecology literature contains a few special graphical methods for two-species models, (e.g. Rosenzweig and MacArthur, 1963, Rosenzweig, 1969) but for the most part these are both complicated and insufficiently general to be worth mastering. Stability analysis for difference equations using equation (4.2.50) can be simplified by involving the Schur–Cohn criteria (May, 1974b, pp. 219–20).

Two-species predator–prey models: The various components of the predator–prey model in Section 4.6A have been studied experimentally for laboratory populations; for insect predators and parasitoids, useful papers written with modelling applications in mind are Hassell, Lawton, and Beddington (1976, 1977), Beddington, Hassell, and Lawton (1976). Of particular interest is the contention by Hassell, Lawton, and Beddington (1977) that even with invertebrate predators type 3 functional responses are likely to be the rule rather than the exception. We know of no reliable fit of *all* the parameters in a predator–prey system that would permit prediction of the population stability as did the model of Hassell, Lawton, and May (1976) which we discussed in Chapter 2; the nearest we can find is a qualitative fit by Tanner (1975) of most of the dimensionless parameter groups in a model of vertebrate predation. Supplemented by a guess at the remaining parameters, this yielded the conclusion that as with single-species models deterministic stability was likely to be the rule rather than the exception. Models with multiple steady states (where the range of applicability of local stability analysis is reduced and 'switching' may be important) are discussed in Holling (1973), Sutherland (1974), May (1977), Murdoch, and Oaten (1975).

Many-species models: Since the appearance of the book by May (1974b) which contains an extensive bibliography up to that date, there has been a publication explosion on the question of the relationship (if any) between complexity and stability in model ecosystems, but as far as we can judge May's broad insight, that unless further constraints are imposed, complexity *per se* begets instability, remains intact. There has also been a large amount of recent work on many-species competition models much of which has been directed to modelling the 'ecological niche'. May (1974a) reviews the deterministic stability of these models, work which has been extended by Abrams (1975, 1976) and McMurtie (1976). For a recent review of niche theory see Pianka (1976). The subtleties involved in the formulation of competition models are discussed by Schoener (1974).

PROBLEMS

(Those marked * are mathematically more demanding than the others.)

1. (Leslie, 1948). A predator–prey model in which both species behave logistically is

$$\frac{dF}{dt} = rF(1 - F/K) - \alpha FC$$

$$\frac{dC}{dt} = sC\left(1 - \frac{C}{\varepsilon F}\right)$$

(a) Scale the above equations so as to reduce the number of parameters from five to two.

(b) Calculate the steady-state populations and show that they are locally stable provided r, K, S, α, ε, are all positive.

(c) Under what conditions is the system overdamped/underdamped?

2. (Maynard Smith, 1974). Two populations are modelled by the Lotka–Volterra predator–prey equations without damping but it is assumed that a fixed number F_R of the prey can find refuge which makes them inaccessible to the predators. The resulting equations are

$$\frac{dF}{dt} = rF - \beta(F - F_R)C$$

$$\frac{dC}{dt} = -\delta C + \gamma C(F - F_R)$$

Calculate the steady states and demonstrate neighbourhood stability.

3. (Nicholson and Bailey, 1935; Beddington, Free, and Lawton, 1975). The population of a parasite (P) and its host (H) is modelled by the difference equations

$$P_{t+\tau} = \alpha H_t(1 - \exp(-aP_t)) \qquad \text{(A)}$$

$$H_{t+\tau} = \alpha H_t \exp(-aP_t) \qquad \text{(B)}$$

where α, a are positive constants.

(a) Calculate the steady-state populations and show that they are positive only if $\alpha > 1$.
(b) Show that if $\alpha > 1$ the steady state is unstable.
(c) Is the divergence from the steady state oscillatory?
(d) These equations assume no self-regulation of the host population. The effect of such self-regulation may be investigated by replacing (B) by

$$H_{t+\tau} = H_t \exp\{\alpha(1 - H_t/K) - aP_t\} \qquad \text{(C)}$$

Is the system still invariably unstable?

4. (May, 1976e). A modification of the logistic equation to describe two mutualistically interacting species results in

$$\frac{dN_1}{dt} = rN_1\left[1 - \frac{N_1}{K_1 + \alpha N_2}\right]$$

$$\frac{dN_2}{dt} = rN_2\left[1 - \frac{N_2}{K_2 + \beta N_1}\right]$$

with α, β, r, K_1, K_2 positive constants. Show that the steady state populations are positive if $\alpha\beta < 1$ and that if this condition is satisfied the steady state is locally stable.

5. The principle underlying the 'competition approximation' is well illustrated by the two-species damped Lotka–Volterra model of Section 4.5. Starting with equations (4.5.12) and (4.5.13), show that if df'/dt' is always zero, then

$$\frac{dc'}{dt'} = -(a - b)c'$$

[Note that this equation describes an overdamped system while from equation (4.4.15) the original system was only overdamped if $b > 4a^2/(1 + 4a)$.]

6.* (MacArthur, 1969). Consider a system of M predators competing for M resources with model equations

$$\frac{dC_i}{dt} = \gamma_i C_i \left[\sum_{j=1}^{M} W_j a_{ij} F_j - T_i \right]$$

$$\frac{dF_i}{dt} = r_i F_i \left[1 - \frac{F_i}{K_i} - r_i^{-1} \sum_{j=1}^{M} a_{ij} C_j \right]$$

where a_{ij} is the probability per unit time that an individual of consumer species i encounters and eats a unit of resource j. K_i, w_i, r_i are respectively the carrying capacity, mean weight and intrinsic growth rate of resource i, γ is a measure of the efficiency with which consumer i converts food into biomass and T_i is the amount of food required per unit time for maintenance of an individual of consumer i.

(a) Using the 'competition' approximation that the resource populations are constant over time derive a set of M differential equations for the consumer populations.

(b) If a function Q is defined by

$$Q \equiv \sum_{j=1}^{M} \left(\frac{w_j K_j}{r_j} \right) \left(r_j - \sum_{k=1}^{M} a_{kj} C_k \right)^2 + 2 \sum_{j=1}^{M} T_j C_j$$

show that if the competition equations have positive steady state solutions, then Q is a Lyapunov function and the steady state is globally stable.

(c) Using the two-species Lotka–Volterra predator–prey model of Section 4.5 as a guide, attempt to find a Lyapunov function for the original set of $2M$ differential equations, i.e. do not make the 'competition' approximation.

7. (Nisbet and Gurney, 1976, McKinstry, 1980). A grotesque simplification of the dynamics associated with the cycling of the element carbon in a closed ecosystem results in the equations (chosen to represent Fig. 1.1).

$$\frac{dx_0}{dt} = k_1 x_1 + k_2 x_2 - A_{01} x_0 x_1 \tag{A}$$

$$\frac{dx_1}{dt} = A_{01} x_0 x_1 - A_{12} x_1 x_2 - k_1 x_1 \tag{B}$$

$$\frac{dx_2}{dt} = A_{12} x_1 x_2 - k_2 x_2 \tag{C}$$

where x_0, x_1, x_2 represent the mass of carbon in respectively the environment, the primary producers, and the consumers. The constants k_1 and k_2 represent rates of respiration and decomposition combined for the producers and consumers respectively. The constant A_{12} characterizes the conversion of producer to consumer biomass while the term $A_{01}x_0x_1$ represents the rate of photosynthesis.

(a) Show that $x_0 + x_1 + x_2$ is a constant (T) equal to the total mass of carbon in the system.
(b) By substituting $x_0 = T - x_1 - x_2$ in equations (B) and (C) obtain a pair of equations in x_1 and x_2.
(c) Show that if the steady state values of x_1 and x_2 are positive, the system is locally stable.
(d) We can very crudely represent the annual variation in insolation by setting

$$A_{01} = A_{01}^*(1 + ae^{i\omega t})$$

with $\omega = 2\pi$ radians year^{-1}. Calculate an expression for the amplitude of the resulting oscillations in x_2.

8. (Goh, 1977). The following model represents interspecific competition between three species:—

$$\dot{N}_1 = N_1(2 - 0.8N_1 - 0.7N_2 - 0.5N_3)$$
$$\dot{N}_2 = N_2(2.1 - 0.2N_1 - 0.9N_2 - N_3)$$
$$\dot{N}_3 = N_3(1.5 - N_1 - 0.3N_2 - 0.2N_3)$$

(a) Locate all the feasible steady states and determine which are locally stable.
(b) Use the result of (a) to guess whether or not the steady state $N_1^* = N_2^* = N_3^* = 1$ is globally stable.
(c) Verify your guess in (b) by solving the equations numerically with initial condition $N_1 = 0.5$, $N_2 = 1.0$, $N_3 = 2.0$.

9.* (Brauer, Soudack, and Jarosch, 1976). The following predator–prey model has been used in a simulation of a system consisting of inorganic nutrient, F, and phytoplankton C.

$$\dot{F} = R - \frac{FC}{F + A}$$

$$\dot{C} = \frac{sAC(F - J)}{(J + A)(F + A)} - E$$

R, A, J, E, and s are constants.
(a) Show that if E, the rate at which plankton are harvested is zero then any non-trivial steady state is locally stable and that the system is overdamped if in addition $R > 4sJ^2/A$.

(b) Show that the phytoplankton, F, will become extinct in a finite time if

$$E > E_c \quad \text{where} \quad E_c = \frac{sAR}{J + A}$$

(c) Show that the steady state is unstable if $[E_s] < E \leqslant E$ where $E_s = 2(J + A)^{-2}\{2sAR + s^2AJ^2 - sAJ[s^2J^2 + 4sR(J + A)]^{1/2}\}$ and show that in this case a limit cycle could be expected.

Chapter 5

The Effects of Spatial Heterogeneity

5.1 INTRODUCTION

One classic definition of the aim of animal ecology is 'to discover the reasons for the distribution and abundance of animals in nature' (Elton, 1927). This definition emphasizes the expectation that the same factors, both external (such as food and water, temperature, predators etc.) and internal (such as territorial behaviour, social interactions etc.) which set the overall size of a population will also determine the way in which it is distributed over the available space. In spite of the difficulties involved in experimental and observational work on factors responsible for the distribution of population there is a growing body of both direct and circumstantial evidence pointing to the particular importance of dispersal in controlling both the total size and the local variations in density of many natural populations. This evidence is supported by several clear and unambiguous laboratory experiments where changes in the possibilities for population movement lead to spectacular changes in population abundance and even to significant shifts in the relative likelihoods of persistence or extinction.

Examples of direct evidence of the importance of dispersal in mammalian populations can be found in comparisons of island and mainland populations of a particular species (e.g. Tamarin's (1977) study of island and mainland voles) or of fenced and unfenced populations (e.g. Krebs, Keller and Tamarin, 1969). There is also evidence that small mammal populations can persist in a patchy environment where each individual patch is too small to sustain a viable population but in which persistence is achieved as a result of a balance between inter-patch migration and local extinction (for example, Smith, 1974). Perhaps even more compelling is the indirect evidence that many populations appear to be regulated at levels well below the apparent carrying capacity of their habitat. Again mice and vole populations provide well-studied examples, while in insect populations there are spectacular examples of biological control processes which reduce populations to levels as low as 1 per cent of their size in the absence of the controlling species, a possibility which is hard to explain by predator–prey models which do not include spatial heterogeneity. Striking laboratory studies illustrating the importance of dispersal include Luckinbill's (1973, 1974) experiments on *Paramecium–Didinium* systems where movement was inhibited by increasing the viscosity of the culture medium, and Huffaker's studies of predator–prey interactions among mites in a complex environment which are the subject of Chapter 10.

While the influence of spatial effects on populations in the real world is well-established, there are formidable problems in constructing mathematically tractable, yet biological meaningful, models incorporating such effects. Two obvious strategies are to construct partial differential equations representing the changes in population density in a particular region, or to subdivide space into discrete patches containing sub-populations which are assumed homogeneous and then to construct a large set of simultaneous ordinary differential equations describing these many sub-populations. Both these approaches all too easily result in over-elaborate mathematics and simplifying assumptions (e.g. a spatially homogeneous or slowly varying environment, identical patches etc.) are normally prerequisites for progress. Even then the mathematical work is usually quite demanding although techniques involving linearization about steady states are available and useful. However, it is perhaps significant that many of the most widely used models involving spatial heterogeneity makes use of some approximation which yields a set of ordinary differential or difference equations such as we studied in Chapters 2 and 4.

In this chapter we review the various strategies outlined above, and then analyse the resulting equations following the now familiar pattern of studying in turn steady states, stability, and the effects of a fluctuating environment.

5.2 MODELLING WITH ORDINARY DIFFERENTIAL OR DIFFERENCE EQUATIONS

A. Searching

The discussion of predator–prey interactions in Chapter 4 envisaged the functional response of the predator as being set solely by the total amount of food available. In many situations an individual animal has to search for food over some geographically extended region, in which case the form of the functional response clearly ought to depend strongly on the spatial distribution of the food. The majority of models involving the effects of searching have been developed for the case of insect host–parasitoid systems, the simplest examples of which are based on assumptions that both species have synchronized generations. The Nicholson–Bailey model is probably the best known model of this type and its derivation illustrates well the technique for describing the effect of searching (Nicholson and Bailey, 1935).

We consider a population of parasitoids which lay eggs in the larvae of some host species. Each host larva can only accommodate one viable parasitoid egg. If we assume that parasitoids search randomly, each covering an area a in its lifetime, then the probability that a given host larva escapes a specified parasitoid is $(1 - a/A)$. Thus, if P_t denotes the population of parasitoids at time t, then the fraction (f) of host larvae which remain unparasitized and hence form the next generation of adults is

$$f = (1 - a/A)^{P_t} \tag{5.2.1}$$

which, by defining

$$\alpha \equiv -\ln\{1 - a/A\} \tag{5.2.2a}$$

we can rewrite as

$$f = e^{-\alpha P_t}. \tag{5.2.2b}$$

Hence, if each adult host produces F eggs, of which a fraction S survive to become larvae, then

$$H_{t+\tau} = (FSH_t)f = FSH_t e^{-\alpha P_t}, \tag{5.2.3a}$$

and, assuming that each parasitized larva gives rise to a single adult parasitoid,

$$P_{t+\tau} = (FSH_t)(1 - f) = FSH_t(1 - e^{-\alpha P_t}). \tag{5.2.3b}$$

It can easily be shown (see Chapter 4 Problem 3) that this model possesses a single stationary state, which is invariably unstable with divergent oscillations. There is a wide range of variations of the basic model in which stability is achieved through relaxation of one or more of the underlying assumptions of random host distribution, random searching and constant searching efficiency. In general, however, extra assumptions are involved which result in the introduction of numerous additional parameters and the models very soon become sufficiently complicated to be of neither strategic nor predictive value.

A rather elegant compromise between realism and tractability (due to May (1978)), involves replacing the random distribution of parasitoid attacks on hosts assumed by Nicholson and Bailey with a 'contagious' distribution (see Fig. 5.1) which in turn is approximated by a negative binomial distribution. In Section 5.2C we give one of the many possible derivations of this model in terms of the behaviour of individuals within the population. For now, it is enough simply to know that the fraction of the host population that escapes parasitism is $(1 + \alpha P_t/k)^{-k}$ where k, which is known as the clumping parameter, describes the distribution of parasitoids. The populations then follow the equations

$$H_{t+\tau} = FSH_t(1 + \alpha P_t/k)^{-k}, \tag{5.2.4a}$$

$$P_{t+\tau} = FSH_t\{1 - (1 + \alpha P_t/k)^{-k}\}. \tag{5.2.4b}$$

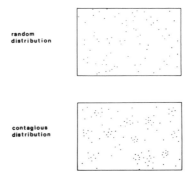

Fig. 5.1. Random and contagious
spatial distributions.

It is a routine exercise in the techniques of Chapter 4 to show that, in contrast to the Nicholson–Bailey model in which the steady state is always unstable, this model exhibits a locally stable stationary state provided $k < 1$. If we note that a random distribution of parasitoids corresponds to the limit of infinite k, then we see at once that substantial aggregation or clumping is required to stabilize the system.

B. Territorial Behaviour

It is well known that in species as diverse as sticklebacks, Arctic wolves and great tits, the establishment and defence of territories by individuals, pairs, or small groups of individuals, is a major factor in regulating population numbers. Probably the best documented examples of territoriality involve bird populations. With a few noteworthy exceptions (e.g. Maynard Smith, 1974, Chapter 12) this topic has received little attention from theoretical ecologists because of the mathematical complexity of even the most artificial models. Even simple geometrical problems such as calculating the expected number of territories of a given area which would be established in a wood by birds arriving consecutively, rapidly leads to difficult, and frequently unsolved, statistical problems.

The subject of this section is one rather elegant approach to modelling territoriality, first used by Lomnicki, which involves neither a proliferation of unmeasurable parameters in the model, nor the need for a lifetime of mathematical experience in order to analyse it. We imagine the total area occupied by a particular population as being, at any instant, divided up into a set of individual territories equal in number to the individuals in the population but highly variable in quality. We describe the quality of a given territory (i.e. the relative availability of food to the individual occupying it) by a rank parameter x, which is just the position of that territory in an ordered list of all the territories into which the area is currently divided. For convenience we chose the convention that $x = 0$ represents the most favourable territory. We now assume that the feeding rate $E(x, F)$ of the individual occupying the x'th ranked territory depends both on the average density of food over the whole area occupied by the population, which we denote by F, and the rank x of the territory it occupies. We cannot derive an explicit expression for the individual feeding function $E(x, F)$, without a detailed knowledge of both the physiology and the behaviour of the species under investigation, but we might expect most such functions to have certain common features which are illustrated in Fig. 5.2.

(a)   There must be a physiological upper limit E_{max} to the rate at which an individual can eat.

(b)   For a fixed value of F, the average food supply, the feeding rate of an individual is a non-increasing function of the rank x of the territory it occupies.

(c)   We would expect the difference in quality of territories occupying adjacent positions in the rank order to decrease as food becomes more abundant.

A possible function exhibiting these features is

$$E(x, F) = \frac{AF}{1 + (AF/E_{max}) + \lambda x}, \qquad (5.2.5)$$

where A, E_{max} are constants and λ can be regarded as a measure of the extent to which individual feeding rates are modified by the quality of the territory occupied.

If the rate at which an individual occupying territory of rank x ingests food is $E(x, F)$ then since the number of territories is by definition equal to the total population of consumers, it is immediately clear that the total rate of

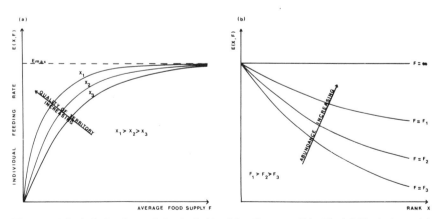

Fig. 5.2 Likely behaviour of the individual feeding rate $E(x,F)$. (a) Variation with average food supply at three fixed values of territory quality. (b) Variation with quality of territory at three fixed values of average food supply.

consumption of food by a population of C consumers must be

$$L(F, C) = \sum_{x=0}^{C-1} E(x, F) \qquad (5.2.6)$$

which, provided the population is not too small, we can approximate by an integral

$$L(F, C) \simeq \int_{0}^{C} E(x, F) \, dx \qquad (5.2.7)$$

If we now further assume that:

(a) in the absence of predation the food species grows logistically with intrinsic growth rate r and carrying capacity K,

(b) all consumer individuals have the same maintenance and replacement cost per unit time, R, and turn any food obtained in excess of this basic requirement into additional offspring with constant efficiency ε,

then we can at once see that the complete dynamics of the system can be expressed as a pair of simple differential equations

$$\dot{F} = rF(1 - F/K) - L(F, C) \qquad (5.2.8a)$$

$$\dot{C} = \varepsilon[L(F, C) - RC], \qquad (5.2.8b)$$

where, from equations (5.2.5) and (5.2.7) we see that

$$L(F, C) = \frac{AF}{\lambda} \ln\left[1 + \lambda C\left\{1 + \frac{AF}{E_{max}}\right\}^{-1}\right]. \qquad (5.2.8c)$$

The complete analysis of this system is somewhat messy and the reader is referred to Gurney, and Nisbet (1979) where the same equations are used with a rather different interpretation. However, it is entirely straightforward to show that equations (5.2.8) have a single non-trivial stationary state (F^*, C^*) given by

$$C^* = \frac{rF^*}{R}\left[1 - \frac{F^*}{K}\right], \qquad (5.2.9a)$$

$$\frac{AF^*}{E_{max}}\left[1 + \frac{AF^*}{E_{max}}\right]^{-1} = \frac{R}{E_{max}}\left[\exp\left\{\frac{r\lambda}{A}\left(1 - \frac{F^*}{K}\right)\right\} - 1\right]\left[\frac{r\lambda}{A}\left(1 - \frac{F^*}{K}\right)\right]^{-1}.$$

$$(5.2.9b)$$

Routine but tedious analysis of equations (5.2.9) then shows;

(a) the steady state will be feasible (i.e. will have both F^* and C^* non-negative) provided only that the parameters are chosen so as to obey the obvious restriction that the highest rate at which an individual occupying the highest quality territory can ingest food shall be greater than his maintenance and replacement cost, i.e.

$$\frac{AK}{1 + AK/E_{max}} > R \tag{5.2.10}$$

(b) if we increase the quality sensitivity parameter λ with all the other parameters held constant then F^* increases monotonically; tending towards $F^* = K$ as λ becomes very large.

(c) the steady state consumer population C^* has its maximum value when $F^* = K/2$ and decreases to zero as $F^* \rightarrow 0$ or K.

The routine application of the techniques of Chapter 4 now shows that all steady states with $F^* > K/2$ are locally stable, and in addition that uniform ($\lambda = 0$) systems are locally stable if they have small K and locally unstable if K is large. Thus, since F^* increases monotonically towards $F^* = K$ as the quality sensitivity parameter λ is increased, it seems reasonable to infer that;

(a) resource-poor (small K) systems are locally stable for all values of the quality sensitivity parameter,

(b) resource-rich (high K) systems, which are unstable if the effective environmental quality is uniform ($\lambda \rightarrow 0$) become stabilized when the advantages accruing to individuals occupying high-quality territory become sufficiently large to raise the steady-state food population above $K/2$,

(c) in both enriched and impoverished systems undue increases in the advantage enjoyed by individuals in high quality territory (i.e. undue increases in λ) reduce the steady-state consumer population to values so low that in any realistic situation their rapid extinction would be certain.

Thus we conclude that while an environment which is either highly uniform or enormously variable will produce instability in a population of territorial animals, a modest degree of variability in environmental quality exerts a strong stabilizing influence. In the presence of such a modest degree of variability the 'paradox of enrichment' does not occur.

C. Patchy environments

There is little future in attempting to model the changes in a population in a patchy environment in terms of models which include detailed descriptions both of the internal dynamics of the component patches and of the process of inter-patch migration. Except where we make the extreme simplifying assumptions which lead to an approximate treatment via partial differential equations—the subject of Section 5.3—any analytic treatment of such models generally leads to rather weak results. Because of this, various authors have developed simplifications which result in more tractable models. This section is devoted to two such simplifications.

The first, due to May, is concerned with a host–parasitoid system where parasites are distributed over a large number of patches *within* which they search randomly as in the Nicholson–Bailey model. If $\pi(P)$ is the probability that a particular patch contains P parasites, then the fraction of the host population that escapes parasitism is

$$\sum_{P=0}^{\infty} \pi(P)(1 - a/A)^P = \sum_{P=0}^{\infty} \pi(P)e^{-\alpha P} \qquad (5.2.12)$$

May's approach is now to approximate the distribution of parasite attacks by a negative binomial, which is empirically observed to fit many of the contagious distributions observed in the field. In this case the fraction of the host population that escapes parasition must be given both by equation (5.2.12) and also by the zero term in a negative binomial distribution. This can only be so if the value of the clumping parameter k satisfies

$$\sum_{P=0}^{\infty} \pi(P)e^{-\alpha P} = (1 + \alpha\bar{P}/k)^{-k} \qquad (5.2.13)$$

where we have denoted by $\bar{P}$ the mean number of parasites *on a particular patch*. If σ_P^2 is the variance in this number, then

$$\bar{P} = \sum_{P=0}^{\infty} P\pi(P),$$

and

$$\sigma_P^2 = \sum_{P=0}^{\infty} P^2\pi(P) - \bar{P}^2 \qquad (5.2.14)$$

On expanding both sides of (5.2.13) in terms of α, and equating terms in α^2 we find that

$$k = \frac{\bar{P}^2}{\sigma_P^2}. \qquad (5.2.15)$$

We now have a model in which the dynamics are given by the equation (5.2.4) but the parameter k introduced empirically in Section 5.2A now has a specific interpretation in terms of the *intra-patch* dynamics, namely that k is inversely proportional to the ratio of the fluctuation intensity σ_P^2 on a particular patch to the mean number of individuals on that patch. Recalling that for overall stability $k < 1$, it follows that a host–parasitoid system with random searching within each patch is stable provided

$$\sigma_P > \bar{P} \qquad (5.2.16)$$

In the next chapter we shall show formally (though the result is intuitively obvious) that this implies rapid local extinction of the parasitoid population on any one patch, and we have the apparently slightly paradoxical result that a high probability of local extinction is necessary for global persistence. The explanation of course is that those patches which at any instant contain no parasitoids constitute a temporary refuge for the hosts and thus the host population is always able to remain 'one step ahead' of the pursuing parasitoids.

It is evident from the foregoing discussion that, in a patchy environment, the balance between colonization and local extinction is of central importance. Our second approach to modelling populations in such environments recognizes this from the outset and makes no attempt to describe the detail of the intra-patch dynamics, attention being instead directed solely to the presence or absence of a species on a particular patch. The simplest conceivable such model involves a single species which maintains itself on a 'universe' of M identical patches. Successful colonization of an empty patch occurs through migration of colonists from other occupied patches and we assume that at any given time, although the total number of migrants is a small fraction of the population, an individual migrant is able to travel considerable distances and hence initiate the colonization of a patch some distance from its previous location. It is then plausible that the probability per unit time that an empty patch is successfully colonized is proportional to the total number of occupied patches in the 'universe'. If at time t, there are $Q(t)$ occupied patches and $E(t)$ ($\equiv M - Q(t)$) empty patches, then the probability $P_C(t)\,\mathrm{d}t$ that in a short time interval $\mathrm{d}t$ one of the empty patches is colonized is

$$P_C(t)\,\mathrm{d}t = \tau_C^{-1}E(t)Q(t)\,\mathrm{d}t = \tau_C^{-1}(M - Q(t))Q(t)\,\mathrm{d}t \qquad (5.2.17)$$

where the constant of proportionality is written as τ_c^{-1} to emphasize that $P_C(t)$ is a probability per unit time. We assume that we can choose $\mathrm{d}t$ to be sufficiently small that the probability of two or more successful colonizations during $\mathrm{d}t$ is proportional to $(\mathrm{d}t)^2$ and can therefore be neglected.

After a patch has been colonized, it is likely that the colony will either become extinct very rapidly (while the population of the patch is still very small)—a situation we describe as 'unsuccessful' colonization—or will persist until extinction is caused through over-exploitation of the resources available within the patch (see Fig. 5.3). Only the second possibility is significant for the global population dynamics, as colonists from short-lived, unsuccessful, colonies can be regarded as originating from their previous patch provided we ignore the few individuals born in an unsuccessful colony who establish a second successful colony, a group unlikely to be numerous enough to be of any global significance. The distribution of lifetimes of patches after successful colonization can only be determined from a detailed knowledge of the intra-patch dynamics, but perhaps the simplest possible assumption is that after successful colonization there is a constant probability per unit time τ_E that the population on the patch will become extinct. The probability $P_E(t)\,\mathrm{d}t$ that during an infinitesimally short time interval $\mathrm{d}t$, a single occupied patch becomes empty would then be

$$P_E(t)\mathrm{d}t = \tau_E^{-1}Q(t)\,\mathrm{d}t. \qquad (5.2.18)$$

The expected change $\mathrm{d}Q(t)$ in the total number of occupied sites between

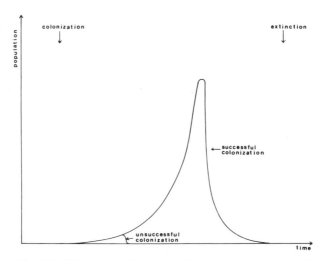

Fig. 5.3. Variation of the population of a single patch
following colonization.

times t and $t + dt$ is clearly

$$dQ(t) = \{P_C(t) - P_E(t)\}\, dt, \qquad (5.2.19)$$

from which we see that the *expected number of occupied sites* changes in accordance with the simple ordinary differential equation.

$$\frac{dQ}{dt} = P_C(t) - P_E(t), \qquad (5.2.20)$$

which for the very simple model defined by equations (5.2.17) and (5.2.18) takes the form of the logistic equation

$$\frac{dQ}{dt} = rQ(1 - Q/K), \qquad (5.2.21)$$

where

$$r = \frac{M}{\tau_C} - \frac{1}{\tau_E}, \qquad (5.2.22)$$

and

$$K = r\tau_C = M - \frac{\tau_C}{\tau_E}. \qquad (5.2.23)$$

The steady state $Q = K$ is of course stable.

Other single species models can easily be developed to take account of such effects as delayed emigration or the need for a 'dead time' during which a patch recovers from over exploitation.

In a precisely similar way we can construct predator–prey (or host–parasite) models in which we recognize four possible states for a particular patch:

(a) empty,
(b) occupied by prey only,
(c) occupied by prey plus predators,
(d) occupied by predators only.

The processes of colonization or extinction are modelled as in the single-species case and the result is a set of four differential equations for the number of patches in each state. A model of this type is used in the case study in Chapter 10.

5.3 MODELLING WITH PARTIAL DIFFERENTIAL EQUATIONS

A. Balance equation for population density

There are situations where the strategems described in the previous section are inapplicable and we cannot avoid grappling with the detail of dispersal and spatial distribution. One modelling procedure which has found wide application in such situations is the use of partial differential equations which describe the changes with respect to both space and time of population density. We imagine a population which is confined to a two-dimensional area A on which is drawn a grid as shown in Fig. 5.4, the side of each small square being of length a. The key assumption which permits us to meaningfully define a population density is that we can choose a such that in most squares the following constraints can be satisfied simultaneously;

(a) a is sufficiently large that the relative fluctuations in the population of each square due to demographic stochasticity are small.

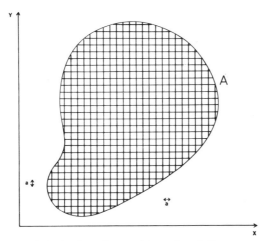

Fig. 5.4. An imaginary grid used to define population density as a function of position.

132

(b) *a* is sufficiently small that the population in each square and the flow of population between squares at a given time varies smoothly with position.

We then define the population density $\rho(x, y, t)$ by

$$\rho(x, y, t) = \frac{1}{a^2} \left[\begin{array}{l} \text{Total population in the square centred} \\ \text{on the point } (x, y) \text{ at time } t. \end{array} \right] \quad (5.3.1)$$

We now recall the fundamental equation of population dynamics (2.1.1) which states that the population in any area can change for only four reasons—births, deaths, immigration and emigration—and apply it to one particular square centred on the point (x, y) as shown in Fig. 5.5. We denote by $F_x(x, y)$ the *x* component of the population flux density, and define

$$F_x(x, y) = \frac{1}{a} \left[\begin{array}{l} \text{Net flow of individuals per unit time} \\ \text{across a line of length } a \text{ centred at } (x, y) \\ \text{and parallel to the } y \text{ axis} \end{array} \right] \quad (5.3.2)$$

where individuals moving to the right and left make respectively positive and negative contributions to the flux density. We define the *y* component of the population flux density $F_y(x, y)$ in a precisely analogous way. If we now apply the fundamental equation to the centre box in Fig. 5.5 we find that if β and δ are the *per capita* birth and death rates in the box, then after accounting for births, deaths, immigration and emigration,

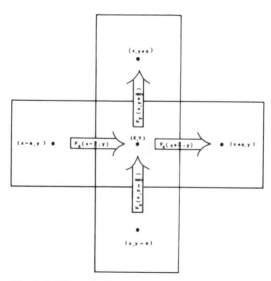

Fig. 5.5 The *x* and *y* components of population
flux density.

$$\frac{\partial}{\partial t}[a^2\rho(x,y)] = (\beta - \delta)a^2\rho(x,y) + a[F_x(x - \tfrac{1}{2}a, y) - F_x(x + \tfrac{1}{2}a, y)$$

$$+ F_y(x, y - \tfrac{1}{2}a) - F_y(x, y + \tfrac{1}{2}a)]. \qquad (5.3.3)$$

We now assume that a is sufficiently small that we can expand the terms on the right hand side by a two-dimensional Taylor expansion (see Appendix C), a procedure whose validity depends critically on our 'smoothness' assumption (b). Then

$$F_x(x \pm \tfrac{1}{2}a, y) \simeq F_x(x, y) \pm \frac{a}{2} \frac{\partial F_x(x, y)}{\partial x}, \qquad (5.3.4)$$

and

$$F_y(x, y \pm \tfrac{1}{2}a) \simeq F_y(x, y) \pm \frac{a}{2} \frac{\partial F_y(x, y)}{\partial y}. \qquad (5.3.5)$$

Equation (5.3.3) then simplifies to the form

$$\frac{\partial \rho}{\partial t} = (\beta - \delta)\rho - \left[\frac{\partial F_x}{\partial x} + \frac{\partial F_y}{\partial y}\right], \qquad (5.3.6)$$

which is simply a restatement of the fundamental principle of population balance in the language of partial differentials.

The notation in partial differential equations involving fluxes can be simplified by introducing a 'vector operator' ∇ defined by

$$\nabla \equiv \mathbf{i}\frac{\partial}{\partial x} + \mathbf{j}\frac{\partial}{\partial y} \qquad (5.3.7)$$

where $\mathbf{i}$ and $\mathbf{j}$ are unit vectors in the x and y directions. If we represent the population flux density by a vector $\mathbf{F}$ where

$$\mathbf{F} \equiv F_x\mathbf{i} + F_y\mathbf{j} \qquad (5.3.8)$$

then we can represent the expression

$$\frac{\partial F_x}{\partial x} + \frac{\partial F_y}{\partial y} \qquad (5.3.9)$$

by the shorthand form $\nabla \cdot \mathbf{F}$ on the understanding that the $\cdot$ represents a scalar product. The reader unfamiliar with and uninterested in vector calculus can safely ignore the reasons for this notation and can regard $\nabla \cdot \mathbf{F}$ as an abbreviation for (5.3.9). In the new notation the balance equation becomes

$$\frac{\partial \rho}{\partial t} + \nabla \cdot \mathbf{F} = (\beta - \delta)\rho. \qquad (5.3.10)$$

Some further insight on this partial differential equation is obtained by integrating over any area A. This yields

$$\iint_A \frac{\partial \rho}{\partial t} \, dx \, dy + \iint_A \nabla \cdot \mathbf{F} \, dx \, dy = \iint_A (\beta - \delta)\rho \, dx \, dy, \qquad (5.3.11)$$

which is simplified by noting:

(a) The operations of differentiation with respect to time and integration over space are independent and the order in which they are performed is of no consequence. Thus

$$\iint_A \frac{\partial \rho}{\partial t} \, dx \, dy = \frac{d}{dt} \iint_A \rho \, dx \, dy = \frac{dN}{dt} \qquad (5.3.12)$$

(b) The term involving population fluxes can be manipulated as follows:

$$\iint_A \nabla \cdot \mathbf{F} \, dx \, dy = \iint_A \left\{ \frac{\partial F_x}{\partial x} + \frac{\partial F_y}{\partial y} \right\} \, dx \, dy$$

$$= \int dy \int \frac{\partial F_x}{\partial x} \, dx + \int dx \int \frac{\partial F_y}{\partial y} \, dy$$

$$= \int dy \left\{ \begin{matrix} F_x \text{ at 'right-hand' boundary} \\ -F_x \text{ at 'left-hand' boundary} \end{matrix} \right\}$$

$$+ \int dx \left\{ \begin{matrix} F_y \text{ at 'top' boundary} \\ -F_y \text{ at 'bottom' boundary} \end{matrix} \right\}.$$

$$(5.3.13)$$

From the definition of the components of flux density (cf. equation (5.3.2)) it follows that those two integrals represent the net loss of population per unit time across the boundaries. (The unconvinced reader should demonstrate this for a rectangular area with the sides of the rectangle parallel to the x and y axes). Thus if I and E are respectively the *total* rates of immigration and emigration,

$$\iint_A \nabla \cdot \mathbf{F} \, dx \, dy = E - I. \qquad (5.3.14)$$

(c) Since $\beta(x, y) \, dx \, dy$ is the per capita birth rate within the box centred at (x, y) then on integrating over the area A

$$\iint_A \beta\rho \, dx \, dy = B, \qquad (5.3.15)$$

where B is the total birth rate. Similarly if D is the total death rate then

$$\iint_A \rho\delta \, dx \, dy = D. \qquad (5.3.16)$$

Thus equation (5.3.11) simply expresses the fact that for the area A

$$\frac{dN}{dt} = B - D + I - E, \qquad (5.3.17)$$

which is where we started in Chapter 2.

B. Random motion

The continuity equation (5.3.10) would become a partial differential equation in the population density ρ if we were able to express the flux density $\mathbf{F}$ in terms of ρ. This is only possible after we have defined the 'microscopic' mechanism (i.e. the behaviour of individuals) responsible for the 'macroscopic' population flux. The simplest such mechanism assumes that each individual moves randomly within the area A. If in a small time interval dt, there is a probability $\tau^{-1} dt$ of an individual moving from the square centred at (x, y) to each of the four neighbouring squares and a negligible probability (of order $(dt)^2$) that he completes a longer journey in this time, then in dt the net flow of individuals across the line in Fig. 5.5 with mid point $(x + \frac{1}{2}a, y)$ is

$$F_x(x + \tfrac{1}{2}a, y)a\, dt = \frac{a^2}{\tau}\{\rho(x, y) - \rho(x + a, y)\}dt \qquad (5.3.18)$$

Taylor expansion where necessary in this equation yields

$$F_x(x, y) + \tfrac{1}{2}a\, \frac{\partial F_x(x, y)}{\partial x} = -\frac{a^2}{\tau}\, \frac{\partial \rho(x, y)}{\partial x}, \qquad (5.3.19)$$

By similar reasoning on the flow between the boxes centred on (x, y) and $(x - a, y)$ we obtain

$$F_x(x, y) - \tfrac{1}{2}a\, \frac{\partial F_x(x, y)}{\partial x} = -\frac{a^2}{\tau}\, \frac{\partial \rho(x, y)}{\partial x}, \qquad (5.3.20)$$

and on adding (5.3.19) and (5.3.20),

$$F_x(x, y) = -D\, \frac{\partial \rho(x, y)}{\partial x}, \qquad (5.3.21)$$

where the diffusion coefficient D is given by

$$D = \frac{a^2}{\tau} \qquad (5.3.22)$$

In a similar way we find that

$$F_y(x, y) = -D\, \frac{\partial \rho(x, y)}{\partial y} \qquad (5.3.23)$$

The vector equation that embodies equations (5.3.21) and (5.3.23) is often written using the ∇ operator in the form

$$\mathbf{F} = -D\nabla\rho, \tag{5.3.24}$$

which on substituting in the continuity equation (5.3.10) yields

$$\frac{\partial\rho}{\partial t} = (\beta - \delta)\rho + D\nabla^2\rho \tag{5.3.25}$$

where the ∇^2 operator is now shorthand for the *scalar* operation $\partial^2/\partial x^2 + \partial^2/\partial y^2$.

C. Biased random motion and directed motion

If the probability per unit time τ^{-1} of an individual jumping from one square to an adjacent square is itself density dependent then the analysis of the previous section goes through unchanged as far as equation (5.3.24) except that the diffusion coefficient now depends on density. For example if dispersal is a response to overcrowding we might expect the jump probability to increase with density; an example of which would be

$$\tau^{-1} = b + c\rho \tag{5.3.26}$$

which results in a flux density of the form

$$\mathbf{F} = -D_0\nabla\rho - D_1\rho\nabla\rho \tag{5.3.27}$$

where

$$D_0 = a^2 b, \qquad D_1 = a^2 c \tag{5.3.28}$$

We call this form for the population flux density *biased random motion*. For this model the partial differential equation in ρ is again obtained by substituting for $\mathbf{F}$ in the balance equation with the result

$$\frac{\partial\rho}{\partial t} = (\beta - \delta)\rho + D_0\nabla^2\rho + D_1\nabla \cdot (\rho\nabla\rho), \tag{5.3.29}$$

where the last term written out in full is

$$\nabla \cdot (\rho\nabla\rho) = \left(\frac{\partial\rho}{\partial x}\right)^2 + \left(\frac{\partial\rho}{\partial y}\right)^2 + \rho\frac{\partial^2\rho}{\partial x^2} + \rho\frac{\partial^2\rho}{\partial y^2} \tag{5.3.30}$$

The biased random motion model is inapplicable to territorial animals since any apparently 'random' motion which may then be observed in fact involves each animal returning regularly to its starting point. The only movements which are of interest in that situation are movements of an individual's 'home' and such movements are likely to be strongly affected by population density (for example, young animals just reaching maturity seeking territory of their own). In particular we would expect that the jump probability τ^{-1} should approach zero at low population densities so that a plausible form might be

$$\tau^{-1} = c\rho \qquad (5.3.31)$$

implying

$$\mathbf{F} = -D_1\rho\nabla\rho, \quad \text{where} \quad D_1 = \tfrac{1}{2}a^2c. \qquad (5.3.32)$$

We call this form for the population flux density *directed motion*.

D. Boundary conditions

Before we can predict the temporal development of population density in a particular area, it is necessary to provide some information on immigration and emigration at the boundaries of the area under study. The simplest case is of course the *closed* population which is confined to a fixed area (island, fenced experimental area, etc.) and for which it is convenient mathematically to assume *reflecting* boundaries across which the population flow is zero. This implies that the population flux density should vanish on the boundaries except in the mathematically possible but thoroughly implausible situation that the flux is parallel to a particular boundary along its entire length. Such 'vortices' of animals are not observed and it is customary to characterize reflecting boundaries by the formal requirement that at all points on the boundary

$$\mathbf{F} = \mathbf{0}, \qquad (5.3.33)$$

which for the special cases of random motion and biased random motion (cf. equations (5.3.21) and (5.3.27) implies

$$\nabla\rho = 0 \quad \text{or equivalently} \quad \frac{\partial\rho}{\partial x} = \frac{\partial\rho}{\partial y} = 0. \qquad (5.3.34)$$

Since many aspects of the population dynamics of closed populations can be modelled without resorting to the use of partial differential equations, these are most commonly encountered in the context of open systems, especially those for which birth and death rates vary with position. If a region where births exceed deaths is surrounded by hostile territory, and the net *per capita* growth rate $g(x, y)$ at a point (x, y) is of the form shown by the continuous curve in Fig. 5.6, then it seems natural to approximate this by the dashed curve in the same figure, so that

$$g(x, y) = \begin{cases} g_0 & \text{if } (x, y) \text{ is inside the favourable area} \\ -\infty & \text{if } (x, y) \text{ is in the surrounding hostile territory.} \end{cases} \qquad (5.3.35)$$

This assumption, which amounts to a statement that any individual leaving the favourable region dies immediately, would appear only applicable to 'lemming-like' mass suicides, but it is probably a reasonable approximation to

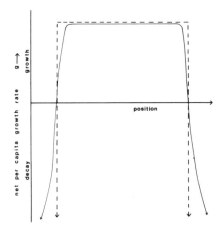

Fig. 5.6. Variation of net per capita growth rate along a transect of a region of favourable environment surrounded by hostile territory.

situations where those individuals excluded from the favourable region are both unable to breed in the surrounding territory and unable to return rapidly to the favourable area. It is an immediate consequence of the assumption that $g(x, y) = -\infty$ outside the favourable area that at all points on the boundary

$$\rho = 0. \tag{5.3.36}$$

This *absorbing* boundary condition that the density vanish on the boundary is popular because it leads to major mathematical simplification, but it is at best an extreme idealization and is wholly inappropriate in many contexts. In the most general type of open system with which we shall be concerned, the sole formal requirement we can make is that if we define an origin within the region of interest, then infinitely far from this origin,

$$\rho = 0 \tag{5.3.37}$$

and

$$\nabla\rho = 0. \tag{5.3.38}$$

5.4 EXPONENTIALLY GROWING OR DECLINING POPULATION

The simplest possible model of a spatially homogeneous population has

$$\frac{dN}{dt} = \lambda N, \tag{5.4.1}$$

which of course represents an exponentially growing or declining population depending on the sign of λ. If the *per capita* birth and death rates in a spatially distributed population are independent of both density and position then the same simple equation results if the population is confined to a closed region. In this case the balance equation

$$\frac{\partial \rho}{\partial t} = (\beta - \delta)\rho - \nabla \cdot \mathbf{F} \tag{5.4.2}$$

can be integrated (following the steps in the derivation of equation (5.3.13)) to yield the result that provided $\mathbf{F} = 0$ at all points on the boundaries, then

$$\frac{dN}{dt} = (\beta - \delta)N . \tag{5.4.3}$$

This result is valid irrespective of the dispersal mechanisms present and reflects the obvious fact that if the probability of an individual birth or death is constant at all points in a closed region, then movement of individuals from place to place within the region has no effect on the total population size.

As soon as birth and death rates vary with position the situation changes dramatically and dispersal may play a vital role in determining whether a population grows or declines. We now illustrate this with a mathematically non-rigorous treatment of a very artificial example but shall subsequently demonstrate the robustness of the conclusions in more realistic contexts. We imagine a population which is confined to a narrow one-dimensional strip of length L, the ends of which are absorbing boundaries as defined in the previous section. Individuals diffuse randomly along the strip, and within the strip the per-capita birth rate is constant and exceeds the per capita death rate which is also constant. The assumption of absorbing boundaries is equivalent to an infinite per capita death rate (and hence zero population) outside the strip, while within the strip the population density is obtained from the equation

$$\frac{\partial \rho}{\partial t} = g\rho + D \frac{\partial^2 \rho}{\partial x^2} \qquad 0 \leq x \leq L, \tag{5.4.4}$$

where

$$g \equiv \beta - \delta > 0, \tag{5.4.5}$$

with the boundary condition

$$\rho(x = 0) = \rho(x = L) = 0. \tag{5.4.6}$$

To investigate this system we initially assume a solution of the form

$$\rho(x, t) = \rho_0(x)e^{\lambda t} \qquad 0 \leq x \leq L \tag{5.4.7}$$

which on substituting in equation (5.4.4) gives the ordinary differential equation

$$\frac{d^2 \rho_0}{dx^2} + \mu^2 \rho_0 = 0 \tag{5.4.8}$$

where

$$\mu = \left(\frac{g - \lambda}{D}\right)^{1/2} \tag{5.4.9}$$

The only solutions of (5.4.8) which are zero at $x = 0$ are of the form

$$\rho_0(x) \propto \sin \mu x. \tag{5.4.10}$$

Such a solution can only be zero at $x = L$ if

$$\mu L = n\pi \text{ radians}, \qquad n = 1, 2, 3, \ldots \tag{5.4.11}$$

i.e. if

$$\lambda = g - \frac{n^2 \pi^2 D}{L^2}, \qquad n = 1, 2, 3, \ldots \tag{5.4.12}$$

Each value of n yields a permissible solution and the most general solution is a superposition of such solutions. The total population thus changes according to the equation

$$N(t) = \int_0^L \rho(x, t) \mathrm{d}x = \sum_{n=1}^{\infty} N_{0n} \exp\left\{\left(g - \frac{n^2 \pi^2 D}{L^2}\right)t\right\} \tag{5.4.13}$$

where N_{0n} are constants. It is clear from this that although births exceed deaths in the region $0 \leq x \leq L$, the population only grows in that region if the exponent in equation (5.4.13) is positive for at least some values of n, a situation which is guaranteed if

$$L > \pi(D/g)^{1/2} = 3.14(D/g)^{1/2}. \tag{5.4.14}$$

The quantity $(D/g)^{1/2}$ called the *diffusion length*, is of the same order of magnitude as the average distance moved by an individual in a generation and the interpretation of equation (5.4.14) is thus that a viable population is only possible on the strip if it is sufficiently long that an individual is likely to reproduce before leaving it.

The above model is unrealistic in two respects, the assumption of one-dimensional motion and the imposition of absorbing boundary conditions. Relaxation of these assumptions merely changes the constant in equation (5.4.14) and not the qualitative conclusion that with random motion there is a certain minimum size below which a habitat is non-viable. For example after a fair amount of mathematical effort we find that in a circular area of diameter L with absorbing boundaries, a population is only viable if

$$L > 4.81 (D/g)^{1/2}. \tag{5.4.15}$$

If alternatively we assume that the transition from favourable to unfavourable habitat is gradual and write the net growth rate (the difference between the per capita birth and death rates) at a distance r from an origin 0 as (for

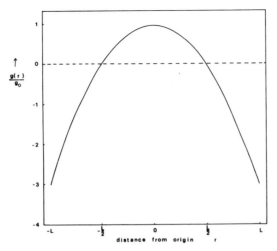

Fig. 5.7. Variation of net growth rate given by equation (5.4.16).

example)

$$g(r) = g_0\left(1 - \frac{4r^2}{L^2}\right), \qquad (5.4.16)$$

which as we show in Fig. 5.7 has a central region of diameter L in which births exceeds deaths, then a viable population is possible only if

$$L > 4(D/g_0)^{1/2}. \qquad (5.4.17)$$

Finally we note that no model which, like the random motion model just discussed, is linear in population density, can possibly exhibit a stable steady state, since if $\rho^*(x, y)$ is a steady state distribution for such a model then so is $\alpha\rho^*(x, y)$ for any value of α. Thus, in general, such linear models can only describe exponentially growing or declining populations. However, what is revealed by the above argument is that in an open system the nature of the dispersal mechanism and the size of the populated area may be as important as crude birth and death rates in determining the rate of growth or decline.

5.5 NEIGHBOURHOOD STABILITY ANALYSIS FOR PARTIAL DIFFERENTIAL EQUATION

A. Local linearization

Given a suitable non-linearity in one or more of the terms representing births, deaths, immigration or emigration, there is the possibility of a steady-state distribution of population density $\rho^*(x, y)$. By linearizing about this steady

state we obtain a linear, partial differential equation whose solutions represent an exponentially growing or declining perturbation from the steady state.
The spirit of this type of linear analysis is thus similar to that used with
ordinary differential equations but, as we have already seen in Chapter 3,
with partial differential equations the resulting algebra is more involved.

If a partial differential equation has a steady state solution $\rho^*(x, y)$ we
obtain the linear equation for the perturbation by setting

$$\rho(x, y, t) = \rho^*(x, y) + \xi(x, y, t), \qquad (5.5.1)$$

where it is assumed that at most points in space

$$|\xi(x, y)| \ll \rho^*(x, y) \qquad (5.5.2)$$

so that terms of order ξ^2 or higher may be neglected. It is furthermore
assumed that those points where this condition is violated play no significant
role in determining the overall population behaviour. For example, a population with density-dependent birth and death rates and random diffusion can
be described by an equation of the form

$$\frac{\partial \rho}{\partial t} = g(\rho)\rho + D\nabla^2\rho. \qquad (5.5.3)$$

With suitable boundary conditions this equation may have a steady-state
solution $\rho^*(x, y)$ which may or may not be spatially uniform. The linear
equation in the perturbation $\xi(x, y, t)$ is obtained by substituting the form
(5.5.1) for $\rho(x, y, t)$, expanding, and neglecting terms of order ξ^2 or higher.
The result is

$$\frac{\partial \xi}{\partial t} = H(x, y)\xi + D\nabla^2\xi. \qquad (5.5.4)$$

where

$$H(x, y) = g(\rho^*) + \rho^*\left(\frac{\partial g}{\partial \rho}\right)^*. \qquad (5.5.5)$$

The partial differential equation obtained by local linearization need not be of
a simple recognizable form and where the dispersal is non-linear it is usually
rather unwieldy. For instance if in the above example we had biased random
motion the term $D\nabla^2\xi$ would be replaced by

$$D_0\nabla^2\xi + 2D_1\nabla\rho^* . \nabla\xi + D_1\rho^*\nabla^2\xi + D_1\xi\nabla^2\rho^*. \qquad (5.5.6)$$

We saw in the previous section that boundary conditions had an important
role in determining whether the solutions of a linear partial differential equation ultimately grow or decline, so further progress requires specifications of
the boundary conditions to be satisfied by the density perturbation ξ. Once
this is done we assume that $\xi(x, y, t)$ is a superposition of solutions of the form

$$\xi(x, y, t) = \xi_0(x, y)e^{\lambda t} \qquad (5.5.7)$$

to obtain a partial differential equation in $\xi_0(x, y)$. The requirement that $\xi_0(x, y)$ satisfies the boundary conditions in principle fixes the value of λ, (though the mathematics involved in the calculation may be difficult) and the sign of the real part of λ of course determines the local stability of the steady state.

In practice it may be difficult to determine the sign of the real part of λ except by tedious numerical means and there is an alternative ploy which may be useful in determining local stability. This is an extension of the concept of the Lyapunov function, and the principal result is that if we can find a function $L(t)$ defined by

$$L(t) = \iint\limits_{\substack{\text{all} \\ \text{accessible} \\ \text{space}}} w(x, y)[\xi(x, y, t)]^2 \, dx \, dy, \qquad (5.5.8)$$

where the 'weighting function' $w(x, y)$ is positive at all accessible points, then local stability is guaranteed if at all times

$$\frac{dL}{dt} \leq 0, \qquad (5.5.9)$$

with equality only if ξ is everywhere zero.

In Sections 5.5B and C we illustrate the above techniques on two examples—one with the population regulated through density dependence in the birth death rates, the other with regulation through non-linear dispersal.

B. An example with density-dependence in the vital rates

As an example of a model of a spatially distributed population which is regulated through density-dependent birth or death rates, we consider equation (5.5.3) and assume for $g(\rho)$ a slight modification of the Gompertz form (cf. Chapter 2, Problem 3), namely

$$g(\rho) = -a \ln\left(\frac{\rho + b}{\rho_0}\right), \qquad (5.5.10)$$

where a, b, ρ_0 are all positive constants. This function resembles the more commonly encountered logistic in many of its qualitative attributes, (see Fig. 5.8) and we select it as its use frequently leads to rather simple mathematics.

The population density now satisfies

$$\frac{\partial \rho}{\partial t} = g(\rho)\rho + D\nabla^2\rho, \qquad (5.5.11)$$

and the most obvious steady state is the trivial one where the density is everywhere zero. In this case the perturbations, which can be thought of as colonizations, obey the equation (obtained from equations (5.5.4) and

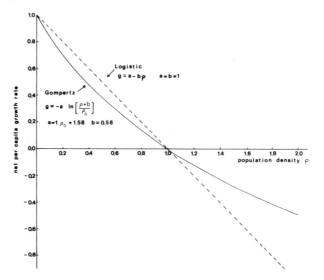

Fig. 5.8. Gompertz and logistic forms for the per capita growth function $g(\rho)$.

(5.5.5))

$$\frac{\partial \xi}{\partial t} = r\xi + D\nabla^2\xi, \tag{5.5.12}$$

with

$$r = a \ln(b/\rho_0). \tag{5.5.13}$$

This type of equation was considered in Section 5.4 and from the arguments in that section it follows that with reflecting boundary conditions the perturbation invariably grows exponentially with time but with absorbing boundaries the population only grows if the diameter of the occupied region exceeds a critical value of order $(D/r)^{1/2}$.

Intuitively we would expect that in those situations where the dispersal is sufficiently weak or the habitat sufficiently large for a small population to grow exponentially, this growth would eventually be stopped by the non-linear logistic term. This is surprisingly awkward to prove, the simplest method being to consider the Liapunov function

$$L = \tfrac{1}{2} \iint\limits_{\substack{\text{occupied} \\ \text{area}}} \xi^2 \, dx \, dy. \tag{5.5.14}$$

Then

$$\frac{dL}{dt} = \iint\limits_{\substack{\text{occupied} \\ \text{area}}} \xi \frac{\partial \xi}{\partial t} \, dx \, dy = \iint\limits_{\substack{\text{occupied} \\ \text{area}}} \{H\xi^2 + D\xi\nabla^2\xi\} dx \, dy, \tag{5.5.15}$$

where the second result is a consequence of equation (5.5.4). The function

$H(x, y)$ is defined in equation (5.5.5) and can be evaluated for this model as

$$H = -a\left[\ln\left(\frac{\rho^* + b}{\rho_0}\right) + \frac{\rho^*}{\rho^* + b}\right] = -a\left[\frac{D\nabla^2\rho^*}{a\rho^*} + \frac{\rho^*}{\rho^* + b}\right] \quad (5.5.16)$$

implying

$$\frac{dL}{dt} = \iint_{\substack{\text{occupied} \\ \text{area}}} \left\{-\frac{a\rho^*\xi^2}{\rho^* + b} - \frac{D\xi^2\nabla^2\rho^*}{\rho^*} + D\xi\nabla^2\xi\right\} dx\, dy \quad (5.5.17)$$

The key to simplifying expressions of this type is to use two results from vector calculus, namely

(a) If θ and ψ are scalar functions of x and y then

$$\theta\nabla^2\psi = \nabla\cdot(\theta\nabla\psi) - \nabla\theta\cdot\nabla\psi \quad (5.5.18)$$

and

(b) If $\mathbf{a}$ is any vector function of x and y (i.e. each component of $\mathbf{a}$ depends on x and y), then

$$\iint_{\substack{\text{closed} \\ \text{area}}} \nabla\cdot\mathbf{a}\, dx dy = \iint_{\substack{\text{perimeter} \\ \text{of area}}} \mathbf{a}\cdot\hat{\mathbf{n}}\, dl \quad (5.5.19)$$

where dl is an element of the perimeter line and $\hat{\mathbf{n}}$ is a unit vector perpendicular to this element. This theorem is proved by an argument similar to that embodied in equation (5.3.13) which is a special case of the general result.

It then follows after some rather heavy manipulation that provided ξ is zero on the boundaries,

$$\frac{dL}{dt} = \iint_{\substack{\text{occupied} \\ \text{area}}} \left\{-\frac{a\rho^*\xi^2}{\rho^* + \varepsilon} - D\left[\nabla\xi + \frac{\xi}{\rho^*}\nabla\rho^*\right]^2\right\} dx\, dy \quad (5.5.20)$$

and hence $dL/dt < 0$ unless $\xi = 0$ everywhere. This completes the proof of the stability of the steady state.

C. An example with density-dependent dispersal

As our second example we consider a population with per capita birth and death rates which are independent of population density but vary with position such that the net *per capita* growth rate $g(x, y)$ varies across a transect of the occupied area in the form shown in Fig. 5.7. We assume that the dispersal is through biased random motion and hence find that

$$\frac{\partial\rho}{\partial t} = g(x, y)\rho + D_0\nabla^2\rho + D_1\nabla\cdot(\rho\nabla\rho) \quad (5.5.21)$$

In this model the diffusion rate is always higher than in the corresponding model with random motion ($D_1 = 0$) and thus a viable population with biased random motion is impossible unless the region of net growth ($g(x, y) > 0$) is at least wide enough to support an exponentially growing population when $D_1 = 0$. In what follows we assume that this is the case.

To simplify our analysis of the model we first scale equation (5.5.21) by setting

$$x' = x/r_0, \qquad y' = y/r_0, \qquad t' = t/t_0, \qquad \rho' = \rho/\rho_0 \qquad (5.5.22)$$

where r_0, t_0, ρ_0 are constants with the dimension of length, time and population density respectively. We choose

$$t_0 = 1/g(x, y)_{max}, \qquad r_0 = (D_0 t_0)^{1/2}, \qquad \rho_0 = D_1^{-1} r_0^2 t_0^{-1}, \qquad (5.5.23)$$

and define

$$g'(x', y') \equiv t_0 g(x, y),$$

and

$$\nabla \equiv \mathbf{i} \frac{\partial}{\partial x'} + \mathbf{j} \frac{\partial}{\partial y'}. \qquad (5.5.24)$$

Then with the new dimensionless variables

$$\frac{\partial \rho'}{\partial t'} = g'(x', y')\rho' + \nabla'^2 \rho' + \nabla' \cdot (\rho' \nabla' \rho'). \qquad (5.5.25)$$

Clearly, any stationary solution of equation (5.5.25) must satisfy

$$g'(x', y')\rho'^* + \nabla'^2 \rho'^* + \nabla'(\rho'^* \nabla' \rho'^*) = 0, \qquad (5.5.26)$$

and to prove the local stability of such a stationary solution we linearize in the perturbation $\xi'(x', y')$ and obtain after some labour

$$\frac{\partial \xi'}{\partial t'} = g'(x', y')\xi' + \rho'^* \nabla'^2 \xi' + 2\nabla \rho'^* \cdot \nabla \xi' + \xi' \nabla'^2 \rho'^* + \nabla'^2 \xi' \qquad (5.5.27)$$

which although linear in ξ is alarmingly complex and unfamiliar. We therefore make no attempt to determine directly the nature of the solutions of this equation but again use a Lyapunov function, in this case choosing

$$L = \frac{1}{2} \iint_{\substack{all \\ space}} (1 + \rho'^*)\xi'^2 \, dx \, dx \qquad (5.5.28)$$

The choice of weighting function (in this case $1 + \rho'^*$) is unfortunately a matter of trial and error, but many trials are possible in the time required for a qualitative study of the partial differential equation (5.5.27). It is a matter now of some very heavy and uninstructive algebra to show that

$$\frac{dL}{dt} = - \iint_{\substack{\text{all} \\ \text{space}}} (1 + \rho'^*) \left\{ \left(\frac{\xi' \nabla \rho'^*}{\rho'^*} - \nabla' \xi \right)^2 + \rho'^* (\nabla' \xi')^2 \right\} dx \, dy$$

$$- \iint_{\substack{\text{all} \\ \text{space}}} \xi'^2 (\nabla' \rho'^*)^2 \, dx \, dy, \tag{5.5.29}$$

which is clearly negative unless ξ is zero everywhere. This completes the proof of the stability of the steady state.

It would appear intuitively obvious from the above argument that with directed motion, which corresponds to $D_0 = 0$, there should always be a locally stable, non-zero, steady state, since the minimum size for a viable area will go to zero with D_0 (cf. equations (5.4.14)–(5.4.17)). This is correct, but because of our choice of scale factors (equation (5.5.23)) the proof of stability requires slight modification, and is the subject of Problem 8.

D. Wave-like disturbances

We noted in previous chapters that for a spatially homogeneous population the approach to a stable steady state may or may not involve a series of damped oscillations depending on whether it is part of an overdamped or an underdamped system. When we take account of the spatial distribution of the population there is the additional possibility that damped oscillations at any particular location might propagate in a 'wave-like' manner. The simplest type of wave-like disturbance—a plane wave travelling without distortion at a speed v in the positive x direction—is represented mathematically by a function $\rho(x - vt)$. This is most easily demonstrated by concentrating on any one point on the wave in Fig. 5.9 and noting that in a small time interval dt, it has moved a distance $v \, dt$. Thus, provided dt is small

$$\rho(x, t) = \rho(x + v \, dt, t + dt) \simeq \rho(x, t) + v \, dt \, \frac{\partial \rho}{\partial x} + dt \, \frac{\partial \rho}{\partial t}. \tag{5.5.30}$$

Hence

$$v \frac{\partial \rho}{\partial t} + \frac{\partial \rho}{\partial x} = 0, \tag{5.5.31}$$

an equation whose general solution is of the form

$$\rho = \rho(u) \quad \text{where} \quad u = x - vt. \tag{5.5.32}$$

If the perturbation in density from a steady state value at some point (x_0, y_0) in space varies sinusoidally as

$$\xi(x_0, y_0, t) = A \cos \omega t \tag{5.5.33}$$

148

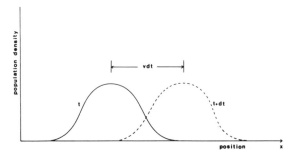

Fig. 5.9. A disturbance in population density propagating parallel to the x-axis. The density at time
$t + dt$ is displaced from that at time t by an amount
$t + dt$.

then if this perturbation propagates along the x axis at speed v,

$$\xi(x, y, t) = \xi\left(x_0, y_0, t - \frac{(x - x_0)}{v}\right) = A \cos(\omega t - kx + \phi)$$

$$= A \cos(kx - \omega t - \phi) \quad (5.5.34)$$

where $k \equiv \omega/v$ is known as the *wave number* and $\phi = kx_0$ is a phase factor.
The quantity k is most easily interpreted by noting that a change in x of $2\pi/k$
changes the argument of the cosine by 2π radians and leaves ξ unchanged in
value. The *wavelength* of the disturbance is hence $2\pi/k$ and it follows that the
wave number (units: radians per unit length) bears the same relationship to
the wavelength or spatial period as does the angular frequency (units: radians
per unit time) to the temporal period.

By similar arguments, a sinusoidal wave travelling in the negative x direction is represented by the expression

$$A \cos(kx + \omega t - \phi), \quad (5.5.35)$$

while waves in the positive and negative y direction are represented by

$$A \cos(ky \pm \omega t - \phi). \quad (5.5.36)$$

The general situation in two-dimensions is illustrated in Fig. 5.10 where we
consider a wave whose direction of propagation makes an angle θ with the x
axis. Equation (5.5.34) is then replaced by

$$\xi(x, y, t) = \xi\left(x_0, y_0, t - \frac{(x - x_0)\cos\theta}{v} - \frac{(y - y_0)\sin\theta}{v}\right)$$

$$= A \cos(\omega t - k_x x - k_y y + \phi)$$

$$= A \cos(k_x x + k_y y - \omega t - \phi) \quad (5.5.37)$$

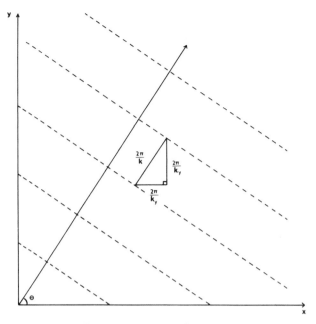

Fig. 5.10. A plane-wave propagating across a two dimensional area.

where

$$k_x = \frac{\omega}{v} \cos \theta = k \cos \theta$$

$$k_y = \frac{\omega}{v} \sin \theta = k \sin \theta \qquad (5.5.38)$$

so that

$$k_x^2 + k_y^2 = k^2. \qquad (5.5.39)$$

The quantities k_x and k_y evidently behave as components of a vector (known as the *wave vector*) formally defined as

$$\mathbf{k} + k_x \mathbf{i} + k_y \mathbf{j}, \qquad (5.5.40)$$

with magnitude equal to the wave number and direction that of the propagating wave. Thus if $\mathbf{r}(= x\mathbf{i} + y\mathbf{j})$ denotes the position of a point, the mathematical representation of a plane wave can be written concisely as (with $\phi = 0$)

$$\xi(\mathbf{r}, t) = A \cos(\mathbf{k} \cdot \mathbf{r} \pm \omega t). \qquad (5.5.41)$$

Finally we recall that it is normally convenient to represent a cosine as the real part of a complex exponential and we shall often write

$$\xi(\mathbf{r}, t) = A e^{i(\mathbf{k} \cdot \mathbf{r} \pm \omega t)}, \qquad (5.5.42)$$

with the understanding that the quantity of biological significance is the real part. In a similar way we describe waves with exponentially growing or declining amplitude by functions of the form

$$\xi(\mathbf{r}.\ t) = A e^{-\mu t} e^{i(\mathbf{k}.\mathbf{r} \pm \omega t)}, \tag{5.5.43}$$

where μ is a (positive or negative) real number.

The importance of wavelike disturbances is two-fold. First, there is the possibility that fluctuations in a few populations might actually propagate in this way, though the examples of which we are aware are either laboratory systems of no ecological significance such as travelling bands of chemotactic bacteria or phototactic algae, or are associated with very specialized situations such as 'waves' of aggregating slime mold amoebae. Much more important is the possibility, discussed more fully in Section 5.6, of Fourier analysing any disturbance in space and time and thus representing it as a superposition of waves of the type described by equation (5.5.42).

E. Diffusion as a stabilizing and destabilizing factor

The formalism in the previous section is particularly appropriate to an investigation of the effect of dispersal on the stability of a spatially uniform, steady state. We consider initially a model of the type described by equation (5.5.3) namely

$$\frac{\partial \rho}{\partial t} = g(\rho)\rho + D\nabla^2 \rho \tag{5.5.44}$$

and assume reflecting boundary conditions so that there is a spatially uniform stationary state. A small perturbation from this state then obeys an equation of the form (cf. equations (5.5.4) and (5.5.5))

$$\frac{\partial \xi}{\partial t} = -\alpha\xi + D\nabla^2\xi, \tag{5.5.45}$$

where we assume $\alpha > 0$). We consider solutions of equation (5.5.45) of the form

$$\xi(\mathbf{r}, t) = A e^{-\mu t} e^{i(\mathbf{k}\cdot\mathbf{r} - \omega t)}. \tag{5.5.46}$$

The result of substituting this expression into the linearized dynamic equation (5.5.45) and equating real and imaginary parts is

$$\omega = 0; \quad \mu = \alpha + Dk^2. \tag{5.5.47}$$

From this we deduce that the return to equilibrium is always non-oscillatory and that spatially uniform disturbances ($k = 0$) approach equilibrium more slowly than spatially heterogeneous ($k \neq 0$) disturbances. An argument analogous to the above can also be applied to single-species models which in their homogeneous form predict oscillatory behaviour; the conclusion being that the general effect of diffusion is to synchronize the oscillations at different points in space.

It is clearly of interest to determine whether there are circumstances in which non-uniform perturbations grow more rapidly (or decay less rapidly) than their uniform counterparts. As far as we are aware this requires at least two species and the simplest, if artificial, example known to us (due to Segal, and Jackson (1972)) involves a predator–prey system which combines co-operative interactions among the prey with interference competition among predators. The equations are

$$\frac{\partial F}{\partial t} = \alpha F + \beta F^2 - \gamma FC + D_1 \nabla^2 F \qquad (5.5.48)$$

$$\frac{\partial C}{\partial t} = \varepsilon FC - \phi C^2 + D_2 \nabla^2 C \qquad (5.5.49)$$

where F, C are respectively the densities of prey and predators and the signs in the equations are chosen so that all the constants are positive. The equations are scaled by setting

$$C' = \alpha^{-1} C \phi, \qquad F' = \alpha^{-1} F \varepsilon, \qquad t' = \alpha t, \qquad x' = x(\alpha/D_2)^{1/2},$$
$$y' = y(\alpha/D_2)^{1/2}, \qquad (5.5.50)$$

whence

$$\frac{\partial F'}{\partial t'} = F'(1 + \Gamma F') - aC'F' + D\nabla'^2 F', \qquad (5.5.51)$$

$$\frac{\partial C'}{\partial t'} = C'(F' - C') + \nabla'^2 C', \qquad (5.5.52)$$

whose behaviour is controlled by the dimensionless groups

$$\Gamma \equiv \beta^*/\varepsilon, \qquad a \equiv \gamma/\phi, \qquad D \equiv D_1/D_2. \qquad (5.5.53)$$

Provided that $\Gamma < a$ and that suitable boundary conditions apply, these equations have a spatially uniform steady state

$$F'^* = C'^* = (a - \Gamma)^{-1}, \qquad (5.5.54)$$

small deviations $(f'(\mathbf{r}, t), c'(\mathbf{r}, t))$ from which are described by

$$\frac{\partial f'}{\partial t'} \simeq (\Gamma F'^*)f' - (aF'^*)c' + D\nabla'^2 f', \qquad (5.5.55)$$

$$\frac{\partial c'}{\partial t'} = F'^* f' - F^* c' + \nabla'^2 c'. \qquad (5.5.56)$$

For stability we require that all solutions of these equations shall be superpositions of components of the form

$$f' = Ae^{-\mu t'}e^{i(\mathbf{k}' \cdot \mathbf{r}' - \omega t')} \qquad (5.5.57)$$

$$c' = Be^{-\mu t'}e^{i(\mathbf{k}' \cdot \mathbf{r}' - \omega t')} \qquad (5.5.58)$$

all with $\mu > 0$. By substituting these trial solutions (5.5.57) and (5.5.58) into the linearized dynamic equations (5.5.55) and (5.5.56) we can show that *either*

$$\mu = \tfrac{1}{2}\{F'^*(1 - \Gamma) + (D + 1)k^2\} \qquad (5.5.59)$$

and

$$\omega^2 = aF'^{*2} + (k^2 + F'^*)(Dk^2 - \Gamma F'^*) - \mu^2. \qquad (5.5.60)$$

or

$$\omega = 0, \qquad (5.5.61)$$

and

$$\mu^2 - \mu(\{1 - \Gamma\}F'^* + (D + 1)k^2) + \{aF'^{*2} + (k^2 + F'^*)(Dk^2 - \Gamma F'^*)\}. \qquad (5.5.62)$$

Routine (if tedious) algebra now serves to show that all possible disturbances decay with time (i.e. $\mu > 0$) provided that

$$\Gamma < 1 \qquad (5.5.63)$$

and

$$D(4a - 2\Gamma - D) > \Gamma^2. \qquad (5.5.64)$$

It is evident from inequality (5.5.64) that this system is only locally stable if the value of the diffusion coefficient ratio (D) lies within a relatively narrow range. Where the diffusion acts as a destabilizing influence, that is where D is outside the stable range, but the other system parameters are such as would produced stability in the absence of diffusion (i.e. $\Gamma < 1$), then a rather subtle pattern of behaviour emerges. It can be shown from equations (5.5.59)–(5.5.64) that for disturbances with wavevectors in the range

$$\frac{1}{2}\left\{\left(\frac{\Gamma}{D} - 1\right)F^* - \sqrt{\left[\left(\frac{\Gamma}{D} - 1\right)^2 F^{*2} - \frac{4}{DF^*}\right]}\right\} < k < \frac{1}{2}\left\{\left(\frac{\Gamma}{D} - 1\right)F^* \right.$$
$$\left. + \sqrt{\left[\left(\frac{\Gamma}{D} - 1\right)^2 F^{*2} - \frac{4}{DF^*}\right]}\right\} \qquad (5.5.65)$$

our trial solutions must have both $\mu < 0$ and $\omega = 0$, whereas for wavevectors outside this range they will have $\omega > 0$ and $\mu > 0$. Hence we see that in this 'diffusion destabilized regime' any components of the initial perturbation which have wavevectors inside the range defined by inequality (5.5.67) will grow exponentially, while those with wavevectors outside this critical range will decay normally. It is particularly vital to notice that all the components of the growing disturbance will have $\omega = 0$ and hence will not propagate. Thus we can deduce that the diffusion destabilized uniform steady state must, after some transient period, be replaced by a stationary non-uniform pattern whose ultimate form will be determined by the non-linearities in the system and/or its boundary conditions.

5.6 DRIVEN SYSTEMS

In the same way that any function of a single variable can be represented as a superposition of sinusoidal components, any function of many variables can be represented as a superposition of propagating waves. Thus for instance a function $x(\mathbf{r}, t)$ which depends on time and two-space dimensions can always be rewritten as

$$x(\mathbf{r}, t) = \frac{1}{8\pi^3} \int_{-\infty}^{\infty} \int_{-\infty}^{\infty} \int_{-\infty}^{\infty} \tilde{\tilde{x}}(\mathbf{k}, \omega) e^{i(\omega t + \mathbf{k}\cdot\mathbf{r})} \mathrm{d}\mathbf{k} \, \mathrm{d}\omega \qquad (5.6.1)$$

where the quantity

$$\tilde{\tilde{x}}(\mathbf{k}, \omega) \equiv \int_{-\infty}^{\infty} \int_{-\infty}^{\infty} \int_{-\infty}^{\infty} x(\mathbf{r}, t) e^{-i(\omega t + \mathbf{k}\cdot\mathbf{r})} \mathrm{d}\mathbf{r} \, \mathrm{d}t \qquad (5.6.2)$$

is known as the Fourier transform of x with respect to time and space.

Multi-dimensional Fourier transforms have essentially similar properties to the simple one-dimensional transforms discussed in detail in Appendix F. In particular if two functions $x(\mathbf{r}, t)$ and $y(\mathbf{r}, t)$ are related by

$$x(\mathbf{r}, t) = \nabla^2 y(\mathbf{r}, t) \qquad (5.6.3)$$

then their transforms are related by

$$\tilde{\tilde{x}}(\mathbf{k}, \omega) = -k^2 y(r, t). \qquad (5.6.4)$$

Thus with the aid of a small number of additional restrictions, the most serious being that the stationary state of the system must be spatially uniform, we can extend the transfer function methods developed in previous chapters to the case of space and time variation in the parameters of a partial differential equation model.

A. A single-species model with density-dependent dispersal

As our first example of the use of transfer functions in spatially extended systems we consider a close relative of the single species model with dispersal by biased random motion, which was analysed in Section 5.5C. Here we assume that the *per capita* growth rate g is dependent only on the local population density $\rho(\mathbf{r}, t)$ and on a single environmental parameter $\phi(\mathbf{r}, t)$, so that

$$\frac{\partial f}{\partial t} = g(\rho, \phi)\rho + D_0 \nabla^2 \rho + D_1 \nabla \cdot (\rho \nabla \rho). \qquad (5.6.5)$$

We further assume that the functional dependence of the *per capita* growth rate on the local population density is chosen so that with $\phi(\mathbf{r}, t)$ set to its average value ϕ^*, and suitable boundary conditions the system has a stable and spatially uniform steady state ρ^*. The deviations $(\xi(\mathbf{r}, t), \eta(\mathbf{r}, t))$ of the population density ρ and the environmental parameter ϕ from their equilibrium values ρ^* and ϕ^* are then related, in the locally linear approximation by

$$\frac{\partial \xi}{\partial t} = \rho^* \left(\frac{\partial g}{\partial \rho}\right)^* \xi + \{D_0 + \rho^* D_1\} \nabla^2 \xi + \rho^* \left(\frac{\partial g}{\partial \phi}\right)^* \eta, \qquad (5.6.6)$$

where the notation * on a partial derivative indicates that it is evaluated at the stationary state (ρ^*, ϕ^*).

Our assumption that the steady state ρ^* is spatially uniform clearly implies that the coefficients in equation (5.6.6) are independent of both space and time, so that Fourier transformation of this equation yields a simple algebraic equation relating the transforms of the deviations,

$$i\omega\tilde{\tilde{\xi}} = \rho^* \left(\frac{\partial g}{\partial \rho}\right)^* \tilde{\tilde{\xi}} - \{D_0 + \rho^* D_1\} k^2 \tilde{\tilde{\xi}} + \rho^* \left(\frac{\partial g}{\partial \phi}\right)^* \tilde{\tilde{\eta}}, \qquad (5.6.7)$$

an elementary rearrangment of which serves to show that

$$\tilde{\tilde{\xi}}(\mathbf{k}, \omega) = T(\mathbf{k}, \omega)\tilde{\tilde{\eta}}(\mathbf{k}, \omega), \qquad (5.6.8)$$

where

$$T(\mathbf{k}, \omega) = \frac{\rho^*(\partial g/\partial \phi)^*}{-\rho^*(\partial g/\partial \rho)^* + \{D_0 + \rho^* D_1\} k^2 + i\omega}. \qquad (5.6.9)$$

B. A two-species model with diffusion

In our second example, although the principles are identical to those of Section 5.6A, the algebra is rather more complex. We consider the spatially extended cousin of the two-species driven system analysed in Section 4.3A, in which two-species which are distributed over a two-dimensional space with densities $\rho_1(\mathbf{r}, t)$ and $\rho_2(\mathbf{r}, t)$ respectively, have population growth rates G_1 and G_2 which depend only on the local population densities and a single environmental parameter $\phi(\mathbf{r}, t)$. For simplicity we shall assume that dispersal is by simple diffusion in both species so that our model dynamics are

$$\frac{\partial \rho_m}{\partial t} = G_m(\rho_1, \rho_2, \phi) + D_m \nabla^2 \rho_m, \qquad m = 1, 2. \qquad (5.6.10)$$

Again assuming that the growth functions and boundary conditions are chosen to yield a stable and spatially uniform stationary state (ρ_1^*, ρ_2^*) when the environmental parameter ϕ is everywhere equal to its average value ϕ^*, we linearize about the stationary state and hence show that in the locally linear approximation the deviations $\xi_m(\mathbf{r}, t)$ of the local population densities from their equilibrium values are related to each other and to the deviation $(\eta(\mathbf{r}, t))$ of ϕ from its equilibrium value, by

$$\frac{\partial \xi_m}{\partial t} = A_{m1}\xi_1 + A_{m2}\xi_2 + D_m\nabla^2\xi_m + \alpha_m\eta, \qquad (5.6.11)$$

where

$$A_{mn} = \left(\frac{\partial G_m}{\partial \rho_n}\right)^*, \qquad (5.6.12)$$

and

$$\alpha_m = \left(\frac{\partial G_m}{\partial \phi}\right)^* \qquad (5.6.13)$$

As before our assumption of a uniform steady state enables us to obtain a simple algebraic relationship between the transforms of the various quantities involved by Fourier transforming equation (5.6.11) with respect to time and space thus

$$i\omega\tilde{\xi}_m = A_{m1}\tilde{\xi}_1 + A_{m2}\tilde{\xi}_2 - D_m k^2\tilde{\xi}_m + \alpha_m\tilde{\eta} \qquad (5.6.14)$$

which after some rearrangement tells us that

$$\tilde{\xi}_m(\mathbf{k}, \omega) = T_m(\mathbf{k}, \omega)\tilde{\eta},$$

where the transfer function $T_m(\mathbf{k}, \omega)$ is now given by

$$T_m(\mathbf{k}, \omega) = \frac{\alpha_n A_{mn} - \alpha_m A_{nn} + \alpha_m D_m k^2 + i\alpha_m\omega}{(\omega_0^2(k) - \omega^2) + i\omega\beta(k)}, \qquad \text{with} \quad \left\{\begin{matrix} m = 1, 2 \\ n = 3 - m \end{matrix}\right\},$$

$$(5.6.15)$$

and

$$\omega_0^2(k) = (A_{11}A_{22} - A_{12}A_{21}) - (D_1 A_{22} + D_2 A_{11})k^2 + D_1 D_2 k^4, \qquad (5.6.16)$$

$$\beta(k) = -A_{11} - A_2 + (D_1 + D_2)k^2. \qquad (5.6.17)$$

It is clear from equations (5.6.9) and (5.6.15) that the dynamic behaviour of both the spatially extended models discussed in this section is closely related to that of their homogeneous counterparts. The single species model yields a transfer function (5.6.9) which simply falls monotonically as ω and/or k increase, while the two-species model is capable of resonant behaviour in which input fluctuations with certain special values of ω and k produce a particularly marked response. The effects of this resonance are discussed more fully in Section 7.5.

5.7 SPATIAL COMPETITION AND LONG RANGE DISPERSAL—THE NEED FOR INTEGRO-DIFFERENTIAL EQUATIONS

The models considered in the previous three sections suffer from two basic weaknesses;

(a) It is assumed that vital rates are either density independent or are controlled solely by the *local* density.
(b) It is assumed that dispersal involves a series of short steps so that we can meaningfully consider very short time intervals during which almost all movement is between adjacent squares.

The first assumption is clearly invalid for species whose individuals make extensive food-gathering trips unless these trips are confined to a rigid exclusive territory; otherwise individuals based at different locations clearly compete to some extent for food. The second assumption is questionable in all but a few special cases (e.g. plankton dispersing through turbulent diffusion) and the effects of relaxing it clearly require investigation.

A model which goes some way to meeting these objections without sacrificing mathematical tractability can be constructed if we describe the food-gathering activities of an individual at $\mathbf{r}$ by a normalized resource capture function $I(\mathbf{r}, \mathbf{r}')$ whose interpretation is that in a perfectly uniform environment, this individual would draw a proportion $I(\mathbf{r}, \mathbf{r}')\,d\mathbf{r}'$ of its total food intake from a small area $d\mathbf{r}'$ (shorthand for $dxdy$) centred at $\mathbf{r}'$. We assume that the single resource on which subsistence depends is distributed in such a way that its density at $\mathbf{r}$ is $R(\mathbf{r})$, so that the total amount of food available to an individual at $\mathbf{r}$ is

$$\hat{R}(\mathbf{r}) \equiv \iint_{\substack{\text{all} \\ \text{space}}} I(\mathbf{r}, \mathbf{r}')R(\mathbf{r}')d\mathbf{r}'. \tag{5.7.1}$$

If $\rho(\mathbf{r})$ is the local population density at $\mathbf{r}$, a measure of the total predation pressure on resources at $\mathbf{r}$ will be

$$\hat{\rho}(\mathbf{r}) = \iint_{\substack{\text{all} \\ \text{space}}} I(\mathbf{r}', \mathbf{r})\rho(\mathbf{r}')d\mathbf{r}'. \tag{5.7.2}$$

The net rate of change of the density of the resource at $\mathbf{r}$ is the difference between the rates of renewal and consumption and will depend on one or more of the following factors: $R(\mathbf{r})$, $\hat{\rho}(\mathbf{r})$ and other environmental factors which determine the suitability of the particular locality for that resource. For simplicity we only consider one of these factors (though the extension to many factors is straightforward in principle) which we denote by $\phi(\mathbf{r})$ and we write

$$\frac{\partial R}{\partial t} = \pi(R, \hat{\rho}, \phi)R. \tag{5.7.3}$$

The rate of change of population density $\rho(\mathbf{r})$ in the absence of dispersal may depend on the local population density (if there is interference competition) and will certainly depend on the food available to an individual at $\mathbf{r}$, $\hat{R}(\mathbf{r})$. Thus neglecting dispersal we obtain an equation of the form

$$\frac{\partial \rho}{\partial t} = g(\rho, \hat{R})\rho. \tag{5.7.4}$$

Equations (5.7.3) and (5.7.4), which embody a simple representation of spatial competition, have deliberatly been formulated in a way which emphasizes the similarity between this situation and that of competition for a spectrum of different resources in a spatially uniform environment (cf. equations (4.6.11) and (4.6.12)).

We now consider the description of dispersal. We assume that the resource is immobile and that dispersal of the consumers is through random motion. However, we do *not* restrict the random 'jumps' to neighbouring cells but simply specify the frequency (τ^{-1}) of the random jumps and the probability $P(\mathbf{r}, \mathbf{r}')\,d\mathbf{r}'$ that a journey commencing at $\mathbf{r}$ will finish in a cell of area $d\mathbf{r}'$ centred at $\mathbf{r}'$. In an environment with no preferred direction (such as might arise with insects moving in a cross-wind) we expect $P(\mathbf{r}, \mathbf{r}') = P(\mathbf{r}', \mathbf{r})$ and consideration of the population balance of a square centred at $\mathbf{r}$ now yields

$$\frac{\partial \rho}{\partial t} = g(\rho, \hat{R})\rho + \tau^{-1} \iint_{\substack{\text{all} \\ \text{space}}} P(\mathbf{r}, \mathbf{r}')\{\rho(\mathbf{r}') - \rho(\mathbf{r})\}d\mathbf{r}' \tag{5.7.5}$$

in place of equation (5.7.4). Clearly this description of random motion is more general than that in Section 5.3B and in Problem 7 we show how the more usual $D\nabla^2\rho$ term derived in that section can be obtained as a limiting case where $P(\mathbf{r}, \mathbf{r}')$ is negligibly small unless $\mathbf{r}$ and $\mathbf{r}'$ are very close together.

Equations (5.7.3)–(5.7.5) are integro-differential equations whose steady states (if any) are determined by the boundary conditions. We initially assume reflecting boundaries and an unvarying homogeneous environment ($\phi(\mathbf{r}, t) = \phi^*$ everywhere). In this case there is a uniform steady state with resource and population densities R^* and ρ^* respectively, but proof of its local stability requires further assumptions on the resource capture function and the jump probability. Since the environment has already been assumed uniform it is reasonable to expect that both $I(\mathbf{r}, \mathbf{r}')$ and $P(\mathbf{r}, \mathbf{r}')$ depend only on the *distance* $|\mathbf{r} - \mathbf{r}'|$ between the points $\mathbf{r}$ and $\mathbf{r}'$ and not individually on $\mathbf{r}$ or $\mathbf{r}'$. We let $\xi(\mathbf{r}, t)$, $\sigma(\mathbf{r}, t)$ be respectively the perturbations in population and resource levels from their steady state values. Then to first order

$$\frac{\partial \sigma}{\partial t} = R^* \left(\frac{\partial \pi}{\partial R}\right)^* \sigma + R^* \left(\frac{\partial \pi}{\partial \rho}\right)^* \xi, \tag{5.7.6}$$

$$\frac{\partial \xi}{\partial t} = \rho^* \left(\frac{\partial g}{\partial \rho}\right)^* \xi + \rho^* \left(\frac{\partial g}{\partial \hat{R}}\right)^* \hat{\sigma} + \tau^{-1} \iint_{\substack{\text{all} \\ \text{space}}} P(\mathbf{r}, \mathbf{r}')\{\xi(\mathbf{r}', t) - \xi(\mathbf{r}, t)\}d\mathbf{r}. \tag{5.7.7}$$

To analyse these equations we take spatial Fourier transforms and use the very powerful *convolution theorem* (see Appendix F) to obtain

$$\frac{\partial \tilde{\sigma}}{\partial t}(\mathbf{k}, t) = R^* \left(\frac{\partial \pi}{\partial R}\right)^* \tilde{\sigma}(\mathbf{k}, t) + R^* \left(\frac{\partial \pi}{\partial \hat{\rho}}\right)^* \tilde{I}(\mathbf{k})\tilde{\xi}(\mathbf{k}, t) \qquad (5.7.8)$$

$$\frac{\partial \tilde{\xi}(\mathbf{k}, t)}{\partial t} = \rho^* \left(\frac{\partial g}{\partial \rho}\right)^* \tilde{\xi}(\mathbf{k}, t) + \rho^* \left(\frac{\partial g}{\partial \hat{R}}\right)^* \tilde{I}(\mathbf{k})\tilde{\xi}(\mathbf{k}, t) + \tau^{-1}(\tilde{P}(\mathbf{k}) - 1)\tilde{\xi}(\mathbf{k}, t).$$

$$(5.7.9)$$

These are simply a pair of ordinary differential equations of the type treated in Chapter 4 and it is a routine application of the techniques of that chapter to show that sufficient conditions for stability are:

(a) the consumer-resource linkage should be of 'predator-prey' type, i.e.

$$\left(\frac{\partial \pi}{\partial \hat{\rho}}\right)^* < 0 \quad \text{and} \quad \left(\frac{\partial g}{\partial \hat{R}}\right)^* > 0 \qquad (5.7.10)$$

and

(b) there should be regulating density-dependence of either or both of the resource or consumer species, i.e.

$$\left(\frac{\partial \pi}{\partial R}\right)^* \leq 0; \qquad \left(\frac{\partial g}{\partial \rho}\right)^* \leq 0; \qquad R^* \left(\frac{\partial \pi}{\partial R}\right)^* + \rho^* \left(\frac{\partial g}{\partial \rho}\right)^* < 0.$$

$$(5.7.11)$$

This condition precludes the type of 'cooperative' interaction which can lead to diffusive instabilies.

These conditions guarantee that the *Fourier transform* of the population distribution approaches a stationary time-independent value, but the distribution itself is obtained by an inverse spatial transform of this quantity, and we have thus derived sufficient conditions for the stability of a uniform stationary state of the original model incorporating spatial competition.

5.8 MILDLY NON-UNIFORM STEADY STATES—TRACKING SPATIAL VARIATIONS IN ENVIRONMENT

In Section 5.6 we discussed the use of transfer functions to describe the effects of time and space variation in the values of parameters appearing in partial differential equations, and showed that the utility of these methods depends crucially on both the stability and the spatial uniformity of the steady state concerned. However, under the usual restriction that deviations from uniformity be in some sense 'small', a minor modification of the technique allows us to consider the time independent non-uniform states which result from time independent variations in some environmental parameter.

We illustrate this by analysing the way in which the steady-state population density predicted by the model of Section 5.7 'tracks' local environmental variations. We assume that the term $\phi(r)$ describing the favourability of the environment at a particular locality for resource production varies as

$$\phi(\mathbf{r}) = \phi^* + f(\mathbf{r}); \qquad |f(\mathbf{r})| \ll |\phi^*| \qquad \text{for all } \mathbf{r}, \qquad (5.8.1)$$

and hence show that in the locally linear approximation the perturbations $\xi^*(\mathbf{r})$ and $\sigma^*(\mathbf{r})$ in the steady-state population and resource densities are related to the perturbation, $f(\mathbf{r})$, in the local favourability function by

$$R^*\left(\frac{\partial \pi}{\partial \phi}\right)^* f(\mathbf{r}) + R^*\left(\frac{\partial \pi}{\partial R}\right)^* \sigma^*(\mathbf{r}) + R^*\left(\frac{\partial \pi}{\partial \rho}\right)^* \hat{\xi}(\mathbf{r}) = 0, \qquad (5.8.2)$$

$$\rho^*\left(\frac{\partial g}{\partial \rho}\right)^* \xi^*(\mathbf{r}) + \rho^*\left(\frac{\partial g}{\partial \hat{R}}\right)^* \hat{\sigma}^*(\mathbf{r}) + \tau^{-1} \iint\limits_{\substack{\text{all} \\ \text{space}}} P(\mathbf{r}, \mathbf{r}')\{\xi^*(\mathbf{r}') - \xi^*(\mathbf{r})\}d\mathbf{r}' = 0.$$

$$(5.8.3)$$

By taking Fourier transforms with respect to space and solving a pair of algebraic simultaneous equations we find that the Fourier transform of the deviation in the steady-state population density is related to that of the deviation in environmental favourability by

$$\tilde{\xi}(\mathbf{k}) = T(\mathbf{k})\tilde{f}(\mathbf{k}), \qquad (5.8.4)$$

where the 'spatial transfer function' $T(\mathbf{k})$ is

$$T(\mathbf{k}) = \frac{-\rho^*(\partial \pi/\partial \phi)^*(\partial g/\partial \hat{R})^* \tilde{I}(\mathbf{k})}{\rho^*(\partial \pi/\partial \rho)^*(\partial g/\partial \hat{R})^* \tilde{I}(\mathbf{k})^2 - \rho^*(\partial \pi/\partial R)^*(\partial g/\partial \rho)^* + \tau^{-1}(\partial \pi/\partial R)^*(1 - \tilde{P}(\mathbf{k}))}.$$

$$(5.8.5)$$

Since by hypothesis the resource capture function and the jump probability distributions are symmetric functions of the argument $(\mathbf{r} - \mathbf{r}')$, their Fourier transforms are real and hence variations in the local population density are either in phase or exactly 180° out of phase with the driving environmental variations (remembering that we are referring to spatial and not temporal phase).

Further investigation of the intimidating expression (5.8.5) is assisted by specifying the form of the resource capture and jump probability functions, and for simplicity we assume both to be symmetric Gaussians with standard deviations σ_I and σ_P respectively, implying that

$$\tilde{I}(\mathbf{k}) = \exp[-\tfrac{1}{2}\sigma_I^2 k^2], \qquad \tilde{P}(\mathbf{k}) = \exp\{-\tfrac{1}{2}\sigma_P^2 k^2\}. \qquad (5.8.6)$$

We note that for most plausible models of the resource dynamics $(\partial \pi/\partial R)^*$ will be non-zero and hence that if there is no intraspecific regulation of the consumers $((\partial g/\partial \rho)^* = 0)$ and no significant dispersal $(\tau \to \infty)$, then

$$T(k) \propto \frac{1}{\tilde{I}(k)} = \exp\{+\tfrac{1}{2}\sigma_I^2 k^2\} \qquad (5.8.7)$$

Thus the effect of spatial competition is to produce very large fluctuations in the steady-state population density in response to fine scale (large k) environmental variations. However, as soon as we permit any self regulation of population in response to local density ($(\partial g/\partial \rho)^*$ non-zero) or dispersal (τ finite) the divergence of the transfer function at large wavenumbers is stopped and if either $(\partial g/\partial \rho)^*$, τ^{-1} or σ_P is sufficiently large that

$$-\left(\frac{\partial g}{\partial \rho}\right)^* + \frac{\sigma_P^2}{\tau \sigma_I^2 \rho^*} > \frac{(\partial \pi/\partial \hat{\rho})^*(\partial g/\partial \hat{R})^*}{(\partial \pi/\partial R)^*} \qquad (5.8.8)$$

the transfer function does not even have a peak and drops off monotonically as k runs from 0 to ∞.

The above discussion is easily illustrated by considering two models investigated by Gurney and Nisbet (1976b). In both models the resource is a plant species which grows logistically and is cropped via a Lotka–Volterra type interaction so that

$$\pi(R, \hat{\rho}) = 1 - R/\phi - \alpha \tilde{\rho}. \qquad (5.8.9)$$

In model A the consumers' numerical response is linear ($(\partial g/\partial \rho)^* = 0$) so that

$$g(\rho, \hat{R}) = \beta \hat{R} = \gamma \qquad (5.8.10)$$

while in model B there is substantial interference competition among the predators which grow logistically with

$$g(\rho, \hat{R}) = \delta(1 - \rho/\hat{R}). \qquad (5.8.11)$$

The transfer function (5.8.5) is easily calculated for both models given the Gaussian resource capture and jump probability functions. Typical results are shown in Fig. 5.11 which illustrates;

(a) the large response of the population density to fine-scale environmental variability caused by 'pure' spatial competition with neither self-regulation of consumers nor dispersal (model A, $\sigma_P/\sigma_I = 0$),

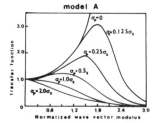 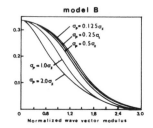

Fig. 5.11. Typical spatial transfer functions. Model A: external consumer control. Model B: strong internal consumer control.

(b) the strong attenuation of this effect caused by dispersal even when the individual steps are relatively short (model A, σ_P/σ_I = 0.125, 0.25),

(c) the damping effect of strong self-regulation (model B).

SOURCES AND SUGGESTED FURTHER READING

Host–parasitoid and Host–parasite models: Extensive list of variants on the basic Nicholson–Bailey model are given by Hassell and May (1973, 1974) and by Beddington, Free, and Lawton (1978). The phenomenological model involving the negative binomial approximation to the parasitoid attack distribution is due to May (1978); the same idea has been used in host–parasite models by Anderson and May (1978) and May and Anderson (1978).

Territoriality: A survey of some of the problems involved in modelling territorial behaviour is in Chapter 12 of Maynard Smith (1974). More recent statistical analyses of models of simultaneous and consecutive establishment of territories and of the partitioning of regions of space into territories include Hasegawa and Tanemura (1976), Tanemura and Hasegawa (1980). Our treatment is based on a representation of social hierarchy proposed by Lomnicki (1978) and developed by Gurney and Nisbet (1979).

Patchy environments: The interpretation of the clumping parameter in the negative binomial distribution in terms of the 'within-patch' variability is due to May (1978). The 'discrete-state models'have been used by Vandermeer (1973), Maynard Smith (1974), Zeigler (1976), Hastings (1977), Gurney and Nisbet (1978a, 1978b).

Partial differential equation models: The reviews by McMurtrie (1978) and Levin (1976) contain extensive bibliographies of the vast literature on this subject. Our treatment of exponentially growing and declining populations and of critical patch sizes has been further developed by Ludwig, Aronson, and Weinberger (1980) and applied to a model of spruce budworm outbreaks (cf. Problem 5, Chapter 2). The difficulties in *formulating* PDE models as deterministic analogues of stochastic models are exposed in a review by Mollison (1977)). The biased random motion' and 'directed motion' models of non-linear dispersal are due to Gurney and Nisbet (1975, 1976a). Further analysis of these models has been performed by Gurtin and MacCamy (1977), Namba (1980), and Newman (1980).

Spatial competition: Our treatment follows an idea of Roughgarden (1974) which was developed by Gurney and Nisbet (1976b), and Roughgarden (1977, 1978).

162

PROBLEMS

(Those marked * are mathematically more demanding than the others.)

1. (May, 1978). Show that for May's model of a host–parasitoid system in a patchy environment (equation (5.2.4));
   (a) the steady-state parasitoid population is larger than for the corresponding Nicholson–Bailey system ($k \to \infty$),
   (b) the steady state is locally stable provided $k < 1$.

2. (Hassell and Varley, 1969; Hassell and May, 1973). A variant of the Nicholson–Bailey model invokes experimental evidence that the searching efficiency of parasitoids can depend on the total parasite population. The new model is

$$H_{t+\tau} = FSH_t \exp\{-QP_t^{1-m}\}$$

$$P_{t+\tau} = FSH_t\{1 - \exp[-QP_t^{1-m}]\}.$$

Calculate the range of values of m for which the system is stable.

3. (Anderson and May, 1978). A simple model of a host–parasite (not parasitoid) system has

$$\frac{dH}{dt} = (a - b)H - \alpha P$$

$$\frac{dP}{dt} = \frac{\lambda PH}{H_0 + H} - (b + \mu)P - \alpha HE\{i^2\}$$

where a is the host birth rate, b the host death rate due to 'natural causes', α the host death rate due to parasitism, μ the instantaneous death rate of parasites within the host, λ the rate of production of eggs per parasite, and H_0 is a constant determining the proportion of parasite eggs that successfully mature and gain entry to a new host. $E\{i^2\}$ is the mean square number of parasites per host and if the parasites are distributed randomly

$$E\{i^2\} = \frac{P^2}{H^2} + \frac{P}{H}$$

while with a negative binomial distribution this becomes

$$E\{i^2\} = \frac{P^2}{H^2}\left(\frac{k+1}{k}\right) + \frac{P}{H}$$

   (a) Show that with the random distribution the steady state populations are positive if

$$a > b \quad \text{and} \quad \lambda > \mu + \alpha + a$$

   (b) Show that with the negative binomial distribution of parasites, there are positive steady states only if

$$a > b \quad \text{and} \quad \lambda > \mu + \alpha + b + \frac{(a - b)(k + 1)}{k}$$

and that the system is stable provided k is finite and positive. (Note that there is a misprint in the statement of the second inequality in the original paper).

4. (McMurtrie, 1978). Show that if individuals disperse through random motion while being carried along in a cross wind of velocity $\mathbf{v}$ then the population flux density is

$$\mathbf{F} = D\nabla\rho + \rho\mathbf{v}$$

5.* Consider a logistic population with diffusion whose dynamics are given by

$$\frac{\partial\rho}{\partial t} = r\rho(1 - \rho/\rho_0) + D\nabla^2\rho$$

confined to a circular region of diameter L with absorbing boundaries. Prove that there is a non-zero stationary distribution only if

$$L > 4.81(D/r)^{1/2}$$

and that this distribution is locally stable.

6.* (MacCamy, private communication). A population has a positive per capita net growth rate G_0 and is confined to a circular region of diameter L with absorbing boundaries. Dispersal is through directed motion. Prove that there is always a stable stationary population distribution irrespective of habitat size.

7. To show the relation between the integral representation (equation (5.7.5)) of random motion and the differential counterpart (equation (5.3.25)), consider motion confined to one dimension with

$$P(x, x') = \frac{1}{\sqrt{(2\pi)}\sigma_P} \exp\left\{-\frac{(x - x')^2}{2\sigma_P^2}\right\}$$

The standard deviation σ_P of this distribution is a measure of the range of the random 'steps' and if σ_P is small we can approximate $\rho(x')$ by a Taylor expansion around the point x.

(a) Show that this leads to an equation of the type (5.3.25) with

$$D = \frac{\sigma_P^2}{2\tau}$$

(b*) Calculate the corresponding expression for D with two-dimensional motion.

8.* (Gurney, and Nisbet, 1975). A population has density-dependent vital

164

rates which vary with position as in Fig. 5.7. Dispersal is through directed motion (cf. equation (5.3.32)). The population density obeys the equation

$$\frac{\partial \rho}{\partial t} = g(\mathbf{r})\rho + D_1\rho\nabla\rho.$$

(a) Scale the variables as in equation (5.5.22) but set

$$t_0^{-1} = g(\mathbf{r})_{max}, \qquad r_0 = (D_1 t_0 p_0)^{-1},$$

to obtain an equation in dimensionless variables.

(b) Prove the stability of a stationary state by considering the Liapunov function

$$L = \iint_{\substack{all \\ space}} \rho'^* \xi^2 \, d\mathbf{r}.$$

Part II

Stochastic Models

Chapter 6

Birth and Death Processes in a Static Environment

6.1 INTRODUCTION

Part I of this book was concerned with *deterministic* models which had the property that populations at any future time could be calculated from knowledge of past and present populations. By contrast if we know that a system with *stochastic* dynamics is in a particular state at a given time we cannot predict its state at any future time. The best we can do is to calculate the probability distribution of outcomes we would obtain if we started many replicates of the system from the same initial state at a particular time, and observed the state of each replicate at a later time. We describe the dynamics of a stochastic system by the equation of motion of this probability distribution.

Much of this chapter is devoted to a rather formal treatment of birth and death processes in a static environment. The only population fluctuations which can be modelled in this way are those due solely to demographic stochasticity (which are normally very small), but the importance of the theory derives less from its immediate applicability (though we do give one example of this in Chapter 10) than from its central position in the theory of environmental stochasticity which is the subject of the next chapter. In particular there are subtleties associated with the mathematical representation of extinction in a variable environment whose resolution depends on realizing that the sole cause of population extinction is a single death in a population consisting of one individual.

The chapter begins with the exact formulation of the equations describing the development with time of the probability distribution for population size, and the derivation of alternative approximations which are more amenable to analysis. We then turn our attention to techniques for solving these equations for the probability distribution and demonstrate how to obtain the gross characteristics (variance and AC_oF) of the fluctuations about statistically stationary and quasi-stationary states. This leads to a discussion of methods of estimating the order of magnitude of the expected time for population extinction and hence to estimates of the ecological stability index defined in Chapter 1. Parts of the formal development have by this stage involved some rather heavy, and not particularly transparent algebra. For this reason, in Section 6.7 we work through in detail the analysis of two birth and death models, the first of which is particularly simple. We strongly recommend the reader who finds difficulty with the formalism to study this first 'logistic' model in parallel with the more intimidating theory. The chapter ends with an application of the theory to a model of population dynamics in patchy environments. This application illustrates rather clearly the robustness of some of the approximations developed in the chapter, and also prepares the ground for one of our case studies—the model of Huffaker's predator–prey cycles in Chapter 10.

6.2 MATHEMATICAL REPRESENTATION OF NON-LINEAR BIRTH AND DEATH PROCESSES

A. Discrete probability distributions

The probability $P(N, t)$ that a population consists of exactly N individuals at time t is defined by considering a very large number (M) of replicate populations, whose individual time histories are called *realizations*. Then

$$P(N, t) \equiv \frac{\text{limiting value}}{\text{as } M \to \infty} \text{ of } \left[\frac{1}{M} \times \frac{\text{Number of replicates containing}}{\text{exactly } N \text{ individuals at time } t} \right]. \quad (6.2.1)$$

A similar limiting procedure enables us to define population dependent birth and death rates $B(N)$ and $D(N)$ by considering a very small time interval dt such that the probability of a single birth between times t and $t + dt$ is $B(N) \, dt$, while that of a single death is $D(N) \, dt$. We assume that the probability of multiple births and deaths is proportional to $(dt)^2$ and is thus negligible if dt is very small.

If the population of a particular replicate is exactly N at time t, then at time $t + dt$ it must be either

(a) $N + 1$ with probability $B(N) \, dt$,
(b) $N - 1$ with probability $D(N) \, dt$, or
(c) N with probability $1 - \{B(N) + D(N)\} \, dt$.

By similar reasoning, a population which at time $t + dt$ contains N individuals must at time t have contained either $N - 1$, N, or $N + 1$ individuals. The probability that it contained $N - 1$ at t and contains N at $t + dt$ is clearly $P(N - 1, t)B(N - 1) \, dt$, and similarly the probability that it contained $N + 1$ at t and contains N at $t + dt$ is $P(N + 1, t)D(N + 1) \, dt$. The probability that it contained N at t and still contains N at $t + dt$ is clearly $P(N, t)[1 - \{B(N) + D(N)\} \, dt]$. Thus, since these are the only three options, the total probability that the population contains N individuals at time $t + dt$

is

$$P(N, t + dt) = P(N - 1, t)B(N - 1)\,dt + P(N + 1, t)D(N + 1)\,dt$$
$$+ P(N, t)[1 - \{B(N) + D(N)\}\,dt], \qquad (6.2.2)$$

which on rearranging and taking the limit $dt \rightarrow 0$ gives

$$\frac{dP(N, t)}{dt} = P(N - 1, t)B(N - 1) + P(N + 1, t)D(N + 1)$$
$$-P(N, t)\{B(N) + D(N)\}. \qquad (6.2.3)$$

For the special case of $N = 0$ this equation takes a slightly simpler form, since the fact that the population size cannot become negative must imply that $D(0) = 0$ and hence that

$$\frac{dP(0, t)}{dt} = P(1, t)D(1) - P(0, t)B(0). \qquad (6.2.4a)$$

In a system which is *closed* and so excludes the possibility of immigration we know in addition that $B(0) = 0$, which enables us to further simplify equation (6.2.4a) to

$$\frac{dP(0, t)}{dt} = P(1, t)D(1), \qquad (6.2.4b)$$

and also to simplify the equation for $dP(1, t)/dt$ with the result

$$\frac{dP(1, t)}{dt} = P(2, t)D(2) - P(1, t)\{B(1) + D(1)\}. \qquad (6.2.5)$$

Equations (6.2.3)–(6.2.5) are sufficient to calculate the population probability distribution at time t from a knowledge of the distribution at a previous time t_0. Just as we started our analysis of deterministic models by identifying a deterministic steady state, so we start the analysis of stochastic models by seeking a *statistically stationary state* in which all the probabilities are constant. However, as we have indicated in Chapter 1, in any model of a closed system with non-zero extinction probabilities, the probability is likely to develop with time in the manner shown in Fig. 1.11 (for convenience reproduced here as Fig. 6.1) in which case no statistically stationary state exists.

To demonstrate this feature more formally we note that no realistic model can permit $D(1)$ to be zero, and hence see from equation (6.2.4b) that if $P(0, t)$ is to be constant then $P(1, t)$ must be zero. But if $P(1, t)$ is zero then it follows from equation (6.2.5) that the only stationary value of $P(2, t)$ is zero and from successive applications of equation (6.2.3) that the only way for $P(N, t)$ to be constant for $N > 2$ is for it to be zero. Thus the only possible statistically stationary state is one in which the possibility of a finite population is zero, i.e. the population is extinct or infinite. Hence, provided the population is bounded, all probability eventually 'leaks' to the $N = 0$ state, from which it cannot escape and which is thus described as 'absorbing'.

Ecologically, the above argument has shown that in an isolated population which cannot grow without limit the probability of ultimate extinction is one;

170

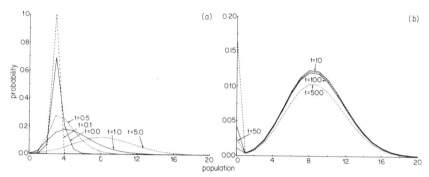

Fig. 6.1. Population probability distribution for a hypothetical population whose size was known exactly at $t = 0$. (a) Transient behaviour ($t = 0 \to t = 10$). (b) Quasi-stationary behaviour ($t = 10 \to t = 500$).

that is to say if we wait long enough there is certain to be a fluctuation large enough to drive the population extinct. However, the expected time to extinction may often be very long in comparison with the time required for significant population changes, in which case there may be a *statistically quasi-stationary state* such as is illustrated in Fig. 6.1(b).

To separate the question of extinction from that of characterizing the statistically quasi-stationary state we define a *conditional probability distribution function* (CPDF) $P_c(N, t)$ by again considering M replicates of the population, and writing

$$P_c(N, t) \equiv \lim_{M \to \infty} \left[\frac{\text{Number of replicates with population } N \text{ at time } t}{\text{Total number of } non\text{-}extinct \text{ replicates at time } t} \right]. \quad (6.2.6)$$

For large values of M the numerator and denominator of the quantity in the square brackets have the values $MP(N, t)$ and $M(1 - P(0, t))$ respectively, so that

$$P_c(N, t) = \frac{P(N, t)}{1 - P(0, t)}. \quad (6.2.7)$$

Differentiating this equation with respect to time gives

$$\frac{dP_c(N, t)}{dt} = \frac{1}{\{1 - P(0, t)\}} \frac{dP(N, t)}{dt} + \frac{P(N, t)}{\{1 - P(0, t)\}^2} \cdot \frac{dP(0, t)}{dt}, \quad (6.2.8)$$

the right-hand side of which is evaluated by substituting for the time derivatives from equations (6.2.3) and (6.2.4b), and making use of equation (6.2.7) to obtain an expression involving solely conditional probabilities. The result is

$$\frac{dP_c(1, t)}{dt} = D(1)P_c(1, t)^2 + D(2)P_c(2, t) - \{B(1) + D(1)\}P_c(1, t), \quad (6.2.9)$$

and

$$\frac{dP_c(N,t)}{dt} = D(1)P_c(1,t)P_c(N,t) + B(N-1)P_c(N-1,t)$$

$$+ D(N+1)P_c(N+1,t) - \{B(N) + D(N)\}P_c(N,t), \qquad N \geq 2. \quad (6.2.10)$$

Clearly, there is no *a priori* reason why these equations cannot have a stable stationary solution given suitable forms for $B(N)$ and $D(N)$. This stationary solution can in practice easily be found using an iterative numerical method described in Section 6.4.

Since the experiments needed to observe the population probability distribution would be immensely costly it is relative unusual to be able to make any direct use of this function. Its principle utility rather lies in enabling us to calculate *expectation values (denoted by $E\{\ \}$)* of more readily accessible quantities. For an arbitrary population dependent quantity $\xi(N,t)$ we define

$$E\{\xi(N,t)\} \equiv \sum_{N=0}^{\infty} \xi(N,t)P(N,t), \qquad (6.2.11)$$

so that, for example, the mean and variance of the population size N are given by

$$m(t) \equiv E\{N(t)\} = \sum_{N=0}^{\infty} NP(N,t), \qquad (6.2.12)$$

and

$$\sigma^2(t) \equiv E\{[N(t) - m(t)]^2\} = \sum_{N=0}^{\infty} N^2 P(N,t) - [m(t)]^2. \quad (6.2.13)$$

respectively.

In cases where it is convenient to separate questions of extinction from those concerning population fluctuations by working with a conditional probability distribution (CPDF) we normally also choose to calculate expectation values conditional on non-extinction (denoted by $E_c\{\ \}$) by performing our average only over those replicates which have not gone extinct by time t. In this case we define a general conditional expectation value by

$$E_c\{\xi(N,t)\} \equiv \sum_{N=1}^{\infty} \xi(N,t)P_c(N,t) = \frac{E\{\xi(N,t)\}}{1-P(0,t)}, \qquad (6.2.14)$$

so that the conditional values for the mean and variance of the population size are

$$m_c(t) \equiv \sum_{N=1}^{\infty} NP_c(N,t) = \frac{m(t)}{1-P(0,t)}, \qquad (6.2.15)$$

and

$$\sigma_c^2(t) \equiv \sum_{N=1}^{\infty} (N - m_c(t))^2 P_c(N,t) = \frac{\sigma^2(t)}{1-P(0,t)}. \qquad (6.2.16)$$

Although it is occasionally possible to make a moderately large number of simultaneous replicate measurements and thus obtain true expectation values experimentally, it is more usual to make prolonged observations of only one or two replicate populations. The time average experimental values thus obtained can under certain circumstances, which are discussed fully in Section 6.5, be equated to the expectation values calculated from equations (6.2.11) or (6.2.14).

B. Diffusion approximations

The equations of motion which we derived in Section 6.2A for the discrete probability distribution $P(N, t)$, are clearly only meaningful if the population size, N, is restricted to integer values. We have already seen in Chapters 2 and 4 that in general the mathematical analysis of models couched in terms of discrete variables is more demanding than that required with continuous variables, and it is therefore tempting to explore the possibility of working with representations in which N is regarded as a continuous variable. One such approach, in which the development with time of the population's probability distribution is calculated from a partial differential equation known as a *diffusion equation*, is the subject of this section.

Diffusion approximations involve some rather subtle mathematics and play a relatively minor role in our subsequent analyses of population fluctuations. However, while the *derivation* of diffusion approximations is fraught with mathematical subtleties, their use is relatively easy. This makes very alluring the somewhat unsound strategy of using them in population ecology without understanding the nature of the approximations involved, a procedure which all too often yields results inapplicable even to the underlying birth and death model, far less to any real population of which the latter can at best be a gross caricature.

A heuristic introduction to the diffusion approximation is obtained by writing down the equation of motion (6.2.3) of the population's probability distribution

$$\frac{dP(N, t)}{dt} = P(N - 1, t)B(N - 1) + P(N + 1, t)D(N + 1)$$

$$- P(N, t)\{B(N) + D(N)\}, \qquad (6.2.17)$$

and trying to use Taylor expansions to approximate the various functions of $N \pm 1$. This involves treating N as a continuous variable which can have non-integer values and re-interpreting $P(N, t)$ as a probability density, which to avoid confusion we shall denote by $p(N, t)$ and define by the formal requirement that $p(N, t)dN$ is the probability that the value of N lies between N and $N + dN$. If we were now to assume that in spite of the fact that the increment between 'states' in the birth and death process is unity we could discard all terms in the Taylor expansions which are of third or higher order, then we would expect that the exact equation (6.2.17) could be approximated by

$$\frac{\partial p(N,t)}{\partial t} = -\frac{\partial}{\partial N}[(B(N) - D(N))p(N,t)]$$

$$+ \frac{1}{2}\frac{\partial^2}{\partial N^2}[(B(N) + D(N))p(N,t)]. \quad (6.2.18)$$

It turns out that we *can* justify the use of equation (6.2.18) as an approximation but that the transition from a discrete to a continuous representation involves a number of hidden assumptions. Without making any pretence at mathematical rigour we now discuss the transition in sufficient detail to emphasize the nature of these assumptions.

Suppose one particular realization contains exactly N individuals at time t. If the probability of multiple births or deaths during some very short time interval dt is negligible, then the true population change dN which occurs during dt is a random variable with possible values $0, \pm 1$, and its statistical expectation value is

$$E\{dN\} = (+1) \times \{\text{Probability of a birth during } dt\}$$

$$+ (-1) \times \{\text{Probability of a death during } dt\}$$

$$+ (0) \times \{\text{Probability of no change during } dt\},$$

$$(6.2.19)$$

which clearly implies

$$E\{dN\} = \{B(N) - D(N)\}\,dt. \quad (6.2.20)$$

By exactly similar reasoning we also find

$$E\{(dN)^2\} = \{B(N) + D(N)\}\,dt. \quad (6.2.21)$$

The equation (6.2.20) for $E\{dN\}$ is straightforward to interpret; essentially it says that the expected population change during a time interval dt is the same as would be predicted by a deterministic model. However *the second moment* $E\{(dN)^2\}$ *has the very distinctive feature of being proportional to* dt *and not to* $(dt)^2$. This important property is the source of most of the difficulties in constructing continuous representations of intrinsically discrete stochastic processes. It can also lead to situations in which some 'normal' procedures in calculus are inapplicable, a point we develop in Chapter 7.

One systematic way of effecting the transition from discrete N to continuous N is to require that in the continuous representation the first two moments of the probability distribution for the change in population dN retain the values given by equations (6.2.20) and (6.2.21). Suppose we allow the 'states' in our birth and death process to move closer together until they are separated by an amount $\varepsilon(\ll 1)$ rather than by one, and assume that in a short time dt the only possible population changes are $0, \pm \varepsilon$. If we write the probabilities (Prob$\{N \to N \pm \varepsilon\}$) that in time dt the population changes by $\pm \varepsilon$ as

$$\text{Prob}\{N \to N + \varepsilon\} = U(N, \varepsilon)\, dt, \qquad (6.2.22)$$

$$\text{Prob}\{N \to N - \varepsilon\} = V(N, \varepsilon)\, dt, \qquad (6.2.23)$$

then clearly

$$E\{dN\} = \varepsilon[U(N, \varepsilon) - V(N, \varepsilon)]\, dt \qquad (6.2.24)$$

and

$$E\{(dN)^2\} = \varepsilon^2[U(N, \varepsilon) + V(N, \varepsilon)]\, dt. \qquad (6.2.25)$$

The requirement that $E\{dN\}$ and $E\{(dN)^2\}$ have the same values for this process as for that described by equations (6.2.20) and (6.2.21) yields the result that, for a specified value of ε, the transition probabilities $U(N, \varepsilon)dt$ and $V(N, \varepsilon)dt$ are related to the original birth and death probabilities by

$$U(N, \varepsilon)\, dt = \frac{1}{2} B(N)\, dt \left(\frac{1}{\varepsilon} + \frac{1}{\varepsilon^2}\right) - \frac{1}{2} D(N)\, dt \left(\frac{1}{\varepsilon} - \frac{1}{\varepsilon^2}\right) \qquad (6.2.26)$$

$$V(N, \varepsilon)\, dt = -\frac{1}{2} B(N)\, dt \left(\frac{1}{\varepsilon} - \frac{1}{\varepsilon^2}\right) + \frac{1}{2} D(N)\, dt \left(\frac{1}{\varepsilon} + \frac{1}{\varepsilon^2}\right), \qquad (6.2.27)$$

which (because of the terms in $1/\varepsilon^2$) will become greater than one and hence unacceptable as probabilities unless *simultaneously* with the transition to continuous N (i.e. letting $\varepsilon \to 0$) we make the transition to continuous time (i.e. letting $dt \to 0$) *keeping the ratio dt/ε^2 finite and small* (relative to the smallest values of $[B(N)]^{-1}$ or $D(N)]^{-1}$). This process of taking the two limits simultaneously is the key to the derivation of the diffusion equation.

In the new representation where the states are separated by intervals of ε, the probability density at time $t + dt$ is

$$p(N, t + dt) = p(N, t) + \{U(N - \varepsilon, \varepsilon)p(N - \varepsilon, t) + V(N + \varepsilon, \varepsilon)p(N + \varepsilon, t)$$

$$- [U(N, \varepsilon) + V(N, \varepsilon)]p(N, t)\}\, dt, \qquad (6.2.28)$$

and hence

$$\frac{p(N, t + dt) - p(N, t)}{dt} = \{U(N - \varepsilon, \varepsilon)p(N - \varepsilon, t) + V(N + \varepsilon, \varepsilon)p(N + \varepsilon, t)$$

$$- [U(N, \varepsilon) + V(N, \varepsilon)]p(N, t)\}. \qquad (6.2.29)$$

There is no apparent objection to Taylor expansion of the various functions of $N \pm \varepsilon$ in this equation, since provided we simultaneously reduce dt, ε can be chosen arbitrarily small. The result, to second order, is

$$\frac{p(N, t + dt) - p(N, t)}{dt} = -\varepsilon \frac{\partial}{\partial N} [\{U(N, \varepsilon) - V(N, \varepsilon)\}p(N, t)]$$

$$+ \frac{1}{2} \varepsilon^2 \frac{\partial^2}{\partial N^2} [\{U(N, \varepsilon) + V(N, \varepsilon)\}p(N, t)]$$

(6.2.30)

which on letting $dt \to 0$, $\varepsilon \to 0$, and using equations (6.2.24) and (6.2.25) to get back to the original birth and death rates becomes

$$\frac{\partial p(N, t)}{\partial t} = - \frac{\partial}{\partial N} [\{B(N) - D(N)\}p(N, t)]$$

$$+ \frac{1}{2} \frac{\partial^2}{\partial N^2} [\{B(N) + D(N)\}p(N, t)] \qquad (6.2.31)$$

which is the *diffusion equation* (6.2.18) we set out to derive.

For completeness we also note that the diffusion equation is sometimes written in the form

$$\frac{\partial p(N, t)}{\partial t} = - \frac{\partial J_p(N, t)}{\partial N} \qquad (6.2.32)$$

where

$$J_p(N, t) \equiv \{B(N) - D(N)\}p(N, t) - \frac{1}{2} \frac{\partial}{\partial N} [\{B(N) + D(N)\}p(N, t)]$$

(6.2.33)

is known as the *probability current*.

By a process exactly analogous to that leading to equation (6.2.31) we can also derive a diffusion approximation to the dynamics of the conditional probability distribution. This derivation provides some *post hoc* justification for our attention to mathematical detail in the preceding paragraphs since in this case a crude Taylor expansion of the discrete equations yields an erroneous diffusion equation (in which probabilities can become negative!). We recognise that each replicate population either has a value between one and infinity or is extinct. We denote by $p_c(N, t) \, dN$ the probability that at time t the population is non-extinct and has a value in the range N to $N + dN$. We assume that for consistency the probability current at $N = 1$ must be equal to $dP(0, t)/dt$, and after a considerable quantity of manipulation find that

$$\frac{\partial p_c(N, t)}{\partial t} = -\frac{\partial}{\partial N}[\{B(N) - D(N)\}p_c(N, t)]$$

$$+ \frac{1}{2}\frac{\partial^2}{\partial N^2}[\{B(N) + D(N)\}p_c(N, t)]$$

$$+ \left[B(1) - D(1) - \frac{1}{2}\left(\frac{\partial B}{\partial N}\right)_{N=1} - \frac{1}{2}\left(\frac{\partial D}{\partial N}\right)_{N=1}\right]p_c(N, t)p_c(1, t)$$

$$- \tfrac{1}{2}[B(1) + D(1)]\left(\frac{\partial p_c}{\partial N}\right)_{N=1}p_c(N, t), \qquad (6.2.34)$$

a rather nasty non-linear equation which is intractable analytically and more difficult to solve numerically than the discrete equations which it purports to approximate. We mention it because it does yield one useful insight. Except for very small populations the last two terms on the right-hand side are always very small compared with the first two; if these are neglected, equation (6.2.34) is identical in form to equation (6.2.31) and we can thus regard a stationary solution of the original diffusion equation as an approximation to the CPDF over the range $N \geqslant 1$.

Finally, we note that expectation values can be obtained from both the conditional and unconditional probability density functions using equations analogous to (6.2.11) and (6.2.14), the result for the conditional expectation value of a general function $\xi(N, t)$ being

$$E_c\{\xi(N, t)\} = \int_{N=1}^{\infty} \xi(N, t)p_c(N, t)\, dN. \qquad (6.2.35)$$

C. Stochastic differential equations

So far we have described stochastic population models in terms of the equation(s) of motion of the population probability distribution. We now explore a rather different representation which is designed to facilitate comparison with analogous deterministic models, and which is particularly useful when modelling populations in a fluctuating environment (see Chapter 7).

We saw in the previous section that in a small time interval dt, the population change (dN) is a random variable with moments

$$E\{dN\} = \{B(N) - D(N)\}\, dt, \qquad (6.2.36)$$

$$E\{(dN)^2\} = \{B(N) + D(N)\}\, dt. \qquad (6.2.37)$$

Thus, provided dt is sufficiently small for us to neglect terms of order dt^2 and higher, the *actual* change in population of any one replicate can be written

$$dN = \{B(N) - D(N)\}\, dt + \eta(t)\sqrt({\{B(N) + D(N)\}\, dt}, \qquad (6.2.38)$$

where $\eta(t)$ is a random variable with zero mean and unit variance. Because N

is restricted to take only integer values, the probability distribution of $\eta(t)$ is strange and equation (6.2.38) is, strictly speaking, merely a cumbersome restatement of the original birth and death model. However, an approximation similar to that involved in deriving the diffusion equation renders it much more tractable.

We argue that, except with very small populations, any change in population which is large enough to significantly affect the birth and death probabilities must be the result of a large number of statistically independent births and deaths. This implies that we can use equation (6.2.38) to describe the population change (dN) which takes place over a relatively long time increment dt, but with $\eta(t)$ now having a probability distribution which is close to normal (by the Law of Large Numbers). If now the time scales inherent in a particular model produce a regime in which we can *both* regard η as normally distributed (implying dt large) *and* regard N as a continuous variable (which, as we showed in Section 6.2B, requires dt very small) then we can meaningfully recast equation (6.2.38) in the form

$$dN = \{B(N) - D(N)\}\, dt + \{B(N) + D(N)\}^{1/2}\, d\omega(t), \qquad (6.2.39)$$

where dN and dt are infinitesimally small, and where $d\omega(t)$, which is known as a *Wiener increment* has the statistical properties

$$E\{d\omega(t)\} = 0 \qquad \text{for all } t, \qquad (6.2.40)$$

$$E\{(d\omega(t))^2\} = dt \qquad \text{for all } t, \qquad (6.2.41)$$

$$E\{d\omega(t)d\omega(t')\} = 0 \qquad \text{unless } t = t'. \qquad (6.2.42)$$

Equations such as (6.2.39) are known as *stochastic differential equations* (SDEs).

We can rewrite equation (6.2.39) in a form which emphasizes the link between a stochastic model and its deterministic counterpart if we divide throughout by dt to obtain

$$\frac{dN}{dt} = B(N) - D(N) + \{B(N) + D(N)\}^{1/2}\gamma(t), \qquad (6.2.43)$$

where

$$\gamma(t) \equiv \frac{d\omega(t)}{dt}. \qquad (6.2.44)$$

The right-hand side of (6.2.43) begs to be interpreted as the sum of 'deterministic' and 'stochastic' contributions to dN/dt. Care must be taken with this formulation however as $\gamma(t)$ thus defined is not a well-behaved mathematical function (e.g. $E\{(\gamma(t))^2\} = \infty$). We shall discuss the properties of $\gamma(t)$, which is known as *Gaussian white noise*, in Sections 6.5 and 7.3.

For further reference we mention here that although the procedure we have given for deriving the SDE (6.2.39) is well-defined and unambiguous, other authors use similar notation with slightly different interpretations. In particular serious problems arise in the integration of SDEs and the reader should not attempt even numerical integration without reference to the discussion in Sections 6.5 and 7.6.

6.3 DENSITY-INDEPENDENT GROWTH AND DECLINE

Most ecologically plausible birth and death models have transition probabilities which show a measure of 'density dependence', i.e. the *per capita* probabilities per unit time of a single birth or death depend on the total population size N. Exact analysis of such models is normally impossible and judiciously selected approximations are essential for progress. However, there are a few models involving density-independent population growth in both closed and open systems for which analytic results are available. In spite of their simplistic nature, these models have pedagogic value as markers against which to compare the more elaborate behaviour of non-linear models, and some (limited) applicability in island biogeography. We therefore study them briefly before continuing with the non-linear models which constitute the main subject matter of this chapter.

A rather general model of this type is the 'birth–death–immigration' model of Karlin and McGregor (1958) where we assume

$$B(N) = \beta N + I, \qquad D(N) = \delta N, \qquad (6.3.1)$$

in which the constants β and δ represent average per capita birth and death rates, and I represents a constant (positive) average rate of immigration. The deterministic analogue of this model is described by the differential equation

$$\frac{dN}{dt} = (\beta - \delta)N + I, \qquad (6.3.2)$$

whose solution grows exponentially if $\beta > \delta$, has a stable steady state N^* ($= I/(\delta - \beta)$) if $\beta < \delta$ and $I \neq 0$, and decays exponentially to zero if $\beta < \delta$ and $I = 0$. The stochastic dynamics are represented by the equations (6.2.3) and (6.2.4a) which now take the form

$$\frac{dP(N, t)}{dt} = (N - 1)\beta P(N - 1, t) + IP(N - 1, t) + (N + 1)\delta P(N + 1, t)$$

$$-\{N(\beta + \delta) + I\}P(N, t), \qquad N \geq 1, \qquad (6.3.3)$$

$$\frac{dP(0, t)}{dt} = \delta P(1, t) - IP(0, t). \qquad (6.3.4)$$

These equations are solved by the mathematical trick of defining a *generating function* $g(z, t)$ as the sum

$$g(z, t) \equiv \sum_{N=0}^{\infty} P(N, t)z^N \qquad (6.3.5)$$

where z is simply a 'dummy' mathematical variable that will disappear in the subsequent analysis. It turns out that in the present type of model $g(z, t)$ is easier to calculate than $P(N, t)$ but, if required, we can always retrieve $P(N, t)$ as the coefficient of z^N when the generating function is expanded in powers of z. Moreover, if we want to calculate *moments* (for example mean population, population variance), this can be done *directly* from the generating function, since for any integer m,

$$E\{N^m\} \equiv \sum_{N=0}^{\infty} N^m P(N, t) = \left[\sum_{N=0}^{\infty} N^m P(N, t) z^N \right]_{z=1} = \left[\frac{\partial^m g(z, t)}{\partial (\ln z)^m} \right]_{z=1}. \tag{6.3.6}$$

Thus the mean population and the fluctuation intensity are derived from the simple relations

$$m(t) = \left[\frac{\partial g(z, t)}{\partial (\ln z)} \right]_{z=1} = \left[z \frac{\partial g(z, t)}{\partial z} \right]_{z=1} = \left[\frac{\partial g(z, t)}{\partial z} \right]_{z=1}, \tag{6.3.7}$$

$$\sigma^2(t) = \left[\frac{\partial^2 g(z, t)}{\partial (\ln z)^2} \right]_{z=1} - [m(t)]^2 = \left[\frac{\partial^2 g(z, t)}{\partial z^2} + \frac{\partial g(z, t)}{\partial z} - \left(\frac{\partial g(z, t)}{\partial z} \right)^2 \right]_{z=1}. \tag{6.3.8}$$

To derive the generating function for our birth–death–immigration model, we multiply both sides of equation (6.3.3) by z^N and sum over N to obtain

$$\frac{d}{dt} \sum_{N=0}^{\infty} P(N, t) z^N = \sum_{N=0}^{\infty} \{ (N - 1)\beta P(N - 1, t) z^N + IP(N - 1, t) z^N$$

$$+ \delta(N + 1) P(N + 1, t) z^N - N(\beta + \delta) P(N, t) z^N$$

$$- IP(N, t) z^N \}. \tag{6.3.9}$$

The mess on the right-hand side of this equation is simplified by noting that

$$\frac{\partial g(z, t)}{\partial z} = \sum_{N=0}^{\infty} NP(N, t) z^{N-1}, \tag{6.3.10}$$

which with a little juggling enables us to simplify equation (6.3.9) to the relatively simple partial differential equation

$$\frac{\partial g}{\partial t} = \{ \beta z^2 - (\beta + \delta)z + \delta \} \frac{\partial g}{\partial z} + I(z - 1)g. \tag{6.3.11}$$

The original set of differential equations (6.3.3)–(6.3.4) can only be solved if we know the probability distribution at some time (say $t = 0$), so we are interested in a solution of equation (6.3.11) satisfying the *initial condition*

$$g(z, 0) = \sum_{N=0}^{\infty} P(N, 0) z^N, \tag{6.3.12}$$

which for the (common) case where the population has a known, certain value N_0 at $t = 0$ is simply

$$g(z, 0) = z^{N_0}. \tag{6.3.13}$$

We also want our probability distribution to be normalized at all times, so we in addition have the *boundary condition*

$$g(1, t) = \sum_{N=0}^{\infty} P(N, t) = 1. \tag{6.3.14}$$

What the above manipulations have achieved is the representation of the birth–death–immigration model in terms of a standard, well-understood type of mathematical equation (the PDE (6.3.11)) in place of the somewhat intractable set of differential equations (6.3.3)–(6.3.4). The solution of equation (6.3.11) can be obtained in about a page of algebra, or more simply, by searching in a suitable book (such as Goel and Richter-Dyn, 1974) with the result

$$g(z, t) = \frac{(\beta - \delta)^{I/\beta}[\delta(e^{(\beta-\delta)t} - 1) + z(\beta - \delta e^{(\beta-\delta)t})]^{N_0}}{[\beta e^{(\beta-\delta)t} - \delta + \beta z(1 - e^{(\beta-\delta)t})]^{N_0 + I/\beta}} \tag{6.3.15}$$

The qualitative behaviour of most birth and death models is adequately summarized by the development with time of the mean population, the variance, and $P(0, t)$ (which for a closed system gives the probability of extinction by time t). All of these can be derived with very little effort from the generating function, the mean and variance by using equations (6.3.7) and (6.3.8), and $P(0, t)$ by setting $z = 0$ to obtain

$$g(0, t) = \left[\sum_{N=0}^{\infty} P(N, t)z^N \right]_{z=0} = P(0, t). \tag{6.3.16}$$

The results are summarized in Table 6.1 along with the asymptotic behaviour as $t \to \infty$ which represents the situation a long time after the (possibly fictional) time $t = 0$ when all replicates contained exactly N_0 individuals.

We see at once from this table that the mean population exactly satisfies the deterministic equation (6.3.2). This is *not* a general property of birth and death models, although it is a feature we hope will be approximately true in robust models. However, the trajectory of the mean population alone does not tell us anything about the behaviour of individual populations which can only be deduced by examining together the variation of the three quantities $m(t)$, $\sigma^2(t)$ and $P(0, t)$. This we now do, considering in turn the three regimes that we identified in the deterministic system;

(a) $\beta > \delta$ with or without immigration,
(b) $\beta < \delta$, no immigration,
(c) $\beta < \delta$, with immigration.

Table 6.1. Characteristics of the birth–death–immigration model with $B(N) = \beta N + I$, $D(N) = \delta N$. The population at $t = 0$ is N_0 with probability one. The mean population, variance, and probability of zero population, at time t are denoted by $m(t)$, $\sigma^2(t)$, and $P(0,t)$ respectively. To simplify the expressions we have set $S = \exp\{(\beta - \delta)t\}$. The table was constructed from information in Goel and Richter-Dyn (1974).

General behaviour

Quantity	$I = 0$ (no immigration)	$I \neq 0$ (with immigration)
$m(t)$	$N_0 S$	$N_0 S + \dfrac{I(S-1)}{(\beta - \delta)}$
$\sigma^2(t)$	$\dfrac{N_0 S(S-1)(\beta + \delta)}{(\beta - \delta)}$	$\dfrac{N_0 S(S-1)(\beta + \delta)}{(\beta - \delta)} + \dfrac{I(S-1)(\beta S - \delta)}{(\beta - \delta)^2}$
$P(0,t)$	$\left[\dfrac{\delta(S-1)}{(\beta S - \delta)}\right]^{N_0}$	$\left[\dfrac{\delta(S-1)}{(\beta S - \delta)}\right]^{N_0}\left[\dfrac{(\beta - \delta)}{(\beta S - \delta)}\right]^{I/\beta}$

Behaviour as $t \to \infty$

Quantity	$I = 0$ (no immigration) $\beta < \delta$	$\beta > \delta$	$\beta = \delta$	$I \neq 0$ (with immigration) $\beta < \delta$	$\beta > \delta$	$\beta = \delta$
S	0	∞	1	0	∞	1
$m(\infty)$	0	$N_0 S$	N_0	$\dfrac{I}{(\delta - \beta)}$	$\left[N_0 + \dfrac{I}{(\beta - \delta)}\right]S$	It
$\sigma^2(\infty)$	$\dfrac{N_0(\beta + \delta)S^2}{(\delta - \beta)}$	$\dfrac{N_0(\beta + \delta)S^2}{(\beta - \delta)}$	$2N_0\beta t$	$\dfrac{I\delta}{(\delta - \beta)^2}$	$\dfrac{N_0(\beta^2 - \delta^2) + I\beta}{(\beta - \delta)^2}S^2$	$\beta I t^2$
$CV = \dfrac{\sigma(\infty)}{m(\infty)}$	∞	Finite	∞	Finite	Finite	Finite
$P(0,\infty)$	1	$\left(\dfrac{\delta}{\beta}\right)^{N_0}$	1	$\left(1 - \dfrac{\beta}{\delta}\right)^{1/\beta}$	0	0

(a) $\beta > \delta$

In this case both mean and variance grow exponentially with time in such a way that the coefficient of variation ($CV \equiv \sigma(t)/m(t)$) settles down at a constant value which can be shown to decrease with increasing N_0 and/or I. However, in spite of the expected exponential growth, eventual extinction of a population is both possible, and if N_0 is small, by no means improbable when the vital rates β and δ are comparable in magnitude. Roughly speaking, in the absence of immigration most of the replicates belong to one of two groups distinguished by their initial behaviour: those that initially grow in size and ultimately 'explode' exponentially, and those that fail to take off and become extinct relatively quickly. Immigration has no significant qualitative effect on the first 'exploding' group, but it does permit extinct replicates to 'restart' thereby reducing to zero the probability of ultimate extinction of a population.

(b) $\beta < \delta$, no immigration

Both mean and variance decay exponentially with time, but now the relative size of the variation between replicates increases steadily, with the result that extinction soon becomes virtually certain. The probability of ultimate extinction is 1 and the mean time to extinction is proportional to $(\delta - \beta)^{-1}$, the constant of proportionality depending on the initial population N_0 (see Problem 6).

(c) $\beta < \delta$, with immigration

This is the only situation in which a true statistically stationary state is achieved and is thus of greater interest than the others for our subsequent study of non-linear models. The coefficient of variation, which at the steady state has a value $(\delta/I)^{1/2}$, can in this case be shown to be equal to the relative fluctuation intensity in a *single replicate* population (a point we discuss in detail in Section 6.5). If $\delta/I \ll 1$, then each individual replicate persists for a long time before extinction, whereas if $\delta/I \geqslant 1$ the pattern followed by each replicate is one of regular colonization and extinction. Examples of each situation are shown in Fig. 6.2.

The above three cases exhaust the possibilities of ecological relevance, but one further piece of insight can be obtained from the special situation where $\beta = \delta$. With no immigration, the deterministic system has a steady state in which the population simply retains its initial value N_0, but it is customary to regard such a steady state as unrealizable in practice since the slightest deviation from exact equality of the vital rates would cause the population to grow or decline exponentially. The present stochastic analysis strengthens this argument by showing that demographic stochasticity alone would be sufficient to ensure steady drift from the 'steady' state N_0 (since from Table 6.1 we see that the variance grows steadily with time).

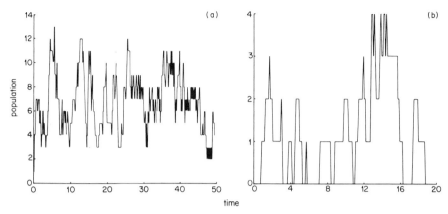

Fig. 6.2. Birth–death–immigration model with a statistically stationary state. (a) $\delta/I \ll 1$—long period of persistence. (b) $\delta/I > 1$—regular colonization and extinction.

The mathematical methods of the present section do not extend readily to cover more complicated forms of birth and death rates. There is no difficulty in obtaining a partial differential equation for the generating function for any non-linear birth and death model, but the equation is normally too complicated to admit an analytic solution. There is no point in developing numerical solutions for the generating function since (as we shall see) the original differential equations for $P(N, t)$ or $P_c(N, t)$ are easily solved numerically. The exact analysis of a model with density-independent regulation has, however, yielded some insight on the basic processes of exponential growth and population extinction which are central to population dynamics. It has also demonstrated the substantial amount of insight that can be gleaned from the three quantities $m(t)$, $\sigma^2(t)$ and $P(0, t)$ on which we shall concentrate throughout the remainder of this chapter and much of Chapter 7.

6.4 STATIONARY AND QUASI-STATIONARY PROBABILITY DISTRIBUTIONS

A. Discrete distributions

We have already argued that the only birth and death models in which a true statistically stationary probability distribution can arise are those where an immigration term causes $B(0)$ to be non-zero; otherwise ultimate extinction or population explosion are certain. It is straightforward to show that in a true stationary state $P^*(N)$

$$B(N)P^*(N) = D(N + 1)P^*(N + 1). \tag{6.4.1}$$

Repeated application of this recurrence relation shows that

$$P^*(N) = \frac{B(1)B(2)\dots B(N-1)}{D(1)D(2)\dots D(N)} B(0)P^*(0), \tag{6.4.2}$$

and hence on normalizing (i.e. ensuring that all the probabilities add to one) we find

$$P^*(N) = \frac{q_N}{\sum\limits_{i=0}^{\infty} q_i}, \qquad (6.4.3)$$

where

$$q_i = \frac{B(1)B(2)\dots B(i-1)}{D(1)D(2)\dots D(i)}, \qquad i > 1, \qquad (6.4.4)$$

$$q_0 = 1/B(0), \qquad q_1 = 1/D(1). \qquad (6.4.5)$$

With a closed population, the population probability distribution is never stationary, but as we have seen, there may be a stationary *conditional* probability distribution which we denote by $P_c^*(N)$. If there is, it can easily be calculated numerically using an argument similar in spirit to that just given. The basic differential equations give us a recurrence relation from which we derive all the probabilities in terms of a single probability $(P_c^*(1))$. In this case the dependence on the parameter $P_c^*(1)$ is non-linear and it cannot be eliminated by a single normalization. However, normalization can be used to refine the estimate of $P_c^*(1)$, and we thus have the following *iterative* scheme which yields all the conditional probabilities to any desired accuracy:

(a)   Guess $P_c^*(1)$.
(b)   Calculate $P_c^*(2)$, $P_c^*(3)$, ... etc. by repeated applications of equation (6.2.10) with dP_c/dt set to zero, stopping at a value of N above which $P_c^*(N)$ becomes negligible.
(c)   Calculate $P_c^*(1)/\sum_N P_c^*(N)$. If the result is significantly different from the old value of $P^*(1)$, repeat (b) with this revised value of $P_c^*(1)$. Continue iterating until desired accuracy is achieved.

This procedure usually converges very rapidly and (if necessary) the calculations are simple enough for a hand calculator; we therefore strongly recommend it as a method for models formulated in terms of birth and death probabilities.

B. Diffusion approximations

On the rare occasions where there is a true statistically stationary state for a population's probability distribution, an approximation to it may be obtained by setting $\partial p/\partial t$ to zero in the appropriate diffusion equation. To simplify the presentation we rewrite the diffusion equation in the form

$$\frac{\partial p(N, t)}{\partial t} = -\frac{\partial}{\partial N}\left[f(N)p(N, t) - \frac{1}{2}\frac{\partial}{\partial N}\{g(N)p(N, t)\} \right], \qquad (6.4.6)$$

where

$$f(N) = B(N) - D(N), \qquad g(N) = B(N) + D(N). \tag{6.4.7}$$

If $\partial p/\partial t$ is to be zero, the quantity in square brackets in equation (6.4.6) (i.e. the probability current) must be independent of N and hence

$$\frac{1}{2} \frac{\partial}{\partial N} \left[g(N)p^*(N) \right] - f(N)p^*(N) = A = \text{Constant}. \tag{6.4.8}$$

where $p^*(N)$ is the stationary probability density. At very large populations ($N \to \infty$), both $p^*(N)$ and $\mathrm{d}p^*(N)/\mathrm{d}N$ must approach zero fast. Thus A = 0 in equation (6.4.8), which can now be solved formally with the result

$$p^*(N) \propto [g(N)]^{-1} \exp\left[2 \int_0^N \frac{f(x)}{g(x)} \, \mathrm{d}x \right]. \tag{6.4.9}$$

The value of the above analysis is actually rather wider than one might at first suppose since it also provides an approach to the more commonly encountered situation where we are seeking an approximation to a *quasi stationary* solution to the diffusion equation, or equivalently, and more usefully, a stationary solution to the 'diffusion-like' equation (6.2.34). In a quasi-stationary state the non-linear terms in equation (6.2.34) are likely to be significantly smaller than the others, so that we may expect to use equation (6.4.9) as at least a first approximation to the true quasi-stationary distribution $p_c^*(N)$. If we do this we must of course regard the distribution as defined on the range $1 \leq N \leq \infty$ and not $0 \leq N \leq \infty$, and must therefore normalize it by

$$\int_1^\infty p_c^*(N) \, \mathrm{d}N = 1. \tag{6.4.10}$$

C. Locally linear approximations

Where there is a statistically quasi-stationary state, we can obtain a very useful approximate solution for the probability distribution by approximating equation (6.2.34) by the simple diffusion equation (6.2.31) and then linearizing about the deterministic stationary state N^*, defined by

$$B(N^*) = D(N^*). \tag{6.4.11}$$

To write down the diffusion equation for a birth and death process we need to evaluate the two functions $f(N)$ and $g(N)$, which we have defined by

$$f(N) \equiv B(N) - D(N) \quad \text{and} \quad g(N) \equiv B(N) + D(N). \tag{6.4.12}$$

If we expand the birth- and death-rate functions about a deterministic steady state, setting

$$n(t) = N(t) - N^*, \tag{6.4.13}$$

and retaining only the leading term in each expansion, then we obtain

$$f(N^* + n) = \lambda n \quad \text{where} \quad \lambda \equiv \left\{ \frac{dB}{dN} - \frac{dD}{dN} \right\}_{N = N^*}, \qquad (6.4.14)$$

$$g(N^* + n) = Q \quad \text{where} \quad Q \equiv \{B(N^*) + D(N^*)\}. \qquad (6.4.15)$$

With these approximations the diffusion equation is simply

$$\frac{\partial}{\partial t} p(N^* + n, t) = - \frac{\partial}{\partial n} \left\{ \lambda n p(N^* + n, t) - \frac{1}{2} \frac{\partial}{\partial n} (Q p(N^* + n, t)) \right\}, \qquad (6.4.16)$$

which has a stationary solution

$$p^*(N^* + n) \propto \exp\{\lambda n^2 / Q\}. \qquad (6.4.17)$$

However, λ as defined above is precisely the quantity which, as we showed in Chapter 2, controls the deterministic stability of a population; thus in the present linear approximation a deterministically stable population (i.e. $\lambda < 0$) has a stationary conditional probability density function which if we set $a = -\lambda$ we can write in the more transparently Gaussian form

$$p_c^*(N) \propto \exp\{-a(N - N^*)^2 / Q\}. \qquad (6.4.18)$$

6.5   GROSS FLUCTUATION CHARACTERISTICS

Calculation of a population's probability distribution is normally a means to an end rather than the end itself if for no other reason than that it is a virtually unmeasurable quantity, and we now concentrate on methods of predicting such quantities as mean, variance, or AC_oF which are experimentally or observationally accessible.

A. Expectation values and time averages

The theoretical picture underlying our formulation of birth and death processes consists of a large number of replicate populations, all started with the same population at time $t = 0$. Within this framework we defined in Section 6.2 $m(t)$ and $\sigma^2(t)$, the mean population and the population variance respectively, as averages over all the replicate populations. We called such averages *expectation values* (denoted by $E\{ \ \}$), and we recall that at any time t the mean population is given by

$$m(t) \equiv E\{N\} = \sum_{N=0}^{\infty} N P(N, t), \qquad (6.5.1)$$

and the population variance by

$$\sigma^2(t) \equiv E\{(N - m(t))^2\} = \sum_{N=0}^{\infty} N^2 P(N, t) - [m(t)]^2. \qquad (6.5.2)$$

In the absence of immigration, both the mean and the variance of a bounded population decay to zero as more and more of the replicate populations become extinct, and it is often more convenient to work with expectation values (denoted by $E_c\{\ \}$) conditional on non-extinction. If a quasi-stationary distribution $P_c^*(N)$ has been reached, these expectation values will not vary with time and we shall use the shorthand notation

$$m_c \equiv m_c(\infty) = \sum_{N=1}^{\infty} N P_c^*(N), \qquad (6.5.3)$$

and

$$\sigma_c^2 \equiv \sigma_c^2(\infty) = \sum_{N=1}^{\infty} N^2 P_c^*(N) - m_c^2. \qquad (6.5.4)$$

Unfortunately expectation values thus defined are seldom measurable, and in the context of studies on a *single* population they are meaningless. The key to relating the analysis in this chapter to measurable quantities is the fact that statistical expectation values can frequently be equated to *time averages* in which a single population is followed over a long period of time. Rigorous proof of the precise conditions required for equality of statistical expectations and time averages belongs to a branch of statistics known as *ergodic theory* and is well beyond the scope of this book, but in broad terms equality is guaranteed if the model population possesses two characteristics:

(a) After a suitably long period of time the population should 'forget' its initial value, i.e. the population at time t should (as $t \to \infty$) be uncorrelated with the population at time zero.

(b) None of the birth or death probabilities $B(N)$ and $D(N)$ should be zero (except when $N = 0$). Thus a population starting from a particular value has in principle the possibility of achieving any other value.

These conditions are met by all the birth and death models we consider, and in situations (such as the studies of stochastic differential equation models with environmental stochasticity in Chapter 7) where a birth and death model is assumed but not always written down explicitly, they will be assumed valid. Thus we can safely test our models by comparing values of conditional mean population m_c and conditional population variance σ_c^2 with experimental or observational estimates based on time averages of the behaviour of a single population which does not become extinct during the period of observation. Such averages (which we denote by $\langle\ \rangle$) are rigorously defined as

$$m_{\text{tim}} = \langle N \rangle \equiv \lim_{T \to \infty} \frac{1}{T} \int_0^T N(t)\, dt, \qquad (6.5.5)$$

$$\sigma_{\text{tim}}^2 = \langle (N - m_{\text{tim}})^2 \rangle \equiv \lim_{T \to \infty} \frac{1}{T} \int_0^T (N - m_{\text{tim}})^2 \, dt, \tag{6.5.6}$$

although in practice they can only be estimated by using large but finite values of T. The time average variance σ_{tim}^2 is central to much of the analysis that follows as it is a measure of the size of the fluctuations in a *single* population. We shall give it the name *fluctuation intensity*.

There is one further interesting quantity whose definition in terms of expectation values is both cumbersome and useless in practice, and which is thus most conveniently defined directly in terms of time averages. This is the *autocovariance function* $C(\tau)$ which, as was mentioned in Chapter 1, is defined as

$$C(\tau) \equiv \langle (N(t) - \langle N \rangle)(N(t - \tau) - \langle N \rangle) \rangle. \tag{6.5.7}$$

B. Direct methods

Once we have calculated the discrete, quasi-stationary, CPDF or its continuous analogue, calculation of m_c and σ_c^2 is simply a matter of evaluating the formulae given in Section 6.5A. But in both the discrete case (where the CPDF will normally have been obtained numerically) and the continuous case (where the lower limit of 1 is likely to make the integral in equation (6.2.35) impossible analytically) numerical calculations will be required. However, the use of locally linear approximations makes possible the derivation of analytic estimates of fluctuation characteristics which prove, in practice, to be remarkably robust.

We have already seen in Section 6.4.C that if we linearize about a deterministic steady state then the diffusion approximation to the CPDF is a Gaussian. Were this probability density defined on the range $-\infty < N < \infty$ and not on the range $1 \leq N < \infty$ we would have

$$m_c = N^*, \qquad \sigma_c^2 = Q/2a. \tag{6.5.8}$$

these results being obtained from a comparison of equation (6.4.18) with the standard form of the normal distribution

$$p(N) \propto \exp\{-(N - m)^2/2\sigma^2\}. \tag{6.5.9}$$

Provided the ratio σ_c/m_c is not too large, i.e. provided most of the probability is concentrated in the meaningful range $N \geq 1$, we expect the expressions in (6.5.8) to be reasonable estimates of m_c and σ_c^2.

An alternative approach to the approximation of m_c and σ_c^2 has as its starting point the SDE (6.2.38). If we retain the notation used in linearizing the diffusion equation, we obtain on applying the same approximations to the SDE

$$dn = -an \, dt + \eta(t)\sqrt{(Q \, dt)} \tag{6.5.10}$$

If we assume that this linear SDE has a statistically stationary state, then, once this state has been reached, expectation values over all replicate populations must be time independent, so that

$$E\{n(t)\} - E\{n(t + dt)\} = E\{dn\} = 0, \qquad (6.5.11)$$

$$E\{n(t)^2\} - E\{n(t + dt)^2\} = E\{n^2\} - E\{(n + dn)^2\} = 0. \quad (6.5.12)$$

Substitution from the SDE (6.5.10) into equation (6.5.11) simply yields $E\{n\} = 0$, but in the case of equation (6.5.12) we find

$$E\{n^2\} = E\{[n(1 - a\ dt) + \eta(t)\sqrt{(Q\ dt)}]^2\} \qquad (6.5.13)$$

$$= E\{n^2(1 - 2a\ dt) + 2n\eta\sqrt{(Q\ dt)} + \eta^2 Q\ dt\} + 0(dt)^{3/2}) \qquad (6.5.14)$$

The zero order terms on both sides of this equation are equal, and demanding equality of the terms in $\sqrt{(dt)}$ yields the result that $E\{n\eta\} = 0$ implying that the value of n at time t is not correlated with the value of η at the same instant. This result, although at first sight surprising in view of the fact that the fluctuations in n are 'driven' by the fluctuations in η is easily understood as soon as we realize that although the value of n is correlated with the value of η at all times prior to t, the value of η at time t is entirely independent of its own previous history and is thus entirely uncorrelated with the current value of n.

If we now equate terms in dt on both sides of equation (6.5.14) we finally obtain

$$0 = -2aE\{n^2\} + QE\{\eta^2\} = -2aE\{n^2\} + Q \qquad (6.5.15)$$

so that

$$\sigma_c^2 = E\{n^2\} - [E\{n\}]^2 = Q/2a. \qquad (6.5.16)$$

Although the results of this derivation agree with our original approximate treatment it is important to realize that rather than being a single 'shot in the dark' approximation it is in fact the first of a systematic series of approximations (see, Bartlett, 1957, 1960) from which, with sufficient effort, any desired accuracy may be obtained. As an example, we now refine our estimate of the mean population. Suppose that to second order in n

$$f(N^* + n) = B(N^* + n) - D(N^* + n) = -an + bn^2, \qquad (6.5.17)$$

so that the SDE (6.5.10) becomes

$$dn = (-an + bn^2)\ dt + \eta(t)\ \{\text{some function of } n\}\sqrt{(Q\ dt)}. \quad (6.5.18)$$

We now take the expectation value of both sides of this equation and use the fact that $E\{dn\}$ and $E\{\eta \times (\text{any function of } n)\}$ are both zero, to obtain

$$E\{n\} = \frac{b}{a} E\{n^2\} = \frac{b}{a} (\sigma_c^2 + [E\{n\}])^2. \qquad (6.5.19)$$

This is a quadratic equation which is easily solved for $E\{n\}$ if we know σ_c^2 and the trick is now to use the *linear* estimate (6.5.16) of this quantity and hence obtain a revised value for $E\{n\}$. We shall illustrate this procedure in an example in Section 6.7.A.

C. Fourier transform methods

There is yet another method of deriving the linear approximation to the population variance which has the major advantages of being applicable to a wider class of models and of yielding in addition the AC_oF. We write the SDE in the form (6.2.43) in which it 'looks' like a normal differential equation and linearize about the deterministic steady state. We obtain

$$\frac{dn}{dt} = -an + Q^{1/2}\gamma(t), \qquad (6.5.20)$$

which, if $\gamma(t)$ were a proper mathematical function of time, would be simply the equation for a deterministic driven system such as we studied in Sections 2.5 and 2.6. Were the equation of this type, we could Fourier transform it and obtain

$$\tilde{n}(\omega) = \frac{Q^{1/2}}{a + i\omega}\tilde{\gamma}(\omega). \qquad (6.5.21)$$

For this expression to be of more than formal interest we require to investigate further the Fourier transform of the white noise $\tilde{\gamma}(\omega)$. White noise as defined in Section 6.2 is only finite if evaluated at finite intervals Δt so if we have values of $\gamma(t)$ at intervals Δt for a long period of time T, then we can approximate $\tilde{\gamma}(\omega)$ by

$$\tilde{\gamma}(\omega) \simeq \Delta t \sum_{j=1}^{T/\Delta t} \gamma(t_j)e^{-i\omega t_j} \quad \text{where} \quad t_j = j\Delta t \qquad (6.5.22)$$

which, using equation (6.2.44), becomes

$$\tilde{\gamma}(\omega) = \Delta t \sum_{j=1}^{T/\Delta t} \frac{\eta(t_j)\sqrt{(\Delta t)}}{\Delta t}e^{-i\omega t_j} = \sqrt{(\Delta t)} \sum_{j=1}^{T/\Delta t} \eta(t_j)e^{-i\omega t_j}. \qquad (6.5.23)$$

In Section 6.2.C we defined $\eta(t_j)$ as a random variable with zero mean and unit variance, and we must thus concern ourselves not with the actual value of the transform $\tilde{\gamma}(\omega)$ but with its statistical properties. Clearly

$$E\{\tilde{\gamma}(\omega)\} = \sqrt{(\Delta t)} \sum_{j=1}^{T/\Delta t} E\{\eta(t_j)\}e^{-i\omega t_j} = 0, \qquad (6.5.24)$$

and

$$E\{|\tilde{\gamma}(\omega)|^2\} = \Delta t \sum_{j=1}^{ } \sum_{k=1}^{ } E\{\eta(t_j)\eta(t_k)\}e^{-i\omega(t_j - t_k)} \qquad (6.5.25)$$

We can simplify equation (6.5.25) considerably by recalling that $\eta(t_j)$ and

$\eta(t_k)$ are uncorrelated unless $t_j = t_k$, and that $\eta(t)$ has unit variance, so that we must have

$$E\{\eta(t_j)\eta(t_k)\} = \begin{cases} 0 \text{ if } t_j \neq t_k \\ 1 \text{ if } t_j = t_k \end{cases} \tag{6.5.26}$$

and hence

$$E\{|\tilde{\gamma}(\omega)|^2\} = \Delta t \sum_{j=1}^{T/\Delta t} 1 = T. \tag{6.5.27}$$

The *spectral density* of any random function $\xi(t)$ is by an extension of equation (F11) defined as

$$S_\xi(\omega) \equiv T^{-1}E\{|\tilde{\xi}(\omega)|^2\} \tag{6.5.28}$$

so in this case the spectral density of the white noise is just

$$S_\gamma = T^{-1}E\{|\tilde{\gamma}(\omega)|^2\} = 1, \tag{6.5.29}$$

and the spectral density of the population fluctuations, $S_n(\omega)$, is

$$S_n(\omega) = \frac{Q}{a^2 + \omega^2}. \tag{6.5.30}$$

In Appendix F (equation (F7)) we show that for any function $n(t)$

$$\langle n(t) \rangle = \frac{1}{T}\tilde{n}(0), \tag{6.5.31}$$

so that in this case we see from equations (6.5.21) and (6.5.24)

$$E\{\langle n(t) \rangle\} = \frac{\sqrt{Q}}{aT}E\{\tilde{\gamma}(0)\} = 0. \tag{6.5.32}$$

But we have already seen (Section 6.5A) that for this kind of model, expectation values and long time averages can safely be equated, so that

$$\langle n(t) \rangle = E\{n(t)\} = E\{\langle n(t) \rangle\} = 0, \tag{6.5.33}$$

i.e.

$$\langle N(t) \rangle = E\{N(t)\} = N^*. \tag{6.5.34}$$

We also show in Appendix F (equation (F19)) that any deterministic function of time with zero mean, say $x(t)$, has a fluctuation intensity σ_{tim}^2 given by

$$\sigma_{tim}^2 = \langle x^2 \rangle = \frac{1}{2\pi}\int_{-\infty}^{\infty} S_x(\omega)\,d\omega \tag{6.5.35}$$

where the spectral density function $S_x(\omega)$ is defined as

$$S_x(\omega) = \lim_{T \to \infty} \frac{|\tilde{x}(\omega)|^2}{T}. \tag{6.5.36}$$

With the modified definition of the spectral density function (equation (6.5.28)) adopted here for random functions of time, equation (6.5.35) must be modified to

$$E\{\langle \xi^2 \rangle\} = \frac{1}{2\pi} \int_{\infty}^{\infty} S_\xi(\omega)\, d\omega, \qquad (6.5.37)$$

and thus, in the present case, again equating expectation and time average values, we see that the population variance is given by

$$\sigma_c^2 = \sigma_{\text{tim}}^2 = E\{\langle n^2 \rangle\} = \frac{Q}{2\pi} \int_{-\infty}^{\infty} \frac{d\omega}{a^2 + \omega^2} = \frac{Q}{2a}, \qquad (6.5.38)$$

the evaluation of the integral being most easily effected by consulting Gradshteyn and Ryshik (1965, p. 217).

These results (equations (6.5.34) and (6.5.38)) for the population mean and variance are of course identical to those obtained by simpler methods, but the advantage offered by the transform method is that it is applicable to more complex problems without extra difficulty. Few, if any, problems that can be solved using Fourier transforms *cannot* be solved by direct methods, but in general direct methods tend to require much more mathematical ingenuity; the power of the transform method is that it is routine, if sometimes tedious. For example in the present problem it is extremely laborious to make a direct calculation of the fluctuation AC_oF, but when using the transform method it can be calculated at once from

$$C(\tau) = \frac{1}{2\pi} \int_{-\infty}^{\infty} S_n(\omega) \cos \omega\tau \, d\omega, \qquad (6.5.39)$$

which we derive from its deterministic analog (equation (F18b)) by again equating time average and expectation values. For the present model, whose spectral density function is given by equation (6.5.30), this expression yields

$$C(\tau) = \frac{Q}{2a} e^{-a\tau}, \qquad (6.5.40)$$

the integral being most easily evaluated by reference to Gradshteyn and Ryshik (1965, p. 406).

6.6. EXTINCTION

One of our principal motives for formulating population models in terms of discrete birth and death processes is to study extinction. We now consider extinction in closed systems where $B(0) = 0$ (ensuring that extinction cannot be 'reversed' by subsequent immigration), and shall concentrate on two fundamental quantities which provide an adequate, qualitative description of extinction in simple models—the probability of ultimate extinction and the mean persistence time of a population that eventually suffers extinction (which we call simply the extinction time). We first review such exact, analytic, results as are available and obtain formal expressions for both quantities of interest—these are summarized at the end of Section 6.6A for the reader uninterested in their derivation. We then restrict our investigation to the (normal) situation where ultimate extinction is certain and relate (in Section 6.6B) extinction characteristics to the population probability distribution, and in particular to the stationary CPDF. This section is the key to our later study of extinction in variable environments (Chapter 7). Finally in Section 6.6C we collect together a few rough and ready approximations that yield analytic 'guesstimates' of extinction times.

A. Exact analytic results

In a closed system, the probability of ultimate extinction is simply the probability $P(0, \infty)$ and can of course be arrived at by numerical solution of the differential equations (6.2.3)–(6.2.5), or in special cases from the asymptotic behaviour of the generating function $g(z, t)$ when $z = 0$ and $t \to \infty$. However, $P(0, \infty)$ can be calculated explicitly in terms of the birth and death probabilities, the derivation being of particular interest as it provides us with a condition for $P(0, \infty)$ to be one, implying certain extinction. To simplify notation, we let E_i be the value of $P(0, \infty)$ when the initial population is i. Then, since the first change of population can only be to $i \pm 1$, we obtain

$$E_i = \left[\begin{array}{c} \text{Probability that} \\ \text{first change is to } i + 1 \end{array} \right] E_{i+1} + \left[\begin{array}{c} \text{Probability that} \\ \text{first change is to } i - 1 \end{array} \right] E_{i-1}$$

$$= \left[\frac{B(i)}{B(i) + D(i)} \right] E_{i+1} + \left[\frac{D(i)}{B(i) + D(i)} \right] E_{i-1}, \qquad i \geqslant 1. \qquad (6.6.1)$$

We know that $E_0 = 1$ and hence E_i can be calculated by repeated applications of equation (6.6.1), provided we know the value of the single parameter E_1. The result for an initial population N_0 is

$$E_{N_0} = E_1 + (E_1 - 1) \sum_{i=1}^{N_0 - 1} S_i, \qquad (6.6.2)$$

where

$$S_i = \frac{D(1)D(2) \ldots D(i)}{B(1)B(2) \ldots B(i)}. \qquad (6.6.3)$$

This somewhat formal looking result is in fact rather useful. First, since E_{N_0} is a probability and is thus constrained to have values between 0 and 1 even as $N_0 \to \infty$, we see immediately that unless the sum converges to a finite limit as $N_0 \to \infty$ we must have $E_{N_0} = E_1 = 1$ for all N. We have therefore proved that in a closed population, ultimate extinction is certain if

$$\sum_{i=1}^{\infty} S_i = \sum_{i=1}^{\infty} \frac{D(1)D(2) \ldots D(i)}{B(1)B(2) \ldots B(i)} = \infty. \qquad (6.6.4)$$

In all closed populations with a single deterministically stable steady state, the death rate exceeds the birth rate for large populations, implying that the terms in the sum steadily increase in magnitude, and the sum itself diverges to infinity. Ultimate extinction is therefore certain and we have confirmed theoretically the picture of the development with time of the probability distribution given in Section 6.1 and illustrated in Fig. 6.1.

From equation (6.6.2) we can also derive an expression for the extinction probability in those few models where equation (6.6.4) is not satisfied (these are models where the population faces a 'choice' between ultimate exponential growth and extinction, a situation commonly modelled in island biogeography). We accept as intuitively obvious (the perfectionist can easily provide himself with a proof!) that unless extinction is certain ($E_{N_0} = 1$ for all values of N_0), then as the initial population N_0 becomes infinite, the extinction probability E_{N_0} approaches zero. It follows by letting $N_0 \to \infty$ in equation (6.6.2) and rearranging the terms, that

$$E_1 = \frac{\sum\limits_{i=1}^{\infty} S_i}{1 + \sum\limits_{i=1}^{\infty} S_i}, \qquad (6.6.5)$$

and by successive applications of equation (6.6.2) that

$$E_{N_0} = \frac{\sum\limits_{i=N_0}^{\infty} S_i}{1 + \sum\limits_{i=1}^{\infty} S_i}. \qquad (6.6.6)$$

The second quantity of major interest in characterizing extinction is the mean time to extinction. We confine our derivation of explicit expressions for extinction times to the (normal) case where ultimate extinction is certain (i.e. equation (6.6.4) is valid), and denote by $\tau_E\{N_0\}$ the mean time to extinction of a population that initially (at $t = 0$) consisted of exactly N_0 individuals. As in the derivation of equation (6.6.1) we consider the first change of population from N_0 which can only be to $N_0 \pm 1$, and argue that

$$\tau_E'\{N_0\} = \begin{bmatrix} \text{Mean time spent} \\ \text{with } N = N_0 \\ \text{before first} \\ \text{change} \end{bmatrix} + \begin{bmatrix} \text{Probability that} \\ \text{first change is to } N_0 + 1 \end{bmatrix} \tau_E\{N_0 + 1\}$$

$$+ \begin{bmatrix} \text{Probability that} \\ \text{first change is to } N_0 - 1 \end{bmatrix} \tau_E(N_0 - 1) \qquad (6.6.7)$$

The last two terms were derived *en route* to equation (6.6.1) and the first can be shown in a few lines of algebra to be $[B(N_0) + D(N_0)]^{-1}$. Thus the extinction times satisfy the recurrence relation

$$\tau_E\{N_0\} = \frac{1}{B(N_0) + D(N_0)} + \frac{B(N_0)}{B(N_0) + D(N_0)} \, \tau_E\{N_0 + 1\}$$

$$+ \frac{D(N_0)}{B(N_0) + D(N_0)} \, \tau_E\{N_0 - 1\}. \tag{6.6.8}$$

We know that $\tau_E\{0\} = 0$ and thus have again produced a situation where all the τ_Es can be calculated in terms of a single parameter $\tau_E(1)$. Routine, if tedious manipulation rather similar to that involved in the derivation of equation (6.6.2) leads to the result

$$\tau_E\{N_0\} - \tau_E\{N_0 + 1\} = \left[\sum_{i=1}^{N_0} q_i - \tau_E\{1\} \right] S_{N_0}, \tag{6.6.9}$$

where the quantities S_i have already been defined in equation (6.6.4) and the q_i (defined in equation (6.4.4)) are the combinations of birth and death probabilities that arose in our discussion of stationary states. Still in the spirit of our previous analysis of ultimate extinction probabilities, we now consider the limiting case $N_0 \to \infty$. It is obvious that the left-hand side of equation (6.6.9) is negative (as extinction from an initial population of $N_0 + 1$ involves a transition to N_0 followed by extinction from N_0). Hence if $\sum_{i=1}^{\infty} q_i$ is infinite, $\tau_E\{1\}$ must also be infinite and we have thus proved that the mean time to extinction from any initial population (which must exceed $\tau_E\{1\}$) is finite only if

$$\sum_{i=1}^{\infty} q_i = \frac{1}{D(1)} + \sum_{i=2}^{\infty} \frac{B(1)B(2) \ldots B(i-1)}{D(1)D(2) \ldots D(i)} < \infty. \tag{6.6.10}$$

When this condition is satisfied, we can deduce with some juggling of equation (6.6.9) that

$$\tau_E\{1\} - \tau_E\{N_0\} = \sum_{m=1}^{N_0-1} \sum_{i=1}^{m} S_m q_i - \tau_E\{1\} \sum_{m=1}^{N_0-1} S_m \tag{6.6.11}$$

which simplifies to give

$$\tau_E\{N_0\} = \tau_E\{1\} + \sum_{m=1}^{N_0-1} S_m \left[\tau_E\{1\} - \sum_{i=1}^{m} q_i \right] \tag{6.6.12}$$

We have thus reduced the problem of calculating the extinction time for an arbitrary population to that of calculating $\tau_E\{1\}$. Furthermore it can be shown that provided the condition (6.6.10) is valid, then

$$\lim_{N_0 \to \infty} \{ S_{N_0}[\tau_E\{N_0\} - \tau_E\{N_0 + 1\}] \} = 0, \tag{6.6.13}$$

the key to the proof being the fact that at large N_0, where births are much less probable than deaths, the transition from N_0 is normally by way of a single death. Thus from equation (6.6.9),

$$\tau_E\{1\} = \sum_{i=1}^{\infty} q_i = \frac{1}{D(1)} + \sum_{i=2}^{\infty} \frac{B(1)B(2)\ldots B(i-1)}{D(1)D(2)\ldots D(i)}, \qquad (6.6.14)$$

and hence from equation (6.6.12)

$$\tau_E\{N_0\} = \tau_E\{1\} + \sum_{m=1}^{N_0-1} S_m \sum_{i=m+1}^{\infty} q_i. \qquad (6.6.15)$$

We now summarize the main results for the reader who has omitted the mathematical argument.

(a) Extinction in a closed population is conveniently described by two sets of parameters S_i and q_i defined by

$$S_i = \frac{D(1)D(2)\ldots D(i)}{B(1)B(2)\ldots B(i)} \qquad (6.6.16)$$

$$q_i = \begin{cases} 1/D(1) & \text{if } i = 1 \\ \dfrac{B(1)B(2)\ldots B(i-1)}{D(1)D(2)\ldots D(i)} & \text{if } i \geqslant 2. \end{cases} \qquad (6.6.17)$$

(b) The probability of ultimate extinction of a population N_0 individuals is:

$$E_{N0} = \begin{cases} 1 & \text{if } \sum_{i=1}^{\infty} S_i = \infty \\ \dfrac{\sum_{i=1}^{\infty} S_i}{1 + \sum_{i=1}^{\infty} S_i} & \text{if } \sum_{i=1}^{\infty} S_i \text{ is finite} \end{cases} \qquad (6.6.18)$$

(c) The mean time to extinction of a population of N individuals is given (provided $E_{N0} = 1$) by

$$\tau_E\{N_0\} = \begin{cases} \displaystyle\sum_{i=1}^{\infty} q_i & \text{if } N_0 = 1 \\ \displaystyle\sum_{i=1}^{\infty} q_i + \sum_{m=1}^{N_0-1} S_m \sum_{i=m+1}^{\infty} q_i & \text{if } N_0 \geqslant 2. \end{cases} \qquad (6.6.19)$$

B. Extinction and the population probability distribution

The analytic expressions in the previous section are cumbersome and with large populations their evaluation can present problems. Moreover, it is very difficult to obtain any 'feel' concerning extinction from such complicated expressions. However, probably the most important weakness of the exact results is that we know of no way of extending the derivation to cover extinction in variable environments. With these difficulties in mind, we now turn to a completely different approach in which we examine formally the development with time of the population probability distribution.

We still confine our attention to closed systems in which extinction is irreversible. The probability of a population persisting to time t and becoming extinct between t and $t + dt$ is then $dP(0, t)$ $(= [dP(0, t)/dt]\, dt)$ and the mean time to extinction is thus

$$\tau_E = \int_{t=0}^{\infty} t\, dP(0, t) = \int_{0}^{\infty} t\, \frac{dP(0, t)}{dt}\, dt. \qquad (6.6.20)$$

Simplification of this expression requires us to know the value of $P(0, \infty)$, the probability of ultimate extinction. We suppose this quantity is known and as it is of course a constant, we can rewrite equation (6.6.20) as

$$\tau_E = -\int_{0}^{\infty} t\, \frac{d}{dt} \{P(0, \infty) - P(0, t)\}\, dt. \qquad (6.6.21)$$

which can be integrated by parts to give

$$\tau_E = -[t\{P(0, \infty) - P(0, t)\}]_{t=\infty} + [t\{P(0, \infty) - P(0, t)\}]_{t=0}$$

$$+ \int_{0}^{\infty} \{P(0, \infty) - P(0, t)\}\, dt. \qquad (6.6.22)$$

The first term vanishes in all but the occasional, pathological, neutrally stable model since $P(0, t)$ normally approaches its limiting value exponentially and we thus conclude that

$$\tau_E = \int_{0}^{\infty} \{P(0, \infty) - P(0, t)\}\, dt, \qquad (6.6.23)$$

which in the very common situation where ultimate extinction is certain becomes

$$\tau_E = \int_{0}^{\infty} \{1 - P(0, t)\}\, dt. \qquad (6.6.24)$$

This result is as far as we can go in totally general terms, and with very small populations it is adequate for numerical evaluation of extinction times. However, we can achieve a very useful simplification in the special case of an ensemble of populations which, prior to extinction, has settled to a quasi-stationary state. In this situation, it follows from the definition (equation (6.2.7)) of the conditional probability distribution, and the assumption of quasi-stationarity that

$$P(1, t) = P_c(1, t)\{1 - P(0, t)\} \simeq P_c^*(1)\{1 - p(0, t)\}. \qquad (6.6.25)$$

In this approximation, we can evaluate $P(0, t)$ since from equations (6.2.4b)

$$\frac{dP(0,t)}{dt} = D(1)P(1,t), \tag{6.6.26}$$

which, with our assumption of a quasi-stationary state $(P_c(1,t)$ give by equation (6.6.25)), simplifies to

$$\frac{dP(0,t)}{dt} = D(1)P_c^*(1)\{1 - P(0,t)\}. \tag{6.6.27}$$

This differential equation is readily solved if we make the reasonable requirement that none of the replicates are extinct at $t = 0$, the result being

$$P(0,t) = 1 - \exp\{-D(1)P_c^*(1)t\}, \tag{6.6.28}$$

the form of which is illustrated in Fig. 6.3.

From equations (6.6.24) and (6.6.28), the expected time to extinction, τ_E, is clearly

$$\tau_E = \int_0^\infty \exp\{-D(1)P_c^*(1)t\}\,dt = [D(1)P_c^*(1)]^{-1}. \tag{6.6.29}$$

In order to use this result, which is of major importance in view of our definition (see Chapter 1) of an ecological stability index directly related to τ_E, we require a value of $P_c^*(1)$. Clearly, in any particular case, we can easily calculate this quantity by using the iterative scheme given in Section (6.4) to obtain a numerical solution for the CPDF. In many cases, however, it is considerably more convenient to be able to obtain an analytic approximation for the extinction time, which in turn requires us to develop approximations to the stationary CPDF. This we do in the next section.

C. Analytic approximations

The most obvious starting point for the development of analytic approximations for the extinction time is the exact formula (6.6.19). With quasi-

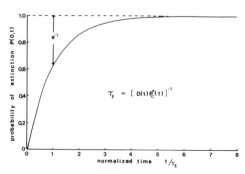

Fig. 6.3. The development with time of $P(0,t)$ for a system already in a quasi-stationary state at $t = 0$.

stationary populations, it is occasionally possible to obtain asymptotic forms valid for large values of N^*, the deterministic steady state, but we have not succeeded in pinning down a general procedure for obtaining such approximations. We do, however, in section 6.7, give an example (due to Falk (1980)) of one such approximation.

A less systematic approach which we have found rather useful, involves approximating the true stationary CPDF by an appropriate discrete probability distribution. Clearly this in general requires that we should first solve numerically for the stationary CPDF in a representative sample of cases, and then consult a suitable compilation of discrete probability distributions (for example, Abramowitz and Segun, 1965, p 929) in order to find an appropriately shaped distribution function. However, in those cases where we have already obtained reasonably reliable estimates of the population mean and variance (m_c and σ_c^2) using one of the approximation techniques discussed above, it is often sufficient to fit a suitable discrete probability distribution to the known values of these quantities. For example, if we find that, for a particular model, $\sigma_c^2 > m_c$ then an obvious candidate for the stationary probability distribution is a negative binomial, for which

$$P_c^*(N) = \frac{(k + N - 1)!}{N!\,(k - 1)!} \left(\frac{m_c}{m_c + k}\right)^N \left(\frac{k}{k + m_c}\right)^k \qquad (6.6.30)$$

where the parameter k can be calculated solely in terms of the population's mean and variance from

$$k = \frac{m_c^2}{\sigma_c^2 - m_c}. \qquad (6.6.31)$$

Thus

$$P_c^*(1) = \frac{k m_c}{m_c + k} \left(\frac{k}{k + m_c}\right)^k = \frac{m_c^2}{\sigma_c^2} \left[\frac{m_c}{\sigma_c^2}\right]^k \qquad (6.6.32)$$

and hence from the fundamental result (6.6.29)

$$\tau_E = [D(1)P_c^*(1)]^{-1} = \frac{\sigma_c^2}{D(1)m_c^2} \left(\frac{m_c}{\sigma_c^2}\right)^{-k} \qquad (6.6.33)$$

which, with a little manipulation, yields a relatively simple expression for the ratio of the mean time to extinction τ_E to the expected lifetime of an individual in uncrowded conditions ($D(1)^{-1}$):

$$\ln(D(1)\tau_E) = \ln\left(\frac{\sigma_c^2}{m_c^2}\right) - \frac{m_c^2}{\sigma_c^2 - m_c} \ln \frac{m_c}{\sigma_c^2} \qquad (6.6.34)$$

If we wish to re-express this result in terms of our ecological stability index, ξ, defined in equation (1.5.1), then we find

$$\xi \equiv \ln \tau_E = \ln\left(\frac{\sigma_c^2}{m_c^2}\right) - \ln[D(1)] - \frac{m_c^2}{\sigma_c^2 - m_c} \ln \frac{m_c}{\sigma_c^2}. \qquad (6.6.35)$$

In the next section we shall demonstrate the considerable robustness of equation (6.5.34) for a model with a relatively simple unimodel probability distribution. However, it is vital to stress that *only* direct calculation of the true CPDF and subsequent accurate fitting of its behaviour will give results of guaranteed accuracy. Unquestioning assumption of any specific probability distribution and consequent uncritical use of equation (6.6.34) or any of its myriad counterparts can lead to serious error.

The techniques for estimating τ_E which we have just described both depend crucially upon the fact that our description of the problem is couched in terms of the birth and death probability functions $B(N)$ and $D(N)$. However, in problems involving environmental variability these probability functions are themselves time dependent and a proper description of the system dynamics in terms of them becomes (as we see in Chapter 7) more difficult to analyse. It is common in such cases to employ an approximate description of the problem formulated directly in terms of an SDE or its equivalent diffusion equation, and although extinction time estimates obtained from such formulations must be treated with considerable care they can often prove useful in qualitative or comparative studies. For this reason we now discuss an alternative approach to the approximation of extinction times starting from the diffusion equation. We assume that, after a short period of time, during which the population effectively 'forgets' its initial condition, there is a period of time comparable in magnitude with τ_E during which the probability density function is of the form

$$p(0, t) = 1 - e^{-t/\tau_E} \qquad (6.6.36)$$

$$p(N, t) = p_0(N)\exp\{-t/\tau_E\} \qquad (N \neq 0) \qquad (6.6.37)$$

with

$$\int_{0^+}^{\infty} p_0(N)\, dN = 1 \qquad (6.6.38)$$

Then on substituting the assumed solution (6.6.37) into the diffusion equation (6.2.31) we obtain

$$-\tau_E^{-1} p_0(N) = -\frac{\partial}{\partial N}\{f(N)p_0(N) - \frac{1}{2}\frac{\partial}{\partial N}[g(N)p_0(N)]\}, \qquad (6.6.39)$$

and have thus reduced the problem of calculating the mean time to extinction to that of finding a value of τ_E for which there is an acceptable (i.e. positive and normalizable) solution $p_0(N)$ to this equation. The mathematical methods for calculating such values of τ_E are very well developed (largely because problems of this type, known as eigenvalue problems, involving partial differential equations are important in physics) but are in general long, involved and uninstructive. However, we can use equation (6.6.39) to derive a very useful and rather general approximation to extinction times. We recall that $p_0(N)$ has been assumed normalized (equation (6.6.38)) and integrate equation (6.6.39) from 0 to ∞ to obtain

$$\tau_E^{-1} = f(\infty)p_0(\infty) - f(0)p_0(0) - \left[\frac{1}{2}\frac{\partial}{\partial N}(g(N)p_0(N))\right]_{N=\infty}$$

$$+ \frac{1}{2}\left[\frac{\partial}{\partial N}(g(N)p_0(N))\right]_{N=0}. \quad (6.6.40)$$

But in a closed population $B(0)$ and $D(0)$ (and hence $f(0)$ and $g(0)$) are zero. Furthermore in most models $p_0(N) \to 0$ very fast (normally at least exponentially) as $N \to \infty$ and equation (6.6.40) thus simplifies in a few lines to

$$\tau_E = 2\left[p_0(0)\left(\frac{dg}{dN}\right)_{N=0}\right]^{-1}. \quad (6.6.41)$$

The utility of this relationship is greatly enhanced by inserting equations (6.6.36) and (6.6.37) into the definition of the conditional probability density function, $p_c(N, t)$ discussed in Section 6.2B

$$p_c(N, t) \equiv \frac{p(N, t)}{1 - p(0, t)} = \frac{p_0(N)\exp\{-t/\tau_E\}}{\exp\{-t/\tau_E\}} = p_0(N) \quad (6.6.42)$$

and hence revealing that if the probability density function does indeed behave as assumed above then the density function for the *probability conditional upon non-extinction* remains stationary with a value $p_c^*(N) = p_0(N)$. In this case we can use equation (6.6.41) to calculate τ_E directly from the extrapolate to $N = 0$ of the stationary conditional probability density function obtained from equation (6.2.34). The generally insanitary nature of this latter equation means that this fact would be of very litle assistance to us were it not for the happy accident that in most cases equation (6.2.34) can be quite closely approximated by the equivalent diffusion equation, so that a workable approximation to $p_0(0)$ can be obtained from the value at $N = 0$ of the stationary solution of the appropriate diffusion equation (6.2.31), where such a solution exists.

Thus we may make a crude first estimate of τ_E from the approximate probability density function calculated from the locally linear approximation to the diffusion equation (6.4.18) which (after appropriate normalization) yields

$$p(N) = \frac{1}{\sqrt{(2\pi)}\sigma_c}\exp\{-(N - m_c)^2/2\sigma_c^2\} \quad (6.6.43)$$

In this approximation

$$\tau_E = 2\left[p_0(0)\left(\frac{dg}{dN}\right)_{N=0}\right]^{-1} = \frac{2}{\sqrt{(2\pi)}\sigma_c}\left[\frac{dg}{dN}\right]_{N=0}^{-1}\exp\{m_c^2/2\sigma_c^2\}, \quad (6.6.44)$$

and our ecological stability index is

$$\xi \equiv \ln \tau_E = \frac{m_c^2}{2\sigma_c^2} - \ln\left[\frac{dg}{dN}\right]_{N=0} - \ln \sigma_c - 0.226 \qquad (6.6.45)$$

In laboratory studies of extinction (cf. Chapter 10) all the terms in the above equation may be significant but in many strategic studies which are concerned with extinction over long periods of time, all but the first two terms are unimportant and we have

$$\xi \simeq \frac{m_c^2}{2\sigma_c^2} - \ln\left[\frac{dg}{dN}\right]_{N=0} \qquad (6.6.46)$$

The latter term in this equation serves primarily to take account of the units we use to measure time and the message to be extracted is thus that *the reciprocal of the relative fluctuation intensity may provide a qualitatively acceptable measure of ecological stability.*

We shall demonstrate by means of examples in Section 6.7 that although the linear estimates of the gross fluctuation characteristics (m_c and σ_c^2) are remarkably robust, the Gaussian approximation (equation (6.6.43)) to the probability distribution and hence to the extinction time is, in general, rather poor, particularly at low population values. Thus, where quantitatively reliable estimates of τ_E are required the use of equation (6.6.43) is not to be recommended. However, it is also clear from our studies that any *changes* which we observe in the value of τ_E obtained from equation (6.6.43) are normally in the same sense as those which the same change in parameters produces in the exact estimate of the same quantity. Thus in any strategic study in which our prime interest is in the way the system stability changes as we vary the model parameters, the estimate of the ecological stability index obtained from equation (6.6.43) provides a satisfactory compromise between accuracy and tractability.

6.7   WORKED EXAMPLES

A. A logistic birth and death model

As our first example of the use of the procedures developed in the preceding sections we consider a birth and death model with

$$B(N) = rN; \qquad D(N) = \frac{rN^2}{K}. \qquad (6.7.1)$$

and note that the deterministic analog of this model always has a globally stable stationary state.

Probability distribution

We first use the iterative method outlined in Section 6.4.A to estimate the exact CPDF for a selection of values of K and illustrate three sample results in

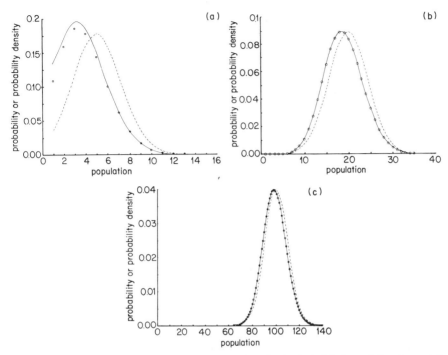

Fig. 6.4. Stationary probability distributions for the logistic birth and death model. The conditional discrete probability distribution is shown by ○, the diffusion approximation by —— and the Gaussian approximation by ----. (a) $K = 5$. (b) $K = 20$. (c) $K = 100$.

Fig. 6.4. On the same graphs we have also plotted the appropriate stationary solution (6.4.9) to the diffusion equation normalized on the range 1 to ∞ in accordance with equation (6.4.10), and the Gaussian approximation (equation (6.4.18)) to the CPDF. These results clearly illustrate the accuracy of both the diffusion approximation and of the Gaussian approximation for all but the smallest populations.

Gross fluctuation characteristics

We next study the mean population and the fluctuation intensity for a number of values of K by the following methods;

(a) exact calculation using the discrete CPDF,
(b) using locally linear approximations to the diffusion equation or the equivalent SDE,
(c) the direct methods discussed in Section 6.5.B.

Having already calculated the discrete CPDF, all that is involved in method (a) is to obtain m_c and σ_c^2 from the formulae

$$m_c = \sum_{N=1}^{\infty} N P_c^*(N), \qquad \sigma_c^2 = \sum_{N=1}^{\infty} N^2 P_c^*(N) - m_c^2. \qquad (6.7.2)$$

Method (b) involves the use of the locally linear approximations to the diffusion equation and SDE discussed in Section 6.4C and 6.5B. In the notation of these sections

$$N^* = K, \tag{6.7.3}$$

$$a \equiv -\lambda \equiv -\left[\frac{dB}{dN} + \frac{dD}{dN}\right]_{N=N^*} = r, \tag{6.7.4}$$

$$Q \equiv B(N^*) + D(N^*) = 2rK \tag{6.7.5}$$

The linear approximation to the diffusion equation is thus (cf. equation (6.4.16))

$$\frac{\partial p(n, t)}{\partial n} = -\frac{\partial}{\partial n}\{-rnp(n, t) - rK\frac{\partial}{\partial n}p(n, t)\} \tag{6.7.6}$$

which has a stationary solution

$$p^*(n) \propto \exp\{-n^2/2K\}. \tag{6.7.7}$$

The linear estimates of mean population and fluctuation intensity are thus

$$m_c = N^* = K, \qquad \sigma_c^2 = K. \tag{6.7.8}$$

The same results can be obtained from the locally linear SDE (6.5.10) which for this model takes the form

$$dn = -rn \, dt + \eta(t)\sqrt{(2rK \, dt)} = -rn \, dt + \sqrt{(2rK)} \, d\omega(t), \tag{6.7.9}$$

where $\eta(t)$ is a normally distributed random variable with zero mean and unit variance. Direct calculation of the linear estimate of the mean population and the population variance is simply a matter of substitution in equations (6.5.11) and (6.5.16). The result is of course exactly the same as was obtained from the linearized diffusion equation. However, where more refined estimates of the mean population are required we can obtain these by noting (cf. equation (6.5.17)) that

$$f(N) = rN - \frac{rN^2}{K} = -rn - \frac{rn^2}{K} \tag{6.7.10}$$

Substitution of the linear estimates of σ_c^2 into equation (6.5.19) thus yields

$$E\{n\} = \frac{-1}{K}\{K + [E\{n\}]^2\}, \tag{6.7.11}$$

the relevant solution of which is

$$E\{n\} = \frac{K}{2}\left\{-1 + \sqrt{\left(1 - \frac{4}{K}\right)}\right\}. \tag{6.7.12}$$

Thus in this (better) approximation the mean population is

$$m_c = \frac{K}{2}\left\{1 + \sqrt{\left(1 - \frac{4}{K}\right)}\right\}. \tag{6.7.13}$$

The results obtained by these various procedures are summarized in Table 6.2, from which we see that for $K > 10$ our locally linear first approximation produces estimates for σ_c^2 and m_c which are within 2 per cent and 18 per cent respectively of the exact values. Thus although the linear approximations are detectably in error they are unlikely to be distinguishable from the exact values in the presence of the sort of experimental error normally encountered in field experiments. However, it is also clear that where high accuracy is needed, this can be provided by the more refined direct methods, which have here yielded estimates of m_c accurate to better than 0.2 per cent for $K \geqslant 10$ and good to 10 per cent even for $K = 5$.

Fourier transform methods

The results in the preceding section together with an estimate of the auto-covariance function can be derived by Fourier transformation of the linearized SDE (6.7.9). We write this equation in the style resembling an ordinary differential equation (cf. equation 6.5.20)), i.e.

$$\frac{dn}{dt} = -rn + \sqrt{(2rK)}\gamma(t) \tag{6.7.14}$$

where $\gamma(t)$ represents Gaussian white noise with unit spectral density, Fourier transformation yields (using equation (F32) to transform the derivative)

$$i\omega\tilde{n}(\omega) = -r\tilde{n}(\omega) + \sqrt{(2rK)}\tilde{\gamma}(\omega), \tag{6.7.15}$$

and hence

$$\tilde{n}(\omega) = \frac{\sqrt{(2rK)}\tilde{\gamma}(\omega)}{r + i\omega} \tag{6.7.16}$$

Table 6.2. Gross fluctuation characteristics for the 'logistic' birth and death model.

	Mean population m_c			Fluctuation intensity σ_c^2	
K	Exact	Linear approximation	Refined estimate	Exact	Linear approximation
5	4.00	5.00	3.62	4.42	5.0
10	8.86	10.00	8.87	10.16	10.0
15	13.91	15.00	13.92	15.1	15.0
20	18.94	20.00	18.94	20.1	20.0
30	28.96	30.00	28.96	30.0	30.0
60	58.98	60.00	58.98	60.0	60.0
100	98.99	100.00	98.99	100.0	100.0

Recalling the definition (equation (6.5.28)) of spectral density, and using the fact that $\gamma(t)$ represents white noise of unit spectral density, we find that the spectral density of the population fluctuation, $S_n(\omega)$, is

$$S_n(\omega) = \frac{2rK}{r^2 + \omega^2} \tag{6.7.17}$$

from which (cf. equations (6.5.35) and (6.5.39)) we deduce that

$$\sigma_c^2 = \frac{1}{2\pi} \int_{-\infty}^{\infty} \frac{2rK}{r^2 + \omega^2}\, d\omega = K, \tag{6.7.18}$$

in agreement with our previous derivations, and that

$$C(\tau) = Ke^{-r\tau}. \tag{6.7.19}$$

Realizations

Judiciously chosen numerical simulations are often of great assistance in gaining a broad understanding of a model's behaviour. To illustrate this point we now construct a number of individual realizations of the birth and death process described by equation (6.7.1), using the following procedure:

(a) Select a starting population N_0
(b) Choose a time increment dt such that $B(N)$dt and $D(N)$dt are both very much less than 1 over the entire range of populations likely to be encountered in the realization.
(c) Use a random-number generator (available in just about all computer libraries) or *in extremis* tables of random numbers, to generate a sequence of random numbers from a uniform distribution over the interval 0 to 1.

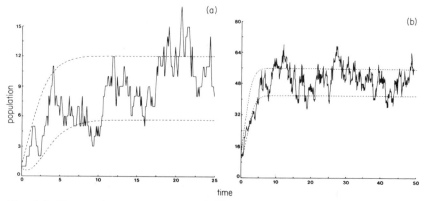

Fig. 6.5. Two realizations of the 'logistic' birth and death model. The broken lines represent the limits $m_c(t) \pm \sigma_c(t)$ within which we should 'normally' find the population. (a) $K = 10$, $N_0 = 1$. (b) $K = 50$, $N_0 = 10$.

(d)   At each time t, take the next random number (R) from the sequence. Then
    (i)   If $R < B(N)\mathrm{d}t$ change $N \to N + 1$
    (ii) If $R > 1 - D(N)\mathrm{d}t$ change $N \to N - 1$
    (iii) If $B(N)\mathrm{d}t \leqslant R \leqslant 1 - D(N)\mathrm{d}t$, do not change N.
(e)   Increment $t \to t + \mathrm{d}t$ and repeat step (4).

Figure 6.5 shows two realizations of the logistic model, one for $K = 10$, the other with $K = 50$. Both realizations illustrate the initial transient followed by the quasi-stationary state in which the population can 'normally' be found within the limits $m_c \pm \sigma_c$.

We can also use individual realizations to assess the robustness of our estimate (equation (6.7.19)) of the AC_oF by explicitly computing it for a number of values of K. Typical results are shown in Fig. 6.6 for a small value of $K(K = 10)$ and a large value $(K = 100)$. The robustness of the approximation (equation (6.7.19)) is obvious.

Extinction times

There are three practicable approaches to the problem of estimating the mean time to extinction for the population represented by this model

(a)   via the exact formula (6.6.19),
(b)   via the CPDF and equation (6.6.29),
(c)   via an analytic approximation to the CPDF.

We see no way of evaluating the exact formula for an arbitrary initial population N_0, but for the present model a rather promising approximation valid for large K can be obtained by arguing that when $N = 1$, the probability of a birth is K times greater than that of a death and the population is 'almost' certain to increase. Thus $\tau_E\{1\}$, the extinction time with an initial population of one, which is always a lower bound to the extinction time, may in this model be a reasonable estimate of its actual value. To compute $\tau_E\{1\}$, we first

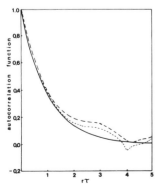

Fig. 6.6. Autocorrelation functions $(ACF = AC_oF/\sigma^2)$ for the 'logistic' birth and death model. Exact results from realizations with $K = 10$ (----) and K = 100 (----), are compared with the linear estimate (——). (Reproduced from Nisbet *et al.*, *Journal of Theoretical Biology*, **68**, 143–160. Copyright by Academic Press Inc. (London) Ltd.

evaluate the parameters q_i in equation (6.4.4) as

$$q_i = \frac{B(1)B(2)\ldots B(i-1)}{D(1)D(2)\ldots D(i)} = \frac{1}{r}\cdot\frac{K^i}{i(i!)}, \qquad i \geq 2, \qquad (6.7.20)$$

$$q_1 = 1/D(1) = K/r. \qquad (6.7.21)$$

Then we estimate the extinction time as (cf. equation (6.6.19))

$$\tau_E \sim \tau_E\{1\} = \frac{1}{r}\sum_{i=1}^{\infty}\frac{K^i}{i(i!)}. \qquad (6.7.22)$$

Summations of this sort are numerically troublesome unless K is small, and asymptotic forms are particularly useful. This particular series can be analysed by a method outline in Murray (1974, p. 6) to obtain

$$\sum_{i=1}^{\infty}\frac{K^i}{i(i!)} \sim K^{-1}e^K \qquad \text{as } K \to \infty. \qquad (6.7.23)$$

Thus our first estimate of τ_E is

$$\tau_E \simeq (rK)^{-1}e^K. \qquad (6.7.24)$$

The second route to the extinction time (via the CPDF) involves using the iterative procedure outlined in Section 6.4 to calculate the value of $P_c^*(1)$ for each value of K and then using the fundamental expression (6.6.29)

$$\tau_E = [D(1)P_c^*(1)]^{-1}. \qquad (6.7.25)$$

Finally, we can approximate the extinction time by one of the techniques in Section 6.6C involving 'guestimates' at the CPDF. The simplest, but least accurate, of these is to assume that the population probability distribution is a Gaussian, so that τ_E is related to the population mean m_c and variance σ_c by equation (6.6.44). Using the linear estimate for m_c and σ_c, given by equation (6.7.8), then yields

$$\ln(r\tau_E) = \frac{K}{2} - \ln\sqrt{K} - 0.226, \qquad (6.7.26)$$

while if we attempt to improve upon this by using the more refined estimate of m_c given by equation (6.7.13) we obtain

$$\ln(r\tau_E) = \frac{K}{2}\left[1 + \sqrt{\left(1 - \frac{4}{K}\right)}\right]^2 - \ln\sqrt{K} - 0.226. \qquad (6.7.27)$$

Secondly we can obtain a potentially more accurate estimate of the extinction time by assuming that the population probability distribution can be closely approximated by a negative binomial distribution so that τ_E, m_c and σ_c^2 are related by equation (6.6.34). In this case we find that using the linear estimates of m_c and σ_c^2 yields (with due attention to the limiting properties of the second term in equation (6.6.34))

$$\ln(r\tau_E) = K \tag{6.7.28}$$

while inserting the more refined estimate of m_c (6.7.13) leads to

$$\ln(r\tau_E) = \ln \frac{4K}{\left[1 + \sqrt{\left(1 - \frac{4}{K}\right)}\right]^2}$$

$$- \frac{K}{2} \frac{\left[1 + \sqrt{\left(1 - \frac{4}{K}\right)}\right]^2}{1 - \sqrt{\left(1 - \frac{4}{K}\right)}} \ln \frac{1 + \sqrt{\left(1 - \frac{4}{K}\right)}}{2}. \tag{6.7.29}$$

The results of all these procedures are shown in Table 6.3 (on page 210) from which it can be seen that as we might expect, the approximation (6.7.24) involving the exact expression for $\tau_E(1)$ and the 'exact' result (6.7.25) given an assumption of quasi-stationarity, are in close agreement. Regarding these values as 'correct' we can assess the analytic approximations, and it can immediately be seen that although the estimates made using the Gaussian assumption change in the right direction and might thus be suitable for comparative or qualitative studies they are systematically in considerable error even at large values of K. By contrast the estimates made using the negative binomial distribution both converge towards the exact result as K becomes large and in particular those made using the refined estimates of m_c are very respectable even for small values of K. This result serves to emphasize the point made earlier in the chapter that correct estimation of the detailed shape of the probability distribution at low values of N is the key to the accurate determination of τ_E.

We thus conclude that, while the crude analytic estimates of extinction time which are readily made using linear techniques are likely to be a useful first approximation of qualitative studies, the *only* completely reliable ways of calculating the absolute value of τ_E are either from the exact result (equation (6.6.19)) or by direct (numerical) calculation of the stationary conditional probability distribution. If a comprehensible and reasonably accurate *analytic* expression for τ_E is required this can almost always be obtained by fitting a suitable function to $P_c^*(N)$. If this procedure is followed, a natural first candidate will often be the negative binomial distribution, but it is vital to remember that there is no prior guarantee that the blind assumption of *any* specific probability distribution will lead to accurate results and it is essential to make appropriate checks on the accuracy of such analytic estimates by comparison with the results of direct numerical calculation.

B. A model with a lower unstable steady state

In order to demonstrate the limitations of techniques involving local linearization we now examine a birth and death model with two non-zero, deterministic steady states. For the model in Section 6.7A the birth and death prob-

Table 6.3. A comparison of extinction time estimates for the 'logistic' model.

Equation	Assumed conditional probability distribution	Estimate of m_c	Estimated value of $\ln r\tau_E$				
			$K = 5$	$K = 10$	$K = 20$	$K = 40$	$K = 80$
6.7.24	Not specified	Not required	3.39	7.70	17.0	36.3	75.6
6.7.25	Exact stationary	Not required	3.84	7.94	17.1	36.4	75.6
6.7.26	Gaussian	Linear	1.47	3.62	8.28	17.9	37.6
6.7.27	Gaussian	Refined	0.28	2.55	7.24	16.9	36.5
6.7.28	Negative binomial	Linear	5.00	10.0	20.0	40.0	80.0
6.7.29	Negative binomial	Refined	3.71	8.59	18.5	38.5	78.5

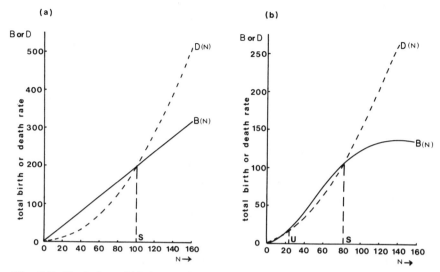

Fig. 6.7. Typical total birth and death rate functions for the models analysed in Section 6.7. The model of part (A) shown in (a), (equation (6.7.1)) has a single, deterministically stable, steady state S, while that of part (B), shown in (b), (equations (6.7.30) and (6.7.31)) has two stationary states: S (stable) and U (unstable)

abilities had the form shown in Fig. 6.7(a); the present model is an example with the form in Fig. 6.7(b). We discussed this situation in Chapter 1 and commented that the deterministic steady state in this case was locally, but not globally, stable since populations of less than U individuals decay to zero rather than increase to D.

In our example of this type of 'two-steady-state' model, we set

$$B(N) = q_1 N\{1 - \exp(-q_2 N)\} - q_3 N^2, \qquad (6.7.30)$$

$$D(N) = q_4 N + q_5 N^2 \qquad (6.7.31)$$

where q_1 to q_5 are constants. Deterministically, the population would follow the equation

$$\frac{dN}{dt} = rN[1 - \theta e^{-N/T} - N/K] \qquad (6.7.32)$$

where

$$r = q_1 - q_4, \qquad \theta = q_1(q_1 - q_4)^{-1}, \qquad T = q_2^{-1}, \qquad K = \frac{q_1 - q_4}{q_3 + q_5}. \qquad (6.7.33)$$

With some algebraic cunning, it can be shown that this model has two-non-zero deterministic steady states as in Fig. 6.7 provided

$$\frac{T}{K}\left[1 + \ln\left\{\frac{\theta K}{T}\right\}\right] < 1 \qquad (6.7.34)$$

and otherwise has no stationary state other than $N = 0$.

Provided the parameters are chosen to satisfy (6.7.34), the two non-zero stationary states can be found (numerically) as the solutions of

$$1 - \theta e^{-N^*/K} = N^*/K. \qquad (6.7.35)$$

Examination of Fig. 6.7(b) suggests that while the upper steady state N_s^* should always exhibit local (but not global) deterministic stability, the lower steady state N_u^* will invariably be deterministically unstable. These suppositions are immediately confirmed by the routine application of the techniques of Chapter 2.

We can now obtain the locally linear approximation to the stationary probability distribution by first using the techniques of Section 6.5 to calculate the mean and variance of the fluctuations about the deterministically stable stationary state

$$m_c \simeq N_s^* \qquad (6.7.36)$$

$$\sigma_c^2 \simeq \frac{q_4 N_s^* + q_5 N_s^{*2}}{2q_3 N_s^* + 2q_5 N_s^* - q_1\{1 + \exp[-q_2 N_s^*]\{q_2 N_s^* - 1\}\} + q_4} \qquad (6.7.37)$$

and then recalling that in this locally linear approximation the stationary probability distribution is a Gaussian with mean m_c and variance σ_c^2.

The accuracy of the linear approximation can now easily be assessed by using the numerical procedure described in Section 6.4 to calculate the exact discrete stationary conditional probability distribution (and hence exact values of m_c, σ^2, and τ_E) for various values of the model parameters. Because of the large number of parameters involved we have not performed exhaustive investigations of the precision of the linear approximation, but have instead only examined a series of values of q_2 with all other parameters being held constant.

We examine first the Gaussian approximation to the discrete probability distribution. It is clear from Fig. 6.8 that the exact discrete probability distribution is essentially unimodal and reasonably well approximated by a Gaussian, provided that the interval $(N_s^* - N_u^*)$ between the stable and unstable stationary states is large compared to the standard deviation of the fluctuations about the upper stationary state. If this is not so there is an appreciable probability that a chance fluctuation will take the population into the unstable region below N_u^*, causing deterministic extinction. The stationary probability distribution in such cases is clearly bimodal and thus very badly approximated by a Gaussian.

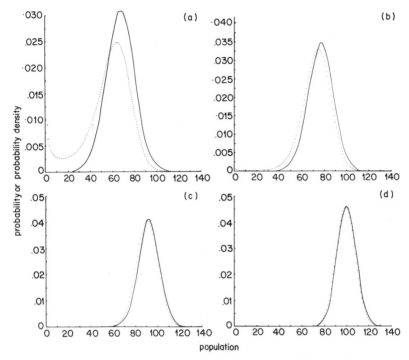

Fig. 6.8. Exact and approximate quasi-stationary probability distributions for the 'two-steady-state model'. .... denotes the exact distribution, —— the Gaussian approximation. (a) $N_s^* = 67.8$, $N_u^* = 26.7$, $\sigma_c = 20.7$. (b) $N_s^* = 77$, $N_u^* = 21$, $\sigma_c = 13.1$. (c) $N_s^* = 92.1$, $N_u^* = 11.5$, $\sigma_c = 9.8$. (d) $N_s^* = 100$, $N_u^* = 0.002$, $\sigma_c = 8.7$.

Fig. 6.9 shows a comparison of exact and approximate results for the relative fluctuation amplitude σ_c/m_c. As we would expect from the discussion above, our locally linear estimates are respectable so long as the fluctuations are small enough to make the probability of an excursion below N_u^* very unlikely. For the values of the parameters examined here this is so as long as σ_c/m_c is less than about 0.2, so that the performance of our linear estimator does not look greatly inferior to its performance in the analysis of the logistic model of Section 6.7A. However, it is clear that this outcome rests strongly on the exact choice of parameter values: a choice which placed N_s^* and N_u^* closer together would make the picture dramatically worse.

Finally we use the approximate value of σ_c^2 (equation (6.7.37)) to obtain a crude estimate of the mean time to extinction τ_E (cf. equation (6.6.44)), namely

$$\tau_E = \frac{2}{(q_1 + q_4)\sigma_c\sqrt{(2\pi)}} \exp\{N_s^{*2}/2\sigma_c^2\}, \qquad (6.7.38)$$

and in Table 6.4 we compare these values with the exact results calculated from the stationary CPDF using equation (6.6.29). It is clear from these

214

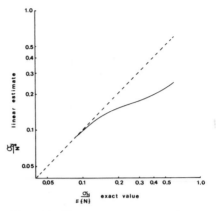

Fig. 6.9. Exact versus approximate values for the relative fluctuation amplitude σ_c/m_c in the two steady state model with $q_1 = 2.5$, $q_3 = q_5 = 0.01$, $q_4 = 0.5$ and q_2 varying.

results that (6.7.38) is a poor approximation to the extinction time except where σ_c/m_c is very small indeed. In view of the crucial dependence of the mean time to extinction on the detailed shape of the stationary CPDF near $N = 1$, this is entirely to be expected.

We conclude that for models with multiple steady states, linear estimates of gross fluctuation characteristics may often provide at least a rough guide to the behaviour of the system, although they must be used with caution and should ideally be systematically cross checked with exact numerical calculations. However, locally linear extinction-time estimates for such models, must be treated with the most extreme caution, and the only really safe course is to use the direct numerical method of Section 6.4 to calculate the CPDF, and then obtain the extinction time from

$$\tau_E = [D(1)P_c^*(1)]^{-1}. \tag{6.7.39}$$

6.8 POPULATION DYNAMICS IN PATCHY ENVIRONMENTS

Although our main interest in the mathematics of birth and death processes derives from applications to the dynamics of homogeneous populations, there are other ecologically important contexts in which the same techniques may be used. All that is required is a quantity which takes integer values, and which changes with time by way of a succession of steps of ± 1, the timing of individual steps being probabilistically controlled. To illustrate this, and to prepare the ground for the case study in Chapter 10, we now discuss one such 'unnatural' application of the formalism, involving the 'discrete-state' representation of populations in patchy environments introduced in Section 5.2C.

Table 6.4. Extinction time estimates for the 'two steady state model' with $q_1 = 2.5$, $q_3 = q_5 = 0.01$, $q_4 = 0.5$.

q_2	1.0	0.25	0.1	0.05	0.035	0.030	0.026	0.021	0.019
σ_c/m_c linear estimate	0.087	0.087	0.087	0.089	0.097	0.105	0.117	0.163	0.025
$\ln \tau_E$ exact	69.7	66.0	57.4	42.0	28.8	22.0	15.3	5.2	3.5
$\ln \tau_E$ equation (6.7.38)	62.5	62.5	62.3	58.7	48.8	41.3	32.2	14.3	3.20

A. The prototype model

We recall that in this type of model we are concerned with the balance between colonization and extinction and not with the detailed dynamics on a particular patch. We consider an arena of M identical patches of which at any time t a number $Q(t)$ are occupied and $E(t)$ ($\equiv M - Q(t)$) are empty. We assume that in an infinitesimally small time interval dt the probability of successful colonization of an empty patch is (cf. equation (5.2.17))

$$P_c(Q)\, dt = \tau_c^{-1} Q(M - Q)\, dt. \qquad (6.8.1)$$

We further assume that over the same time interval dt, the probability of extinction on an occupied patch is (cf. equation (5.2.18))

$$P_E(Q)\, dt = \tau_L^{-1} Q\, dt, \qquad (6.8.2)$$

where τ_L is the mean lifetime of a colony on a single site. We shall not repeat the discussion of these assumptions in Chapter 5 except to reiterate that equation (6.8.1) implies that all occupied patches, irrespective of their location, have equal probability of providing colonists for a particular empty patch, while (6.8.2) has little to commend it except maximal mathematical simplicity, a point to which we shall return in section 6.8B.

With these assumptions, an arena of M patches which at time t has Q occupied patches will at time $t + dt$ have either:

(a) $Q + 1$ occupied patches with probability $P_c(Q)dt$,
(b) $Q - 1$ occupied patches with probability $P_E(Q)dt$,
(c) Q occupied patches with probability $1 - [P_c(Q) + P_E(Q)]dt$.

This is *exactly* the mathematical situation we encountered in Section 6.2 and analysed in the next few sections. In the spirit of these investigations we now try to obtain a robust approximation of the statistics of patch occupancy by pretending that $Q(t)$ is a continuous variable whose dynamics are described by the stochastic differential equation (cf. equation (6.2.39))

$$dQ(t) = \{P_c(Q) - P_E(Q)\}\, dt + \{P_c(Q) + P_E(Q)\}^{1/2}\, d\omega(t) \qquad (6.8.3)$$

We further approximate by linearizing equation (6.8.3) about the steady state occupancy Q^*, which is given by (cf. equation (5.2.23))

$$Q^* = M - \tau_c/\tau_L, \qquad (6.8.4)$$

and finding (with $q \equiv Q - Q^*$)

$$dq(t) = -aq(t) + b^{1/2}\, d\omega(t), \qquad (6.8.5)$$

where

$$a = \tau_L^{-1}[Q^*/(M - Q^*)], \qquad b = 2Q^*/\tau_L \qquad (6.8.6)$$

This SDE is identical to equation (6.5.10) whose properties have now been investigated by a superfluity of methods. Thus the intensity of the fluctuations in patch occupancy is (cf. equation (6.5.16))

$$\sigma_Q^2 \equiv E\{[Q - Q^*]^2\} = b/2a = M - Q^*, \qquad (6.8.7)$$

while the spectral density and AC_oF are (cf. equation (6.5.30) and (6.5.40))

$$S(\omega) = \frac{b}{a^2 + \omega^2}, \qquad C(\tau) = \sigma_Q^2 e^{-a\tau}. \qquad (6.8.8)$$

Extinction in this model occurs if all the patches become empty simultaneously. As the population contains no obvious mechanism for synchronizing the dynamics of different patches, we should expect the mean time to extinction of the entire system to increase very rapidly with M, the total number of patches. To demonstrate this, we invoke the argument of Section 6.6 that an acceptable qualitative description of extinction can be obtained from the relative fluctuation intensity σ_Q^2/Q^{*2} which has the form (deduced from equation (6.8.7))

$$\frac{\sigma_Q^2}{Q^{*2}} = \frac{(M - Q^*)}{Q^{*2}} \qquad (6.8.9)$$

It is clear from equation (6.8.9) that as the average fraction of occupied patches decreases, there comes a point where the relative fluctuation intensity grows steeply, implying rapid extinction. In the crudest approximation equation (6.6.46) the time to extinction is given *very* roughly by

$$\tau_E \simeq \tau_L \exp\left\{\frac{Q^{*2}}{2(M - Q^*)}\right\} \qquad (6.8.10)$$

and thus for the entire system to persist (say) of the order of 100 times longer than the population on a single patch we would require (assuming M reasonably large)

$$\frac{Q^*}{M} \le 3M^{-1/2}. \qquad (6.8.11)$$

Refining our estimate of extinction time and changing our arbitrary criterion for persistence (to say $\tau_E = 50\tau_L$ or $1000\ \tau_L$) changes the constant in equation (6.8.11), but we can safely conclude that in this model, population persistence achieved through a balance between colonization and extinction is only possible if the average proportion of occupied patches is greater than a critical minimum value of order of magnitude $M^{-1/2}$.

B. Robustness

This grotesquely oversimple model can only be of any scientific value if its main predictions survive when the model is modified or elaborated to add increased realism. This requirement that the *model* be robust against structural changes is of course additional to the need for robustness of any mathematical approximations made in its analysis. However, the work discussed earlier in the chapter (supported by numerical checks on this model) gives us confidence in the robustness of the approximations involving local linearization, so we now turn our attention to the question of robustness of the model itself.

By far the most questionable features of the prototype model are the assumptions:

(a) that the population of a patch has a constant probability per unit time (independent of its past history) of becoming extinct.
(b) that all patches, irrespective of their geographical location, are equally likely to provide colonists to a particular patch.

We recently devoted a paper (Gurney and Nisbet, 1978a) to the effects of these and other approximations so we shall confine ourselves to restating the principal results of that investigation.

To assess the importance of the detailed dynamics of extinction on a particular patch, we constructed a model identical in all respects to the prototype except that the population on each patch persisted for a *fixed lifetime* τ_L. We found that, to within the accuracy of a numerical integration that arose in the calculation (0.1%!), the relationship (6.8.7) between mean patch occupancy and fluctuation intensity was unchanged. All that was changed was the temporal structure (as represented by the spectral density function or the AC_oF) of the fluctuation in occupancy, the fixed lifetime having a (predictably) noticeable effect in situations where $Q/^*M$ approached 1, implying almost all

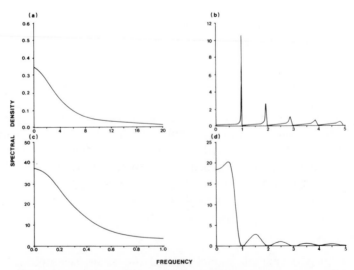

Fig. 6.10. Plots of spectral density against frequency ($f = \omega/2\pi$) for the fluctuations in patch occupancy in the prototype model ((a) and (c)) and in the single lifetime model ((b) and (d)) with $M = 100$, $Q^* = 96$ ((a) and (b)), $Q^* = 65$ ((c) and (d)).

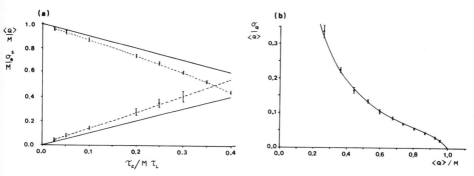

Fig. 6.11. Comparison of the behaviour of the prototype model (———) with that of a model postulating only nearest neighbour colonization (ⵏ). (a) Plot of average occupancy and fluctuation intensity against τ_L. (b) Plot of relative fluctuation amplitude against average occupancy.

sites were occupied at any given time. Examples of the relevant spectral density functions are shown in Fig. 6.10.

To assess the importance of the 'geographical' assumption (b) we studied a variant of our prototype model resembling the 'stepping-stone' models used in population genetics. We assumed that the patches were arranged on a two-dimensional square grid but that an empty patch could only receive colonists from a populated *nearest-neighbour* patch. Thus the probability that a potentially colonizable patch is in fact colonized during a time interval dt is proportional to the number of its nearest neighbours which are occupied. Extinction was still described by equation (6.8.2) implying a constant probability per unit time of extinction of a specified occupied patch. The resulting model was (and is!) well beyond our analytic capabilities, so we constructed a large number of numerical realizations from which we deduced the statistics of patch occupancy. Some results for a 10×10 grid are reproduced in Fig. 6.11 where we see (graph (a)) that there is a systematic discrepancy of up to 40 per cent between the 'stepping-stone' model and our prototype. This discrepancy is largely due to edge-effects—36 of the 100 patches do not have 4 nearest neighbours and are thus 'anomalous'—but clearly it will be important for all but the largest values of M. However, the interrelation between the fluctuation intensity and the mean patch occupancy is, within statistical uncertainty, unchanged from the prototype model (graph (b)) and we thus have considerable confidence that the criterion for persistence (equation (6.8.11)) should be applicable, irrespective of the detailed mechanism of recolonization of an empty patch.

SOURCES AND SUGGESTED FURTHER READING

General theory of non-linear birth and death processes: This is covered in many texts on stochastic processes—we found Karlin and Taylor (1975), pp. 131–150, particularly readable and informative especially on extinction.

Goel and Richter-Dyn (1974) combine a wide-ranging survey of theory with a number of applications. The first two chapters of Pielou (1969) constitute a very readable introduction to both density-dependent and density-independent birth and death processes but the mathematical methods are not pursued in depth.

Exactly Soluble Models: These have been studied by an impressive array of statisticians. Chapter 1 of Goel and Richter-Dyn (1974) contains a useful summary of results and sources.

Nonlinear Models: Interest in the formulation of non-linear birth and death models, exact numerical investigation of their properties, and the development of analytic approximations appears to date from the work by Bartlett (e.g. Bartlett 1957, 1960, 1966; Bartlett, Gower, and Leslie, 1960). Bartlett's contributions include the use of local linearization to approximate gross fluctuation characteristics estimation of extinction times by extrapolating a probability distribution to $N = 0$.

Patchy Environments: The treatment in Section 6.8 follows Gurney and Nisbet (1978a). Computer simulations of this type of model have been reported by Maynard Smith (1974), Hilborn (1975), Gilpin (1975) and Zeigler (1976).

References on diffusion approximations and stochastic differential equations are given in Chapter 7, and on Fourier analysis in Appendix F.

PROBLEMS

(Those marked * are mathematically more demanding than the others.)

1. (de Angelis, 1976). The population of the Giant Canada Goose at Waubay National Wildlife Refuge, South Dakota was censused once per year in spring from 1945–1962 with the result

    $$m = 159, \qquad \sigma_N^2 = 3710$$

    To investigate these fluctuations de Angelis considered a birth and death model with

    $$B(N) = a_1 N - b_1 N^2, \quad D(N) = a_2 N + b_2 N^2$$

    (a) Show that for this model, to a good approximation

    $$\sigma_N^2 = \frac{a\gamma}{2b^2}, \qquad m = \frac{a}{b} - \frac{b\sigma_N^2}{a}$$

    where $a = a_1 = a_2$ $\quad b = b_1 + b_2,$ $\quad \gamma = (b/a)(a_1 + a_2) - (b_1 - b_2)$

    (b) The best fit to the proposed birth and death rates for this population gave

$a_1 = 0.81,$ $a_2 = 0.061,$ $b_1 = 0.00025,$ $b_2 = 0.00016.$

(Note: there is a sign error in b_1 on p. 233 of original paper). Show that the model predicts a fluctuation intensity much smaller than is observed and suggest reasons for the discrepancy.

2. (Scott and Rines 1975). Sir Peter Scott, Robert Rines and every travel agent within 200 miles of Loch Ness would like us to believe that a small population of *Nessiteras rhombopteryx* has persisted for up to 12 000 years in Loch Ness. If Nessie's population dynamics were given by the model of Section 6.6.A what is the minimum value of K (the carrying capacity of Loch Ness) that would make likely such persistence if the mean lifetime of an individual *Nessiteras* in uncrowded conditions were, (a) 2 years, (b) 10 years, (c) 50 years.

3. The model in Section 6.6A had density-dependent mortality but density-independent fertility. If a population were regulated solely through its birth-rate a possible representation would have

$$B(N) = \begin{cases} \alpha N - \beta N^2, & N < \alpha/\beta \\ 0, & N \geq \alpha/\beta \end{cases}, \qquad D(N) = \delta N, \alpha > \delta.$$

where α, β, δ are constants

(a) Calculate the linear estimates of mean population and of fluctuation intensity.
(b) Calculate the crude estimate (6.6.46) of the mean time to extinction and attempt to refine this estimate by using a suitable, discrete probability distribution to fit the mean and variance.

4. (MacArthur and Wilson, 1963; Goel and Richter-Dyn, 1974). The following model purports to describe the dynamics of the total *number S* of bird species present on an island. We let $C(S)dt$ and $E(S)dt$ be the probabilities during dt of respectively successful colonization by a new species and extinction of an existing species. We assume the source of colonists is a 'pool' of S_T species and set

$$C(S) = \begin{cases} \beta(S_T - S), & S < S_T \\ 0, & S \geq S_T \end{cases}, \qquad E(S) = \delta S.$$

By making a suitable linear approximation, show that the relative magnitude of the fluctuations in S is approximately

$$\frac{\sigma_S^2}{S^{*2}} = \frac{\delta}{\beta S_T}.$$

The following two problems are intended to illustrate the relationship between the deterministic and stochastic models of a declining population approaching extinction.

5. Consider a population in which all recruitment has ceased, modelled as a birth and death process with

$$B(N) = 0, \qquad D(N) = \delta N$$

(a) Using Table 6.1 and equation (6.6.24) show that if at time $t = 0$ the population is N_0 then the extinction time is

$$\tau_E\{N_0\} = \int_0^\infty [1 - (1 - e^{-\delta t})^{N_0}] \, dt$$

(b) With the aid of a suitable change of variable (such as $u = 1 - \exp\{-\delta t\}$) evaluate this integral to show that

$$\tau_E\{N_0\} = \frac{1}{\delta} \sum_{i=1}^{N_0} \frac{1}{i}$$

(c) Hence show that for large values of N_0, the mean time to extinction is approximately $\delta^{-1} \ln N_0$, which is equal to the time required for the analogous deterministic model population to decline in size from N_0 to 1.

[Mathematical hints:

(i) $\dfrac{1 - x^{N_0}}{1 - x} = 1 + x + x^2 + \ldots + x^{N_0 - 1}$ \qquad for any x

(ii) $\displaystyle\sum_{i=1}^{N_0} \frac{1}{q} \sim \ln N_0$ \qquad as $N_0 \to \infty$.

6.* Consider a birth and death model with

$$B(N) = \beta N, \qquad D(N) = \delta N,$$

(a) Show that if $N = 1$ at $t = 0$, then the mean time to extinction is

$$\tau_E\{1\} = -\frac{1}{\beta} \ln\left(1 - \frac{\beta}{\delta}\right)$$

(b) Using Table 6.1 and equation (6.6.24), show that if at time $t = 0$, the population is N_0, then

$$\tau_E\{N_0\} = \frac{1}{\delta} \sum_{j=0}^\infty \left(\frac{\beta}{\delta}\right)^j \sum_{i=0}^{N_0-1} \frac{1}{i+j+1}.$$

(c) Hence show that

$$\tau_E\{N_0\} < \frac{\ln N_0}{(\beta - \delta)}.$$

7.* (Gurney and Nisbet, 1978a). The 'prototype' model of population dynamics in a patchy environment can be modified to incorporate a 'dead' or 'unavailable' phase between extinction of a patch population through over-exploitation of resources and recovery of the patch sufficiently to permit successful recolonization. We now recognize three possible patch states (empty and available, occupied, and 'dead') and imagine a 'universe' of M sites, of which Q are occupied and U are dead. We assume that during dt, the probability that one of the U dead sites recovers is

$$P_R(U)\,dt = \tau_D^{-1}U\,dt,$$

that one of the Q occupied sites goes extinct is

$$P_E(Q)\,dt = \tau_L^{-1}Q\,dt,$$

and that one of the $[M - Q - U]$ available sites becomes successfully colonized is

$$P_c(Q, U)\,dt = (M\tau_c)^{-1}Q(M - U - Q)\,dt$$

(a) Show that the evolution of $Q(t)$, $U(t)$ can be described by a pair of coupled stochastic differential equations with deterministic steady states

$$Q^* = \frac{M(1 - \tau_c/\tau_L)}{(1 + \tau_D/\tau_L)} \qquad U^* = \frac{M(1 - \tau_c/\tau_L)}{(1 + \tau_L/\tau_D)}$$

(b) Linearize about this steady state to show that small deviations $q(= Q - Q^*)$ and $u(= U - U^*)$ obey the SDEs

$$\dot{q} = -(Q^*/M\tau_c)(q + u) + (Q^*/\tau_L)^{1/2}(\gamma_1 - \gamma_2)$$

$$\dot{u} = -u/\tau_D - q/\tau_L + (Q^*/\tau_L)^{1/2}(\gamma_2 - \gamma_3)$$

where γ_1, γ_2, γ_3 are independent white-noise terms of unit spectral density.

(c) By Fourier transforming these equations and noting that $E\{\tilde{\gamma}_i^*\tilde{\gamma}_j\} = 0$ unless $i = j$, show that the spectral density of the fluctuations in $Q(t)$, the patch occupancy, is

$$S_Q(\omega) = \frac{(2Q^*/\tau_L)(A + \omega^2)}{(\omega_0^2 - \omega^2) + \beta^2\omega^2}$$

where

$$A = (Q^*/M\tau_c)^2 + \tau_D^{-2} + Q^*/M\tau_c\tau_D$$

$$\omega_0^2 = (Q^*/M\tau_c)(\tau_D^{-1} + \tau_L^{-1})$$

$$\beta = Q^*/M\tau_c + \tau_D^{-1}$$

(d) Hence calculate the intensity of fluctuations in patch occupancy (the necessary integral is in Table 7.2) and show (by direct calculation for a few selected values of τ_D) that unless τ_D (the mean recovery time) is significantly greater than τ_L (the mean duration of the population on a single patch), the plot of σ_0/Q^* against Q^*/M is not significantly different from Fig. 6.11b. This is further confirmation of the robustness of the prototype model.

Chapter 7

Variable Environments

7.1 INTRODUCTION

Chapter 6 yielded a recipe for calculating the various characteristics of fluctuations due to demographic stochasticity, but it was evident from the examples studied that the relative intensity of these fluctuations typically scales inversely with mean population and is thus very small in the vast majority of natural populations. In this chapter we therefore extend our repertoire of modelling techniques to cover fluctuations driven by environmental variability, which in all but the most stable environments will swamp the effects of demographic stochasticity.

Historically, most 'strategic' studies of the effects of environmental variability on population dynamics have proceeded by an heuristic approach in which one or more of the parameters in a deterministic equation are permitted to 'wobble' and the resulting population fluctuations studied. This approach is useful (and indeed is the source of most existing insights on the consequences of variable environments) but it has severe limitations which become most apparent when questions of extinction arise. Because of these difficulties we approach the question of environmentally driven fluctuations rather cautiously through successive modifications of the basic formalism of birth and death processes, first to cover deterministic environmental variations (Section 7.2) and then to incorporate environmental stochasticity (Section 7.3). Even in this development, we are forced to compromise on mathematical rigour but at least the assumptions made are well defined.

Although the mathematics in Sections 7.2 and 7.3A and B is seldom immediately applicable, it constitutes the foundation from which, in Section 7.3D, we develop heuristic methods of estimating fluctuation intensities and extinction times. The recipes in this section are based on local linearization, and are in many respects the crux of our analytic treatment of stochastic models. Notwithstanding the somewhat abstruse nature of the preceding mathematical theory, they are really very easy to apply and the majority of the problems at the end of the chapter have the objective of providing practice in their use. The locally linear approximation is also the natural context in

225

which to discuss the question of quasi-repetitive disturbances. Thus in Section 7.4 we examine the description and modelling of quasi-cycles in homogeneous populations, while in Section 7.5 we give a parallel treatment of 'wave-like' disturbances in spatially distributed systems.

Having shown in Section 7.3 that the exact study of non-linear birth and death processes in a randomly varying environment is fraught with great difficulty, we explore in Section 7.6 the possibility of developing a more tractable approximate treatment based upon stochastic differential equations. Our broad conclusions are that although locally linear approximations in this vein are rather robust the pitfalls associated with the inclusion of even the simplest non-linearity render such extensions almost worthless. Thus, in cases where non-linear dynamics are central to the problem we advocate the rejection of the apparently convenient fiction of environmental randomness and a return to the well-defined, if tedious, methods of Section 7.2.

This chapter completes our exposition of modelling techniques, the remainder of the book being devoted to case studies. Because of the somewhat underdeveloped state of the art, our treatment of stochastic models has unavoidably taken the form of a compendium of techniques, all of which are unsatisfatory in some respects. There is thus a danger that mastering the route(s) through the mathematical maze becomes an end in itself that deflects attention from the business in hand which is the construction and interpretation of models. We therefore conclude with a brief overview (section 7.7) of modelling strategy in which we step back from the technicalities and discuss the sequence of decisions involved in the construction and analysis of stochastic models.

7.2 SINGLE-SPECIES MODELS WITH ENVIRONMENTAL VARIABILITY

A. Exact calculations

Chapter 6 was devoted to an analysis of the very restrictive class of birth and death models in which the probabilities of a birth or death do not depend explicitly on time. To incorporate environmental variability into the models we assume that some time-dependent, external factor $\phi(t)$ influences the probabilities per unit time of a birth or death. The effect of this is to introduce 'driving' into the differential equations (6.2.3)–(6.2.5) that describe the temporal development of the population probability distribution; written out in full for a closed population these equations now become

$$\frac{dP(0, t)}{dt} = P(1, t)D(1, \phi(t)), \tag{7.2.1}$$

$$\frac{dP(1, t)}{dt} = P(2, t)D(2, \phi(t)) - P(1, t)\{B(1, \phi(t)) + D(1, \phi(t))\} \tag{7.2.2}$$

$$\frac{dP(N,t)}{dt} = P(N+1,t)D(N+1,\phi(t)) + P(N-1,t)B(N-1,\phi(t))$$
$$- P(N,t)\{B(N,\phi(t)) + D(N,\phi(t))\}. \qquad (7.2.3)$$

From a knowledge of $P(N,t)$ we can of course calculate the various characteristics of the population fluctuations. We recall that the mean population and the population variance are defined as expectation values, i.e. as averages over the instantaneous states of a large number of replicate populations, namely

$$m(t) \equiv E\{N(t)\} = \sum_{N=0}^{\infty} N(t)P(N,t), \qquad (7.2.4)$$

$$\sigma^2(t) \equiv E\{[N(t) - m(t)]^2\} = \sum_{N=0}^{\infty} [N(t)]^2 P(N,t) - [m(t)]^2, \qquad (7.2.5)$$

and in a varying environment, these quantities fluctuate in response to the driving term $\phi(t)$. However, as was the case in a static environment, provided the density dependence of the vital rates precludes unlimited growth, the solution of the differential equations for the population probability is characterized by monotonic increase in $P(0,t)$, the probability of extinction by time t, and a simultaneous decline to zero of the other probabilities $P(N,t)$, $N \neq 0$. Both the probability of extinction and the nature of the variations in the surviving replicate populations are thus influenced by the driving term $\phi(t)$, but the quantities $m(t)$ and $\sigma^2(t)$ embody both effects in a somewhat confusing manner. It is therefore advantageous to separate the two effects by again defining a conditional probability distribution function (CPDF) which represents the fraction of *non-extinct* replicates containing a given number of individuals. The conditional mean and variance are then defined (as previously) by

$$m_c(t) \equiv E_c\{N(t)\} = \sum_{N=1}^{\infty} N(t)P_c(N,t) = m(t)/(1 - P(0,t)), \qquad (7.2.6)$$

$$\sigma_c^2(t) \equiv E_c\{[N(t) - m(t)]^2\} = \sum_{N=1}^{\infty} [N(t)]^2 P_c(N,t) - [m(t)]^2$$
$$= \sigma^2(t)/(1 - P(0,t)). \qquad (7.2.7)$$

A simple example provides a clear illustration of the benefits of separating the questions of characterizing fluctuations and predicting extinction. We consider the 'logistic' model of Section 6.7A but assume a sinusoidal variation in the death probabilities. Thus we solve numerically the differential equations (7.2.1)–(7.2.3) with

$$B(N) = rN; \qquad D(N, \phi(t)) = \frac{rN^2}{K}(1 + \phi(t)), \qquad (7.2.8)$$

where

$$\phi(t) = b \cos \omega t. \qquad (7.2.9)$$

228

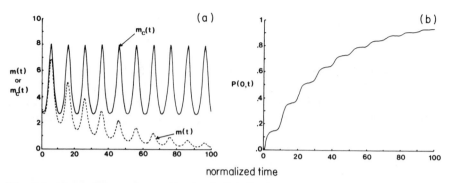

Fig. 7.1. Numerical results for the 'logistic' time-dependent, birth and death model defined by equations (7.2.8) and (7.2.9) with $K = 5, a = 0.6, f = \omega/2\pi = 0.1r$. We set $P(3,0) = 1$, representing a situation where each replicate initially contained exactly three individuals. In graph (a) we display mean population $m(t)$ (-----) and conditional mean population $m_c(t)$ (———). In graph (b) we show the time development of the extinction probability $P(0,t)$.

The conclusions from one such calculation are shown in Fig. 7.1. The very small 'carrying capacity' K was chosen so as to emphasize the decline in the mean population $m(t)$ in contrast with the persisting oscillations in the conditional mean, both of which are evident in Fig. 7.1(a). Figure 7.1(b) shows the effect of the environmental variation on the probability of extinction; $P(0, t)$ can only increase with time as extinction of a closed population is irreversible, but it increases in a series of steps which coincide with the times when the population is expected to drop to low values. These statistical properties, which of course refer to large numbers of replicate populations, are reflected in the behaviour of single populations, and Fig. 7.2 illustrates the behaviour

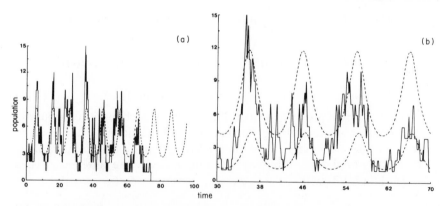

Fig. 7.2. A single realization of the driven 'logistic' birth and death model with the same choice of parameters as in Fig. 7.1. (a) The entire time-history of the population (———) compared with the conditional mean (-----). (b) Part of the time history of the population (———) compared with the heuristic limits $m_c(t) \pm \sigma_c(t)$ (-----) within which we might 'normally' expect to find the population.

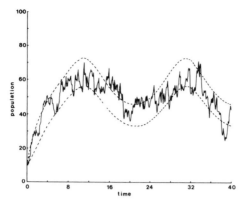

Fig. 7.3. A single realization (——) of the driven logistic birth and death process with $K = 50$, $a = 0.25$, $f = \omega/2\pi = 0.05r$. The realization was started with $N = 10$ at $t = 0$. The broken lines are the heuristic limits $m_c(t) \pm \sigma_c(t)$ within which we should 'normally' expect to find the population size.

of a single realization of the model with the same parameters as in Fig. 7.1, while Fig. 7.3 illustrates the behaviour of a much large population with smaller demographic fluctuations. If the population probability distribution were normal, we would expect a non-extinct replicate to spend of the order of two thirds of its time within the limits $m_c(t) \pm \tau_c(t)$ (one standard deviation above and below the mean). The skewness of the real PDF should not affect this observation overmuch and it is evident that the realizations in Figs. 7.2 and 7.3 behave very much in accordance with this prediction.

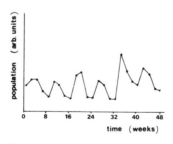

Fig. 7.4. Mean population of six replicates of a system in which *Tribolium castaneum* was supplied with food at a rate which varied as a square wave with a period of 8 weeks. (From Jillson, 1980.) (Reprinted by permission from *Nature*, **288**, 699–700. Copyright © 1980 Macmillan Journals Limited.)

Lest the theory so far appear somewhat distant from biological reality, we conclude this section by mentioning some experiments by Jillson (1980) in which a number of replicate populations of the flour beetle *Tribolium castaneum* were cultured in an environment where the rate of supply of medium (flour plus brewer's yeast) was initially held constant at 20 g per fortnight and then switched periodically between 32 g per fortnight and 8 g per fortnight. The set-up can (very) loosely be visualized as an implementation of 'square-wave' variations in carrying capacity. Without going to the length of constructing a detailed model of these experiments, we can at this point usefully note, first, the similarity of Jillson's experimental and our theoretical systems (both involving a number of distinct replicate populations subjected to the same environmental variation), and secondly, the similarity of the qualitative behaviour of the experimental mean population (shown in Fig. 7.4) to that in the driven birth and death model (see Figs. 7.1 and 7.3).

B. Approximate calculation of gross fluctuation characteristics

The preceding section contains a rigorous recipe for the exact calculation of gross fluctuation characteristics, but as it involves an infinite (or after truncation, very large) set of differential equations which do not appear amenable to much analytic simplification, such exact calculation requires a formidable quantity of numerical work unless the populations being modelled are exceptionally small. With larger populations, it is clearly desirable to develop approximations in which population is regarded as a continuous variable for all purposes except the calculation of extinction probabilities. When modelling populations in static environments, the most useful approximations of this type involved a stochastic differential equation (SDE) and we now extend this formalism to cover the case of a varying environment.

Given explicit time dependence of the birth and death probabilities through the external parameter $\phi(t)$, the continuous SDE still takes the form which we derived as equation (6.2.39) for a static environment, namely

$$dN(t) = \{B(N, \phi(t)) - D(N, \phi(t))\} \, dt + \{B(N, \phi(t)) + D(N, \phi(t))\}^{1/2} \, d\omega(t).$$

$$(7.2.10)$$

The corresponding diffusion equation is spectacularly intractable because of the explicit time dependence of B and D, and there is thus no serious prospect of calculating the evolution with time of even the continuous approximation to the true discrete population probability distribution. However, we saw in Chapter 6 that, for small demographic fluctuations about a deterministic steady state, there was a variety of locally linear methods of deriving the gross fluctuation characteristics without first obtaining the probability distribution. Since deterministic variations in total birth and death rates can similarly be treated through local linearization (see e.g. the discussion of transfer functions in Chapter 2), an obvious approach to treating the combined effects of demographic stochasticity and environmental variability would appear to be linearization of equation (7.2.10) about the deterministic steady state N^* that would arise if $\phi(t)$ remained constant at its mean value ϕ^*. Retaining the notation of previous chapters and setting

$$n(t) \equiv N(t) - N^*, \qquad f(t) \equiv \phi(t) - \phi^*, \tag{7.2.11}$$

we obtain after linearization

$$dn(t) = \lambda n(t)dt + \alpha f(t)dt + Q^{1/2}d\omega(t), \tag{7.2.12}$$

where

$$\lambda \equiv \left[\frac{\partial B}{\partial N} - \frac{\partial D}{\partial N} \right]_{\substack{N=N^* \\ \phi=\phi^*}}, \qquad \alpha \equiv \left[\frac{\partial B}{\partial \phi} - \frac{\partial D}{\partial \phi} \right]_{\substack{N=N^* \\ \phi=\phi^*}}, \tag{7.2.13}$$

$$Q \equiv B(N^*, \phi^*) + D(N^*, \phi^*).$$

Provided the deterministic steady state is stable ($\lambda < 0$), the solution of the linearized equation (7.2.12) is the sum of a transient initial condition-dependent term which eventually decays towards zero, and a persisting term which represents the combined demographic and externally driven fluctuations. The latter is normally our main concern and it is most easily derived by recasting (7.2.12) in the style

$$\frac{dn}{dt} = \lambda n + \alpha f(t) + Q^{1/2}\gamma(t) \tag{7.2.14}$$

with $\gamma(t)$ representing Gaussian white noise of unit spectral density, and then Fourier transforming to obtain after a little algebraic juggling

$$\tilde{n}(\omega) = \frac{\alpha \tilde{f}(\omega)}{i\omega - \lambda} + \frac{Q^{1/2}\tilde{\gamma}(\omega)}{i\omega - \lambda}. \tag{7.2.15}$$

As we argued in Section 6.5, the spectral density of fluctuations containing a non-deterministic component is most conveniently defined as the expectation value of the spectral density discussed in Appendix F. Thus, from equation (7.2.15), we deduce that the spectral density of the population fluctuations is given by

$$S_n(\omega) = \lim_{T \to \infty} E\left\{ \frac{|\tilde{n}(\omega)|^2}{T} \right\}$$

$$= \lim_{T \to \infty} \frac{1}{T} \left[\frac{\alpha^2}{\omega^2 + \lambda^2} E\{|\tilde{f}(\omega)|^2\} + \frac{Q}{\omega^2 + \lambda^2} E\{|\tilde{\gamma}(\omega)|^2\} \right.$$

$$\left. + \frac{\alpha Q^{1/2}}{\omega^2 + \lambda^2} E\{\tilde{f}(\omega)\tilde{\gamma}^*(\omega) + \tilde{f}^*(\omega)\tilde{\gamma}(\omega)\} \right]. \tag{7.2.16}$$

We can simplify this rather intimidating expression by noting that:

(a)   The driving function, $f(t)$, is deterministic so that

$$\lim_{T \to \infty} \frac{1}{T} E\{|\tilde{f}(\omega)|^2\} = S_f(\omega), \qquad (7.2.17a)$$

where $S_f(\omega)$ is the simple spectral density defined in Appendix F.

(b)   The spectral density of $\gamma(t)$ is (cf. equation (6.5.29)) unity, so that

$$\lim_{T \to \infty} \frac{1}{T} E\{|\tilde{\gamma}(\omega)|^2\} = 1. \qquad (7.2.17b)$$

(c)   The Wiener increment $d\omega(t)$ in equation (7.2.12) is taken from a probability distribution which is unaffected by the driving fluctuations. Thus $\gamma(t)$ and $\phi(t)$ are uncorrelated, so that

$$E\{\tilde{f}(\omega)\tilde{\gamma}(\omega)^*\} = E\{\tilde{f}^*(\omega)\tilde{\gamma}(\omega)\} = 0. \qquad (7.2.17c)$$

The final result for the spectral density of the population fluctuations is thus

$$S_n(\omega) = \frac{\alpha^2 S_f(\omega)}{\omega^2 + \lambda^2} + \frac{Q}{\omega^2 + \lambda^2}. \qquad (7.2.18)$$

The two terms on the right-hand side of this equation are both familiar, the first from Chapter 2 where we were concerned with the deterministic response to environmental variations and the second from Chapter 6 which was devoted to demographic stochasticity. Thus the result of local linearization is to decouple environmentally driven fluctuations from those due to demographic stochasticity. This is in fact a quite general feature of the technique, and in all the more elaborate models to be considered later in this chapter we shall obtain, after lineariaztion, expressions for the spectral density of the population fluctuations which have the general form

$$S_n(\omega) = |T(\omega)|^2 S_f(\omega) + \text{demographic stochasticity term} \qquad (7.2.19)$$

where $T(\omega)$ is the transfer function obtained from a routine analysis of the deterministic response to $f(t)$.

We now use the spectral density function given in equation (7.2.18) to infer the intensity σ_{tim}^2 and autocovariance function $C(\tau)$ of the population fluctuations. On putting our extended definition of spectral density (equation (6.5.28) or (7.2.16)) into the standard results (equations (F18) and (F19)), we see at once that

$$E\{\sigma_{\text{tim}}^2\} = \frac{1}{2\pi} \int_{-\infty}^{\infty} S_n(\omega) \, d\omega = \frac{\alpha^2}{2\pi} \int_{-\infty}^{\infty} \frac{S_f(\omega) \, d\omega}{\omega^2 + \lambda^2} + \frac{Q}{2|\lambda|}, \qquad (7.2.20)$$

and

$$E\{C(\tau)\} = \frac{1}{2\pi} \int_{-\infty}^{\infty} S_n(\omega) \cos \omega\tau \, d\omega$$

$$= \frac{\alpha^2}{2\pi} \int_{-\infty}^{\infty} \frac{S_f(\omega) \cos \omega\tau \, d\omega}{\omega^2 + \lambda^2} + \frac{Q}{2|\lambda|} e^{-|\lambda||\tau|} \qquad (7.2.21)$$

For normal birth and death models the values obtained for *long* time averages do not vary significantly between replicates, and thus equations (7.2.20) and (7.2.21) effectively give us the results we would obtain from a single population.

As an illustration of the application of equations (7.2.20) and (7.2.21) we consider the case of a sinusoidal driving function $f(t) = f_0 \cos \omega_0 t$. In this case the appropriate spectral density function is

$$S_f(\omega) = \frac{\pi f_0^2}{2} [\delta_{\text{Dirac}}(\omega - \omega_0) + \delta_{\text{Dirac}}(\omega + \omega_0)] \qquad (7.2.22)$$

so that

$$\sigma_{\text{tim}}^2 = E\{\sigma_{\text{tim}}^2\} = \frac{f_0^2 \alpha^2}{2(\omega_0^2 + |\lambda|^2)} + \frac{Q}{2|\lambda|}, \qquad (7.2.23)$$

$$C(\tau) = E\{C(\tau)\} = \frac{f_0^2 \alpha^2 \cos \omega_0 \tau}{2(\omega_0^2 + |\lambda|^2)} + \frac{Q}{2|\lambda|} e^{-|\lambda||\tau|} \qquad (7.2.24)$$

An example of the type of ACF described by equation (7.2.24), in this case calculated from the 'logistic' birth and death model with a sinusoidally varying death rate (equations (7.2.8) and (7.2.9)), is shown in Fig. 7.5(b). This shows clearly that the ACF of the population fluctuations exhibits the oscillating

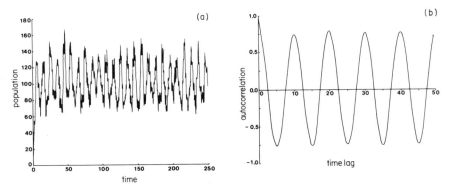

Fig. 7.5. A single realization of the 'logistic' birth and death model with sinusoidal modulation of the death rate (graph (a)) together with its autocorrelation function (graph (b)).

'tail' at large value of $|\tau|$ which we identified in Chapter 1 as being characteristic of *phase-remembering quasi-cycles*. The temporal pattern of such fluctuations is illustrated by a realization of the same model (Fig. 7.5(a)) which clearly shows the superposition of demographic 'jitter' on well-marked determinisitic cycles.

C. Extinction

As was emphasized in Chapter 6, there is only one mechanism for extinction of a closed population—a single death in a population of exactly one individual. For the single species birth and death models presently under investigation, this implies that the only rigorous method of estimating extinction probabilities is to calculate the development with time of $P(0, t)$ and then to use the result (equations (6.6.20) and (6.6.24))

$$\tau_E = \int_{t-0}^{\infty} t \, dP(0, t) = \int_0^{\infty} t \, \frac{dP(0, t)}{dt} \, dt \qquad (7.2.25)$$

$$= \int_0^{\infty} (1 - P(0, t)) \, dt. \qquad (7.2.26)$$

Thus for example, the curve in Fig. 7.1(b) could be used for numerical evaluation of τ_E in the particular model for which it was derived.

Given the time-consuming nature of exact calculations for even the simplest model, there is clearly a need for some kind of approximate method of calculating extinction times in models incorporating the effects of environmental variability. To the best of our knowledge this is a somewhat underdeveloped area mathematically, though it is possible to identify the likely route towards fruitful approximations. Since from equations (7.2.1) and (6.2.7)

$$\frac{dP(0, t)}{dt} = P(1, t)D(1, \phi(t)) = (1 - P(0, t))P_c(1, t)D(1, \phi(t)),$$

$$(7.2.27)$$

then on integrating this equation formally with initial condition $P(0, 0) = 0$ (all replicates non-extinct at $t = 0$) we obtain

$$P(0, t) = 1 - \exp\left\{-\int_0^t P_c(1, t')D(1, \phi(t')) \, dt'\right\}, \qquad (7.2.28)$$

and hence (using equation (7.2.26))

$$\tau_E = \int_0^{\infty} \exp\left[-\int_0^t P_c(1, t')D(1, \phi(t')) \, dt'\right] dt. \qquad (7.2.29)$$

With a static environment, we approximated this integral by replacing $P_c(1, t')$ by its stationary value $P_c^*(1)$, the result being an approximation to the extinction time (equation (6.2.29))

$$\tau_E = [D(1)P_c^*(1)]^{-1}, \tag{7.2.30}$$

which was good provided transients involving the initial conditions decayed over a characteristic time much less than τ_E. In a variable environment the function $P_c(1, t)$ consists of an initial-condition-dependent transient plus a persisting part which we denote by $P_{cp}(1, t)$, and it seems natural to base an analogous approximation to τ_E on the replacement of the complete CPDF $P_c(1, t)$ by $P_{cp}(1, t)$, with the result

$$\tau_E = \int_0^\infty \exp\left\{-\int_0^t P_{cp}(1, t')D(1, \phi(t')) \, dt'\right\} dt. \tag{7.2.31}$$

This is as far as we can progress without further assumptions on the nature of the external perturbation $\phi(t)$. We therefore now restrict our discussion to the case of periodic (but not necessarily sinusoidal) variations, which have $\phi(t) = \phi(t + P)$ for all t, and assume that the period P is substantially less than τ_E. We define

$$z(t) \equiv P_{cp}(1, t)D(1, \phi(t)), \tag{7.2.32}$$

and find after a little algebra that

$$(t - P)\theta \leqslant \int_0^t z(t') \, dt' \leqslant (t + P)\theta, \tag{7.2.33}$$

where

$$\theta = \frac{1}{P}\int_0^P z(t) \, dt = \frac{1}{P}\int_0^P P_{cp}(1, t)D(1, \phi(t)) \, dt. \tag{7.2.34}$$

On inserting this result in equation (7.2.31) we obtain

$$\theta^{-1}e^{-P\theta} \leqslant \tau_E \leqslant \theta^{-1}e^{+P\theta}, \tag{7.2.35}$$

an inequality whose usefulness derives from the fact that in many applications (for example, the 'logistic' model with driven death rate analysed later in this section) $P\theta \ll 1$ and hence $e^{-P\theta}$ and $e^{+P\theta}$ are very close to 1. It thus follows that

$$\tau_E \approx \theta^{-1} = \left[\frac{1}{P}\int_0^P D(1, \phi(t))P_{cp}(1, t) \, dt\right]^{-1}, \tag{7.2.36}$$

an expression which is clearly a generalization of the static result (7.2.30).

The principal importance of equation (7.2.36) derives from the fact that estimation of τ_E now involves a single integral over a period rather that a double integral over the entire time history of the system. Since in general the integral will have to be calculated numerically, this represents an enormous reduction in computational effort, as it is now only necessary to calculate $P_c(1, t)$ (from the differential equations (7.2.1)–(7.2.3)) over a long enough time interval for transients to become small and one cycle of the persisting oscillations to be observed. To appreciate the amount of effort thus saved we need only note that the number of differential equations involved in the calculation is of the order of the maximum population attained with significant probability, while τ_E (and hence the time interval over which the integrand of equation (7.2.31) is significantly different from zero) tends to scale exponentially with population size. The gain is thus very great for all but the smallest populations.

A second, more speculative, aspect of the result (7.2.36) is that it appears to hold out some promise of a further round of analytic approximations involving local linearization of the differential equations for the CPDF in order to relate the persisting fluctuations $P_{cp}(1, t)$ to the driving term $\phi(t)$. We are aware of no work in which this approach has been followed, but its potential can be seen with the aid of an example. We consider (again) the 'logistic' birth and death model with sinusoidal variations in carrying capacity. Parametrized slightly differently from equation (7.2.8) to simplify the ensuing mathematics, this model states

$$B(N) = rN, \qquad D(N) = \frac{rN^2}{K_0(1 + \phi(t))} = \frac{rN^2}{K(t)} \qquad (7.2.37)$$

where

$$\phi(t) = b \cos \omega t, \qquad \omega = 2\pi/P. \qquad (7.2.38)$$

We recall from Chapter 6 that if the carrying capacity is constant at K_0 then the binomial approximation to the CPDF has a very large clumping parameter and the distribution is approximately Poisson. We further recall that for logistic models the characteristic return time to equilibrium is r^{-1} and that at low frequencies ($\omega \ll r$) the mean population 'tracks' variations in carrying capacity. It is tempting to imagine that similar 'tracking' behaviour might occur with $P_c(1, t)$ in which case the instantaneous value of $P_c(1, t)$ will be the same as would arise in a static environment if the carrying capacity were held constant at $K(t)$. Thus provided

$$r^{-1} \ll P \ll \tau_E, \qquad (7.2.39)$$

we can plausibly guess that as long as $K(t) \gg 1$

$$P_{cp}(1, t) \simeq \frac{K(t)}{e^{K(t)} - 1} \simeq K(t)e^{-K(t)}, \qquad (7.2.40)$$

and hence

$$D(1, \phi(t))P_{cp}(1, t) \simeq r \exp\{-K_0(1 + b \cos \omega t)\}. \qquad (7.2.41)$$

The evaluation of τ_E using equation (7.2.36) is a little tricky but the conclusion is very simple; for large values of K_0, (i.e. $K_0 \rightarrow \infty$)

$$\ln(r\tau_E) \sim K_0(1 - b) \qquad (7.2.42)$$

This calculation, as well as illustrating the potential of a new approximation method, exposes a point of some general importance. The extinction time is enormously reduced by the action of even quite moderate environmental variations (if $K_0 = 100$, a 14 per cent modulation in carrying capacity will reduce τ_E by a factor of a million!). This is because downswings in population lead to massive increases in the probability of extinction with little compensating gain in safety during population upswings. Furthermore, with all but the smallest populations the mean times to extinction predicted by static birth and death models are so large as to be meaningless in an ecological context, and we are forced to conclude that virtually all ecologically useful models of extinction will invoke environmental variability.

7.3 ENVIRONMENTAL STOCHASTICITY

A. 'Deterministic' and 'random' environmental variation

The analysis of Section 7.2 presupposes an exact deterministic representation of $\phi(t)$, the external variable influencing birth and death processes and this is of course an unattainable ideal. In practice, as we noted in Chapter 1, complicated variations are often represented as the superposition of a *deterministic* component whose form is readily predictable at all future times and *random fluctuations* or *noise* which are described statistically. As an example of this procedure we show in Fig. 7.6 the decomposition of a 10-year run of montly temperature data taken at Recife, Brazil. The obvious periodicity of the raw data is reflected in a large peak in the spectral density, but if a deterministic representation of the seasonal variation is removed before performing the spectral analysis, the result is the type of spectrum that would arise with pink noise (defined in Section 7.3C).

Given the convenience (and proven utility in statistical forecasting) of such representations it would clearly be useful to generalize still further our

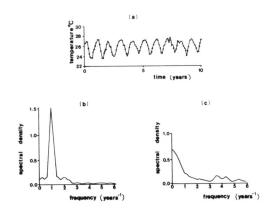

Fig. 7.6. The decomposition of a 10-year run of monthly temperature data. (Reproduced by permission from Chatfield, 1975.) (a) Ten years of monthly average air temperature at Recife, Brazil. (b) Estimated spectral density of the raw data. (c) Estimated spectral density of the seasonally adjusted data.

analysis of birth and death processes to cover the effects of random environmental variation. To effect this extension we first set up a formal framework for the analysis (Section 7.3B), and then consider the various types of 'noise' that might constitute plausible inputs to a population model (Section 7.3C). We then show (sections 7.3D and E) how local linearization can be used to give a powerful and simple recipe for estimating gross fluctuation characteristics and extinction times in the presence of environmental noise.

B. Formal representation of environmental stochasticity

As in Section 7.2 we consider a model in which the probabilities per unit time of a single birth and a single death are written as $B(N, \phi(t))$ and $D(N, \phi(t))$ respectively, but we now regard $\phi(t)$ as a random variable. The birth and death process is thereby rendered *doubly stochastic*, since *for each* realization of the environmental variable there is a normal birth and death model of the type already discussed. Our existing formalism is clearly inadequate for this problem and we must seek a suitable extension of it.

Corresponding to a single realization $\phi_i(t)$ of the environmental variable ϕ, there is a population PDF $P_i(N, t)$ obtained by integrating the basic differential equations (7.2.1)–(7.2.3) provided $\phi_i(t)$ is sufficiently well-behaved to permit the integration. If the result of the integration is ambiguous (as would arise if $\phi_i(t)$ were a realization of white noise) then the rules of integration must be specified *a priori*. We now consider a large number M_ϕ of such realizations and define the *'overall PDF'* by

$$P(N, t) \equiv M_\phi^{-1} \sum_{i=1}^{M_\phi} P_i(N, t). \qquad (7.3.1)$$

We define *'overall expectation values'* in two stages. Given a single realization $\phi_i(t)$ of the environmental process, the expectation value of an arbitrary function $f(N, t)$ is defined in the usual way by

$$E_i\{f(N, t)\} \equiv \sum_{N=0}^{\infty} f(N, t)P_i(N, t). \qquad (7.3.2)$$

Then given many (M_ϕ) realizations of $\phi(t)$, we introduce an *expectation value with respect to environmental variability*, defined for a function $g(N, t, \phi(t))$ by

$$E_\phi\{g(N, t, \phi(t))\} \equiv M_\phi^{-1} \sum_{i=1}^{M_\phi} g(N, t, \phi_i(t)). \qquad (7.3.3)$$

These two definitions lead naturally to a definition of *"overall expectation value"* as

$$E_T\{g(N, t, \phi(t)\} \equiv E_\phi\{E_i\{g(N, t, \phi(t))\}\} = M_\phi^{-1} \sum_{i=1}^{M_\phi} \sum_{N=0}^{\infty} g(N, t, \phi_i(t))P_i(N, t).$$

$$(7.3.4)$$

It is now straightforward to prove that for any function $f(N, t)$ that does not depend explicitly on $\phi(t)$, the overall PDF is a well-behaved probability distribution and

$$E_T\{f(N, t)\} = \sum_{N=0}^{\infty} f(N, t)P(N, t), \tag{7.3.5}$$

an immediate consequence of this result being that population means and variances can be defined in the usual way as

$$m(t) \equiv E_T\{N\} = \sum_{N=0}^{\infty} NP(N, t), \tag{7.3.6}$$

$$\sigma^2(t) \equiv E_T\{(N - m(t))^2\} = \sum_{N=0}^{\infty} N^2 P(N, t) - [m(t)]^2. \tag{7.3.7}$$

The key to our analysis of 'demographic' fluctuations in static environments was the introduction of the CPDF which immediately conferred two benefits:

(a) In many models $P_c(N, t)$ rapidly approached a stationary distribution $P_c^*(N)$. Thanks to this stationarity we could appeal to ergodic theorems for permission to relate statistical expectation values (which are normally unmeasurable but are readily calculable) to time averages over the history of a single non-extinct population. Without this correspondence the theory would be largely inapplicable.

(b) The problem of estimating the expected time to extinction was greatly simplified in those situations where this time greatly exceeded that required for establishing the stationary CPDF.

In the case of a variable environment there are two possible ways of defining a CPDF:

(a)
$$P_c^{(1)}(N, t) \equiv E_\phi\{P_{ci}(N, t)\} = \frac{1}{M_\phi} \sum_{i=1}^{M} \frac{P_i(N, t)}{1 - P_i(0, t)}, \tag{7.3.8}$$

or

(b)
$$P_c^{(2)}(N, t) \equiv \frac{P(N, t)}{1 - P(0, t)}. \tag{7.3.9}$$

That the appropriate choice of definition (a) is shown by considering our second objective—the prediction of expected times to extinction. For a single realization $\phi_i(t)$ we have (cf. equation (7.2.31))

$$\tau_{Ei} = \int_0^{\infty} (1 - P_i(0, t)) \, dt = \int_0^{\infty} \exp\left\{-\int_0^t P_{ci}(1, t')D(1, \phi(t')) \, dt'\right\} dt. \tag{7.3.10}$$

We comment from our previous work on deterministic environmental variations that while $D(1, \phi(t))$ is unlikely to vary enormously in any anticipated problems (at most tens of per cent either way) we can expect $P_{ci}(1, t')$ to fluctuate over many orders of magnitude. We thus argue that if ϕ_i^* is the mean value of $\phi_i(t)$, then

$$\tau_{Ei} \sim \int_0^\infty \exp\left\{-D(1, \phi^*)\int_0^t P_{ci}(1, t')\,dt'\right\}dt \qquad (7.3.11)$$

and hence, provided the vast majority of the 'power' in the fluctuations in $\phi_i(t)$ is at frequencies greater than a constant P^{-1}, then

$$\tau_{Ei} \sim \left[D(1, \phi^*)P^{-1}\int_0^P P_{ci}(1, t)\,dt\right]^{-1} \qquad (7.3.12)$$

The final step in the argument is to assume that the *overall* CPDF is stationary and that some kind of ergodic theorem holds. This implies for large P that

$$E_\phi\left\{P^{-1}\int_0^P P_{ci}(1, t)\,dt\right\} = P^{-1}\int_0^P E_\phi\{P_{ci}(1, t)\}\,dt = P_c^*(1) \qquad (7.3.13)$$

provided definition (a) (equation (7.3.8)) is used to define the overall CPDF. Thus

$$E_T\{\tau_E^{-1}\} \equiv E_\phi\{\tau_{Ei}^{-1}\} \sim D(1, \phi^*)P_c^*(1). \qquad (7.3.14)$$

However, we are normally (at best) interested only in the order of magnitude of τ_E and moreover are as likely to be wanting an estimate of expected probabilities per unit time of extinction as of the extinction time itself. We thus make no distinction at this point between $E\{_E^{-1}\}$ and $1/E\{\tau_E\}$ and regard

$$E_T\{\tau_E\} \sim [D(1, \phi^*)P_c^*(1)]^{-1} \qquad (7.3.15)$$

as a loose estimate of the expected time to extinction.

C. Types of noise

If we are to represent environmental variation in simple models as the sum of deterministic and random parts, we must have at our disposal suitable ways of characterizing each. Modelling the deterministic part of $\phi(t)$ is normally a matter of guesswork or simple curve-fitting depending on one's current position on the 'strategic-tactical' continuum, but the choice of appropriate representations of random fluctuations requires somewhat more thought.

Intuitively, an obvious candidate for representation of random environmental variation is the *random walk*. In discrete time, this involves $\phi(t)$ changing in a series of discrete jumps, each totally independent of its predecessor; in continuous time $\phi(t)$ changes via a series of steps proportional to Wiener increments (introduced in Section 6.2) $d\omega(t)$ with the properties (cf. equations (6.2.40) and (6.2.41))

$$E\{d\omega(t)\} = 0, \qquad E\{d\omega(t)^2\} = dt. \qquad (7.3.16)$$

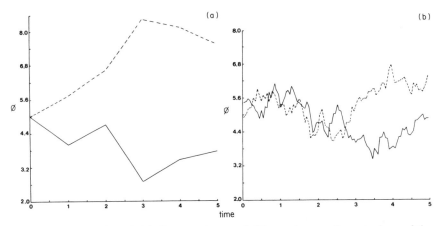

Fig. 7.7. Examples of, (a) discrete-time, and (b) continuous-time versions of the random walk.

We recall from Chapter 6 that the distinctive properties of the Wieₙer process are consequences of the second equation which requires that the mean square displacement over a very short time interval be proportional to dt and not $(dt)^2$ as with a deterministic process. Examples of discrete and continuous random walks are shown in Fig. 7.7

In line with the policy adopted throughout the book we concentrate on the continuous-time formalism and consider a model in which

$$d\phi(t) = D^{1/2}\, d\omega(t) \qquad (7.3.17)$$

where D is a constant with the units of ϕ^2/time, the notation being chosen to emphasize the similarity with random motion in space (cf. Section 5.3). By considering the time from 0 to t as made up of a large number of infinitesimally small increments, we find that if the value of $\phi(t)$ at $t = 0$ is known with certainty and denoted by ϕ_0, then

$$m_\phi \equiv E\{\phi(t)\} = \phi_0, \qquad \sigma_\phi^2 \equiv E\{[\phi(t) - \phi_0]^2\} = Dt. \qquad (7.3.18)$$

From these equations we can summarize the most important properties of the random walk as follows:

(a) The value of $\phi(t)$ is in no way 'regulated' or 'controlled'; at any instant, the best estimate we have of future values of $\phi(t)$ is simply the current value, whose precision as an estimator decreases rapidly with time.

(b) The root-mean-square displacement $\sqrt{(E\{[\phi(t) - \phi_0]^2\})}$, which is a measure of the expected size of the change in value of ϕ over the time interval 0 to t increases steadily, albeit slowly (as $t^{1/2}$), with time. This is illustrated in Fig. 7.8. The statistical distribution of $\phi(t)$ is thus non-stationary even in the limit of large t.

242

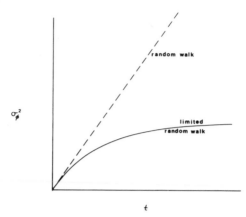

Fig. 7.8. Variation with time of the mean square displacement for a random walk and for a limited random walk.

Many environmental variables behave in a way that over short time intervals resembles the random walk but in the long term appears to be regulated about some well-defined average value ϕ^*. To describe this type of fluctuation we define a new process which we initially call a *limited random walk* in which the expected intensity of the fluctuation ultimately approaches a stationary value in the manner shown in Fig. 7.8.

One mathematically rather simple form for a limited random walk with ϕ_0 equal to the stationary mean value ϕ^*, has

$$\sigma_\phi^2 = D\tau_c(1 - e^{-t/\tau_c}), \qquad (7.3.19)$$

where the constant τ_c can be interpreted as a 'coherence time' such that the fluctuations appear like a random walk over times significantly less than τ_c and appear regulated on time scales greatly exceeding τ_c. For this model it is a matter of relatively simple manipulation to show that the autocovariance function $C(\tau)$ is

$$C(\tau) = D\tau_c e^{-\tau/\tau_c}, \qquad (7.3.20)$$

from which the spectral density of the fluctuations can be calculated using the Wiener–Khinchin relation (see Appendix F, equation (F18a)) with the result

$$S(\omega) = \frac{2D\tau_c^2}{1 + \omega^2\tau_c^2}. \qquad (7.3.21)$$

The form of these functions is sketched in Fig. 7.9 where we see that low frequencies predominate in the spectral representation of the fluctuations. For this reason the limited random walk is frequently (and more memorably) described as *pink noise*.

From time to time we encounter situations where the random part of the environmental variations has a coherence time much smaller than the time

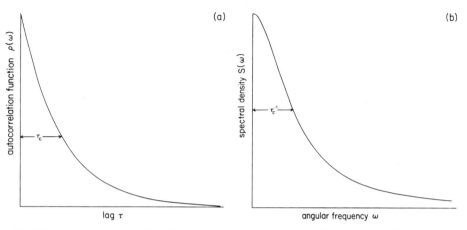

Fig. 7.9. Autocorrelation function (a), and spectral density (b), for a quantity following a limited random walk (pink noise).

required for significant population change. In this case, over all frequencies
for which the magnitude of the transfer function relating population and
environmental fluctuations is significant, the value of the spectral density is
virtually constant and for the purposes of modelling population fluctuations
we can reasonably regard the environmental spectrum as flat. This idealization which is known as *white noise* corresponds formally to the limiting case of
pink noise with

$$\tau_c \to 0, \qquad D \to \infty, \qquad D\tau_c^2 \text{ constant;} \qquad (7.3.22)$$

however, since in reality environmental noise is at best pink with a small but
finite τ_c, the subtleties associated with the existence of this limit need not
concern us. In practice, to use the white noise approximation we simply
assume a constant spectral density S and ignore the microscopic mechanisms
responsible for the value taken by S in any particular case.

Our present approach to the fiction of white noise might appear at odds
with Chapter 6 (and most texts on signal analysis) where white noise was
defined as the formal derivative of a Wiener process and then *proved* to have
a constant spectral density. There are good reasons for this divergence of
approach; in the analysis of demographic stochasticity white noise was very
much a subsidiary concept emerging naturally from the mathematics and its
interpretation was then of minor importance. By contrast, we are here
directly *modelling* environmental variations which are never in reality white
noise, and the justification for treating environmental variation in a particular
population model as white noise must rely on an empirically observed separation of time scales between population and environmental changes. Thus for
example the fluctuations represented in Fig. 7.6(c) might be regarded as
white noise, pink noise, or a static environment by ecologists studying respectively voles, mosquitoes or bacteria!

However plausible the preceding rationalization of the white noise approximation, there remains the conceptual difficulty that white noise has infinite variance. This does not imply that we would observe infinitely large excursions in our environmental variable, since any measurement of necessity involves *averaging* over some finite (though possibly small) time interval T_m. If for example our instrument measures a simple time-average of $\phi(t)$, then we are really measuring

$$\phi_m(t) \equiv \frac{1}{T_m} \int_{t-\frac{1}{2}T_m}^{t+\frac{1}{2}T_m} \phi(u)\, du, \qquad (7.3.23)$$

which to assist analysis we rewrite as the *convolution* (see Appendix F) of $\phi(t)$ with a rectangular pulse, i.e.

$$\phi_m(t) = \frac{1}{T_m} \int_{-\infty}^{\infty} \phi(t-u)H(u)\, du, \qquad (7.3.24)$$

where

$$H(u) = \begin{cases} 1 & \text{if } |u| \le \frac{1}{2}T_m \\ 0 & \text{otherwise} \end{cases}. \qquad (7.3.25)$$

We can thus use the convolution theorem (F46) to relate the Fourier transforms of $\phi_m(t)$ and $\phi(t)$, the result being

$$\tilde{\phi}_m(\omega) = T_m^{-1} \tilde{\phi}(\omega)\tilde{H}(\omega). \qquad (7.3.26)$$

Furthermore, evaluation of $H(\omega)$ is straightforward since

$$\tilde{H}(\omega) = \int_{-\infty}^{\infty} H(u)e^{-i\omega u}\, du = \int_{-\frac{1}{2}T_m}^{\frac{1}{2}T_m} e^{-i\omega u}\, du = T_m \frac{\sin \frac{1}{2}\omega T_m}{\frac{1}{2}\omega T_m}, \qquad (7.3.27)$$

and hence

$$\tilde{\phi}_m(\omega) = \tilde{\phi}(\omega) \frac{\sin \frac{1}{2}\omega T_m}{\frac{1}{2}\omega T_m}. \qquad (7.3.28)$$

If the environmental variation is modelled as white noise of spectral density S, it is an immediate consequence of equation (7.3.28) that the spectral density of the measured noise is

$$S_m(\omega) = S \cdot \frac{\sin^2(\frac{1}{2}\omega T_m)}{(\frac{1}{2}\omega T_m)^2}, \qquad (7.3.29)$$

from which the variance of the measured noise is readily calculable as

$$\sigma_{\phi m}^2 = \frac{1}{2\pi} \int_{-\infty}^{\infty} S_m(\omega)\, d\omega = \frac{2S}{\pi T_m} \int_0^{\infty} \frac{\sin^2 u}{u^2}\, du = \frac{S}{T_m}, \qquad (7.3.30)$$

the last step involving integration by parts plus the use of a known integral (Gradshteyn and Ryzhik, 1965, p. 405). Thus any measurement of white noise detects predominantly that part of the spectrum with frequencies lower than T_m^{-1} and produces a (continuous) series of measured values with a variance determined by the measuring instrument.

Having concluded that pink and white noise, which are characterized by particular forms of spectral density function, might be used to model environmental variation, and furthermore that the modelling decision 'pink versus white' is a quantitative one involving identification of time scales, we cannot totally duck (by reference to statistics texts) the question of measurement of spectral-density functions. Figure 7.10(a) shows the spectral density of a single realization of white noise sampled at regular time intervals. It is evident that such spectra are jagged and far from flat, a feature which is *not* due to the finite run length but rather to the statistical nature of the noise. In fact it can easily be shown that for a single realization of white noise with theoretical spectral density S, the experimentally determined spectral density (known as the periodogram and derived using equation (F11) or a close relative) is a random variable with mean S and variance proportional to S^2 (see, for example Chatfield, 1975, pp. 137–8). Mathematically, we circumvent this problem by defining (cf. equation (6.5.28)) the spectral density of white noise as an expectation value or average over a large number of realizations. As an example of the effect of this change in definition we show in Fig. 7.10(b) the average spectral density from five distinct realizations of the type which yielded the spectral density function shown in Fig. 7.10(a). This procedure is, however, of little interest to the modeller, who cannot normally conjure up a large number of distinct but statistically equivalent realizations of the environment under investigation. Instead when investigating a single experimental time series, we *smooth* the periodogram by calculating an appropriate weighted average of points over a 'window' of frequencies. This of course reduces the resolution with respect to frequency of points on the

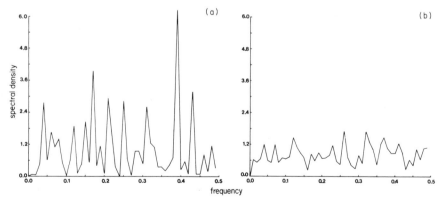

Fig. 7.10. Spectral density functions for, (a) a single realization of white noise with theoretical spectral density equal to unity, and (b) the average of five such realizations. The spectral density of the average is clearly smoother than the spectral density of the single realization.

periodogram but does enable us to determine the *shape* of the underlying spectrum. We thus conclude that the form of the spectrum of environmental noise is measurable and that this spectrum can reasonably be regarded as an 'input' to a population model.

D. Local linearization

After selecting a representation for environmental noise in any particular model, it might appear a relatively trivial matter to modify the previous analysis (see Section 7.2) of SDEs with deterministically varying birth and death probabilities to cover environmental stochasticity. In fact, major mathematical obstacles are found (and are discussed later in the chapter) unless we restrict ourselves to a *linearized* analysis of the now familiar type. Fortunately, the results of this type of analysis turn out more robust than we could reasonably have anticipated, and for this reason we have isolated in this section the basic recipe for estimating gross fluctuation characteristics and extinction times.

As in previous chapters we denote by ϕ^* the average value of $\phi(t)$ over a long period of time and consider small displacements of $\phi(t)$ from this mean value. The displacement at any particular instant is assumed separable into a deterministic part $f_{\text{det}}(t)$ and a random part $f_{\text{ran}}(t)$. Thus we have

$$\phi(t) = \phi^* + f_{\text{det}}(t) + f_{\text{ran}}(t). \tag{7.3.31}$$

By what amounts to a rerun of the argument preceding equation (7.2.12), we find that after linearization, the dynamics of the population fluctuations can be approximated by the SDE

$$\frac{dn(t)}{dt} = \lambda n(t) + \alpha f_{\text{det}}(t) + \alpha f_{\text{ran}}(t) + Q^{1/2}\gamma(t), \tag{7.3.32}$$

where as before

$$\lambda \equiv \left\{ \frac{\partial B}{\partial N} - \frac{\partial D}{\partial N} \right\}_{\substack{N=N^* \\ \phi=\phi^*}}, \qquad \alpha \equiv \left\{ \frac{\partial B}{\partial \phi} - \frac{\partial D}{\partial \phi} \right\}_{\substack{N=N^* \\ \phi=\phi^*}}, \tag{7.3.33}$$

and $\gamma(t)$ represents white noise of unit spectral density. Fourier transformation and some reorganization of terms in equation (7.3.32) yields (cf. equation (7.2.15))

$$\tilde{n}(\omega) = \frac{\alpha \tilde{f}_{\text{det}}(\omega)}{i\omega - \lambda} + \frac{\alpha \tilde{f}_{\text{ran}}(\omega)}{i\omega - \lambda} + \frac{Q^{1/2}\tilde{\gamma}(\omega)}{i\omega - \lambda} \tag{7.3.34}$$

in which the three terms on the right-hand side show that within the region of applicability of local linearization, the effects of deterministic environmental variability, environmental stochasticity and demographic stochasticity are additive. The interpretation of (7.3.34) is helped if we recast it in the form

$$\tilde{n}(\omega) = T(\omega)[\tilde{f}_{\text{det}}(\omega) + \tilde{f}_{\text{ran}}(\omega)] + \begin{bmatrix} \text{demographic} \\ \text{stochasticity} \\ \text{term} \end{bmatrix}, \qquad (7.3.35)$$

and recognize that $T(\omega)$ is simply the transfer function introduced in Chapter 2 and used regularly thereafter. As was the case with deterministic models we shall find that the form (7.3.35) persists through many elaborations (multi-species, time-delays, discrete generations etc.) and hence the response of a model population to environmental noise is readily handled with the same mathematical tools as were developed for deterministic variations.

Provided the deterministic and random parts of the environmental fluctuations are uncorrelated (and it is virtually a matter of definition that they should be), then on averaging over a large number of realizations of the environmental process, we obtain

$$E_\phi\{\tilde{f}_{\text{det}}(\omega)\tilde{f}_{\text{ran}}^*(\omega)\} = E_\phi\{\tilde{f}_{\text{det}}^*(\omega)\tilde{f}_{\text{ran}}(\omega)\} = 0. \qquad (7.3.36)$$

If additionally, the white demographic noise is uncorrelated with the driving environmental variations, then on considering the doubly stochastic process involving a large numer of replicate populations corresponding to each one of the (large number of) environmental realizations, we have

$$E\{[\tilde{f}_{\text{det}}(\omega) + \tilde{f}_{\text{ran}}(\omega)]\tilde{\gamma}^*(\omega)\} = E\{[\tilde{f}_{\text{det}}(\omega) + \tilde{f}_{\text{ran}}(\omega)]^*\tilde{\gamma}(\omega)\} = 0.$$
$$(7.3.37)$$

Thus the spectral density of the fluctuations in population is (cf. equation (7.2.16))

$$S_n(\omega) = \lim_{T\to\infty} \frac{1}{T} E\{|\tilde{n}(\omega)|^2\}$$

$$= \frac{\alpha^2 S_{\phi,\text{det}}(\omega)}{\omega^2 + \lambda^2} + \frac{\alpha^2 S_{\phi,\text{ran}}(\omega)}{\omega^2 + \lambda^2} + \frac{Q}{\omega^2 + \lambda^2}, \qquad (7.3.38)$$

where $S_{\phi,\text{det}}(\omega)$ is the spectral density of the deterministic driving fluctuations (and will normally consist of a discrete set of delta functions) and $S_{\phi,\text{ran}}(\omega)$ is the spectral density of the environmental noise. Again, because of the possibilities of subsequent generalization it is useful to rewrite (7.3.38) in terms of the transfer function with the result

$$S_n(\omega) = |T(\omega)|^2[S_{\phi,\text{det}}(\omega) + S_{\phi,\text{ran}}(\omega)] + \begin{bmatrix} \text{demographic} \\ \text{stochasticity} \\ \text{term} \end{bmatrix}. \qquad (7.3.39)$$

We have thus reduced the problem of approximating the spectral density of the population fluctuations to three distinct parts;

(a) Modelling demographic stochasticity or further approximating by neglecting it.

(b)   Modelling the spectrum of the environmental fluctuations.
(c)   Calculating the transfer function by the techniques developed in Part I
      of this book.

Once the spectral density is known, calculation of the fluctuation intensity
and autocovariance function is simply a matter of using the familiar equations
(F18b) and (F19), i.e.

$$\sigma_{\text{tim}}^2 = \frac{1}{2\pi} \int_{-\infty}^{\infty} S_n(\omega)\, d\omega \qquad \text{and} \qquad C(\tau) = \frac{1}{2\pi} \int_{-\infty}^{\infty} S_n(\omega) \cos \omega\tau\, d\omega.$$

$$(7.3.40)$$

As always, however, estimating the mean time to extinction is more tricky.
Here, the only way to avoid a very tricky calculation is to decide *a priori*
whether the deterministic or the random variations are more likely to play the
dominant role in reducing the population to levels where extinction is likely.
If the former is the case we are back with all the difficulties encountered in
Section 7.2C but with the additional complication of environmental noise,
and as far as we are aware this is mathematically unexplored territory. However, the situation is much simpler if the random noise is believed to be the
prime cause of extinction. In this case we require one further input to our
model, namely the *probability distribution* of the environmental noise. If this
is approximately Gaussian then so will be the probability distribution of the
population fluctuations provided the SDE linking the driving and population
fluctuations is linear. (This is a consequence of a standard theorem in probability theory—see, for example, Bendat and Piersol (1971, p. 94).) We then
use the value of this Gaussian density function at $N = 1$ to estimate the mean
time to extinction using equation (7.3.15) with the result

$$\tau_E \sim [D(1, \phi^*)P_c^*(1)]^{-1} \sim [D(1, \phi^*)]^{-1}\sqrt{(2\pi)}\sigma_{\text{tim}} \exp\left\{\frac{(N^* - 1)^2}{2\sigma_{\text{tim}}^2}\right\}.$$

$$(7.3.41)$$

Within the accuracy of the present work where we are ignoring demographic
stochasticity $(N^* - 1)$ is indistinguishable from N^* and this result thus
simplifies to

$$\tau_E \sim [D(1, \phi^*)]^{-1}\sqrt{(2\pi)}\sigma_{\text{tim}}\exp\{N^{*2}/2\sigma_{\text{tim}}^2\}. \qquad (7.3.42)$$

E. Elaborations

Our basic recipe for calculating fluctuation intensities and AC$_o$Fs was presented in the context of a single-species model with the underlying dynamics
describable by a birth and death process. The method is of course applicable
to a wide range of models, the key to most extensions being equation (7.3.39)
relating population and driving fluctuations through the result

$$S_n(\omega) = |T(\omega)|^2[S_{\phi,\text{det}}(\omega) + S_{\phi,\text{ran}}(\omega)] + \begin{bmatrix} \text{demographic} \\ \text{stochasticity} \\ \text{term} \end{bmatrix}, \quad (7.3.43)$$

which generalises to all those situations for which in Chapters 2–5 we derived transfer functions.

Where demographic stochasticity can be neglected, the only difficulty that arises in using equation (7.3.43) is the evaluation of the integrals that yield the fluctuation intensity and the AC_0F. The seriousness of this difficulty depends on the complexity of the representation of the environmental fluctuations; with anything more elaborate than pure sinusoids or white and pink

Table 7.1. Integrals encountered in calculations of fluctuation intensity for differential equation models 'driven' by white or pink noise. The general integral is of the type (Gradshteyn and Ryzhik, 1965, p 218).

$$I_n = \int_{-\infty}^{\infty} \frac{g_n(\omega)\,d\omega}{h_n(\omega)h_n(-\omega)}$$

where

$$h_n(\omega) = a_0\omega^n + a_1\omega^{n-1} \ldots + a_n,$$
$$g_n(\omega) = b_0\omega^{2n-2} + b_1\omega^{2n-4} + \ldots + b_{n-1}.$$

(The coefficients in both polynomials may be complex and the polynomial $h_n(\omega)$ has all its roots in the upper half-plane.)

Integral	Context
$I_1 = \dfrac{\pi b_0}{a_0 a_1}$	One-species, white noise
$I_2 = \dfrac{\pi i(a_0 b_1 - a_2 b_0)}{a_0 a_1 a_2}$	Two-species, white noise One-species, pink noise
$I_3 = \dfrac{\pi i(-a_2 b_0 a_3 + a_0 b_1 a_3 - a_0 a_1 b_2)}{a_0 a_3(a_0 a_3 - a_1 a_2)}$	Three species, white noise Two-species, pink noise
$I_n = \dfrac{\pi i \det \begin{bmatrix} b_0 & b_1 & b_2 & ..: & b_{n-1} \\ a_0 & a_2 & a_4 & \cdots & 0 \\ 0 & a_1 & a_3 & \cdots & 0 \\ \vdots & \vdots & \vdots & & \\ 0 & 0 & 0 & \cdots & a_n \end{bmatrix}}{a_0 \det \begin{bmatrix} a_1 & a_3 & a_5 & \cdots & 0 \\ a_0 & a_2 & a_4 & \cdots & 0 \\ 0 & a_1 & a_3 & \cdots & 0 \\ \vdots & \vdots & \vdots & & \\ 0 & 0 & 0 & \cdots & a_n \end{bmatrix}}$	n-species, white noise $(n-1)$-species, pink noise

noise the integrals will almost always require numerical computation. However, in the special cases where the driving fluctuations are modelled as white or pink noise, the integrals obtained are of a type extensively used in control theory and are well documented. In Table 7.1 we have listed the integrals commonly encountered in calculations of fluctuation intensity for differential equation models and to illustrate the use of the table we consider the integral

$$I = \frac{1}{2\pi} \int_{-\infty}^{\infty} \frac{r^2 S \, d\omega}{r^2 + \omega^2} = \frac{r^2 S}{2\pi} \int_{-\infty}^{\infty} \frac{d\omega}{(r + i\omega)(r - i\omega)} \qquad (7.3.44)$$

that would arise in a logistic model with white noise variations in carrying capacity. The denominator is of the form $h_1(\omega)h_1(-\omega)$ and of the two brackets it is clearly $r + i\omega$ that has a root ($\omega = +ir$) in the upper half-plane. Thus we identify

$$b_0 = \frac{r^2 S}{2\pi}, \qquad a_0 = i, \qquad a_1 = r, \qquad (7.3.45)$$

from which it follows that

$$I = \frac{\pi i b_0}{a_0 a_1} = \frac{rS}{2}, \qquad (7.3.46)$$

This is in agreement with the result obtained by elementary means, namely

$$I = \frac{r^2 S}{2\pi} \left[\frac{1}{r} \tan^{-1} \frac{\omega}{r} \right]_{-\infty}^{\infty} = \frac{rS}{2}. \qquad (7.3.47)$$

The reader with no inclination to become involved in heavy integration may still want to apply the basic recipe to obtain 'ballpark estimates' of gross fluctuation characteristics in simple models. For this reason we have constructed a second table (Table 7.2) with formulae for fluctuation intensity and for ACF (the general expressions for which were too gruesome to include in Table 7.1) in three of the simplest types of model driven by white noise.

7.4   QUASI-CYCLIC FLUCTUATIONS

A. Identifying and describing quasi-cycles

Many deterministic models exhibit, at least for some values of the controlling parameters, limit cycles or driven oscillations which are cyclic in the precise mathematical sense that for all t and all integer n

$$N(t + nP) = N(t). \qquad (7.4.1)$$

Such mathematically perfect cycles are of course never observed in real populations, and if we wish to draw a distinction between those population fluctuations which are in some sense repetitive and those which are not we require a more subtle test than that provided by equation (7.4.1). The reader who

Table 7.2. Transfer functions, fluctuation intensities and ACF ($= \mathrm{AC_oF}$/fluctuation intensity) for three simple types of population model. The 'driving' variable $f(t)$ is assumed to be white noise with spectral density S in the differential equation models and with variance S/τ_g in the difference equation model.

Type of model	Linearized equations	Transfer function $\tilde{n}(\omega)/\tilde{f}(\omega)$	Fluctuation intensity	ACF $\rho(\tau)$
Single-species differential equation	$\dot{n} = \lambda n + \alpha f(t)$	$T(\omega) = \dfrac{\alpha}{i\omega - \lambda}$ $\quad \lambda < 0$	$\dfrac{\alpha^2 S}{2|\lambda|}$	$e^{-|\lambda||\tau|}$
Two-species differential equation	$\dot{n}_i = A_{i1}n_1 + A_{i2}n_2 + \alpha_i f(t)$ $(i = 1, 2)$	$T_i(\omega) = \dfrac{\psi_i + i\omega\alpha_i}{(\omega^2 - \omega_0^2) + i\omega\beta}$	$\dfrac{(\psi_i^2 + \omega_0^2\alpha_i^2)S}{2\omega_0^2\beta}$	$Be^{-\lambda_1|\tau|} + Ce^{-\lambda_2|\tau|}, \quad \beta \geq 2\omega_0$ $e^{-\frac{1}{2}\beta\tau}\dfrac{\cos(\omega_1\tau - \phi)}{\cos\phi}, \quad \beta < 2\omega_0$
Single-species difference equation	$n_{t+\tau_g} - n_t = \lambda\tau_g n_t + \alpha\tau_g f_t$	$T(\omega) = \dfrac{\alpha\tau_g}{e^{i\omega\tau_g} - (1 + \lambda\tau_g)}$	$\dfrac{\alpha^2 S}{|\lambda|(2 - |\lambda\tau_g|)}$	$\{1 - |\lambda\tau_g|\}^{\tau/\tau_g}$

Notation: $\beta = -(A_{11} + A_{22});$ $\quad \omega_0^2 = A_{11}A_{22} - A_{12}A_{21};$ $\quad \psi_i = A_{ii}\alpha_j - A_{jj}\alpha_i$ $\quad$ with $j = 3 - i;$ $\quad \omega_1 = \frac{1}{2}(4\omega_0^2 - \beta^2)^{1/2};$

$$\phi = \tan^{-1}\left[\frac{\beta[\psi_i^2 - \alpha_i^2\omega_0^2]}{2\omega_1[\omega_0^2 + \alpha_i^2\omega_0^2]}\right]; \quad \lambda_1 = \frac{1}{2}\beta + \frac{1}{2}(\beta^2 - 4\omega_0^2)^{1/2}; \quad \lambda_2 = \frac{1}{2}\beta - \frac{1}{2}(\beta^2 - 4\omega_0^2)^{1/2}$$

believes that visual examination of the raw data will serve this purpose should make a brief scan of the published literature which contains numerous examples of pink noise being erroneously identified as cyclic after cursory examination of short runs of data. We argued in Chapter 1 that the appropriate measure of repetitiveness in a fluctuating population was provided by the autocorrelation function

$$\rho(\tau) \equiv \frac{C(\tau)}{C(0)} = \frac{1}{\sigma_{\text{tim}}^2} \langle (N(t) - \langle N \rangle)(N(t + \tau) - \langle N \rangle) \rangle. \quad (7.4.2)$$

We have since (in Section (7.3)) outlined a recipe for the approximate calculation of the ACF in a wide range of models, and a more precise quantitative discussion of quasi-cycles is thus now in order.

We describe fluctuations as non-cyclic if the ACF decays monotonically to zero at large values of the lag τ, with at most a finite (usually small) number of zero crossings at small τ. By contrast, with mathematically perfect cycles satisfying equation (7.4.1) the ACF itself exhibits perfect cycles which persist to $\tau = \pm\infty$. The intermediate case of *quasi-cyclic* fluctuation yields an ACF whose oscillations decline in amplitude as $|\tau|$ increases, and in Chapter 1 we distinguished two subcategories;

(a) *phase-remembering* quasi-cycles whose ACF after an initial decline shows cycles of essentially constant amplitude as shown in Figs. 1.6(b) and 7.11,

(b) *phase-forgetting* quasi-cycles whose ACF consists of damped oscillations whose amplitude decays to zero at long lags, as shown in Figs. 1.6(c) and 7.12.

This classification of quasi-cycles covers a wide range of fluctuation patterns from those which clearly resemble perfect cycles to those from which a cyclic component can only be extracted after the most rigorous statistical analysis. Moreover we are studying quasi-cyclic fluctuations as a route to insight on population regulation and not because of their intrinsic fascination; we thus require a quantitative measure of the *extent* to which any particular fluctuation is cyclic.

Because of the very different statistical properties of phase-remembering and phase-forgetting quasi-cycles we are forced to adopt a different measure for the two categories. *Phase-remembering* quasi-cycles always contain a truly cyclic component and are conveniently characterized by the relative magnitudes of this component and the remaining 'noise'. More precisely, we define a quantity R_N (known to engineers as the signal to noise ratio) to be the ratio of the variance attributable to the cyclic component to that attributable to the (aperiodic) noise. Thus for example if a fluctuating quantity were modelled as the superposition of a sinusoid on a background of pink noise (a very appropriate model for the temperature variations in Fig. 7.6) the $AC_o F$ would be of the form

$$C(\tau) = Ae^{-\mu|\tau|} + B \cos \omega_p\tau, \qquad (7.4.3)$$

the total fluctuation intensity ('signal' plus 'noise') would be

$$\sigma^2 = C(0) = A + B = \sigma^2_{\text{aperiodic}} + \sigma^2_{\text{periodic}}, \qquad (7.4.4)$$

and the signal to noise ratio would be

$$R_N = \frac{\sigma^2_{\text{periodic}}}{\sigma^2_{\text{noise}}} = \frac{A}{B}. \qquad (7.4.5)$$

Fig. 7.11 illustrates the ACF obtained from equation (7.4.3) for several fluctuations with the same underlying noise (i.e. the same values of A and μ) but with different signal to noise ratios R_N (effected by varying B). The graphs show clearly that the phase remembering nature of the cycles is only revealed by the form of the ACF beyond some critical lag whose value increases as R_N is decreased. Bearing in mind that an ACF derived from a run of length T is only statistically reliable for lags less than about $T/4$, it is clear that R_N is involved in determining the ease with which phase-remembering cycles may be identified as such (i.e. the minimum length of data run required). Indeed on re-examining equation (7.4.3) we see that to unambiguously identify phase remembering cycles with an ACF of the form (7.4.3) we require a run length

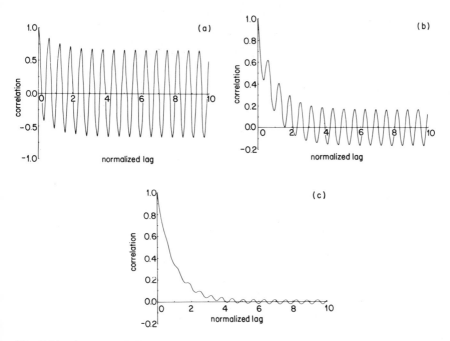

Fig. 7.11. Autocorrelation functions for phase-remembering quasi-cycles obtained from equation (7.4.3) with $A = 1$, and $\mu = 1$. (a) $R_N = 2.0$ (b) $R_N = 0.2$. (c) $R_N = 0.02$.

T satisfying

$$T \gg \frac{1}{\mu} \ln\left(\frac{A}{B}\right) = \frac{1}{\mu} \ln\left(\frac{1}{R_N}\right). \tag{7.4.6}$$

In practice we require a run of about

$$T \sim \frac{10}{\mu} \ln\left(\frac{1}{R_N}\right) \tag{7.4.7}$$

to observe reliably a 'tail' of persisting oscillations comparable in length with the coherence time of the noise.

Phase-forgetting quasi-cycles can similarly be characterized by a quantity which measures the ease with which they can be identified. An appropriate quantity (which we call the *coherence number*) is the number of cycles over which the amplitude of the oscillations in the ACF decays by a predetermined factor which for convenience we take to be e^{-1}. In the simple, but commonly encountered, case of a quantity with an ACF of the form

$$\rho(\tau) = e^{-\mu|\tau|} \cos \omega\tau, \tag{7.4.8}$$

we have

$$n_c = \omega/(2\pi\mu). \tag{7.4.9}$$

In contrast to the previous case, phase-forgetting quasi-cycles do not contain a truly cyclic component and the problem of identifying them is not merely a matter of long runs of data. It is clear that even with an ACF like equation (7.4.8) which is always damped oscillatory in form, the cyclic nature of the fluctuations will be completely submerged if the population's 'memory' is short in comparison with the cycle period ($n_c \ll 1$), while if it is long compared to the cycle period, the fluctuation will appear almost perfectly cyclic. We thus adopt a somewhat arbitrary criterion for 'effectively quasi-cyclic' (as opposed to 'effectively non-cyclic') fluctuations, namely

$$n_c \geq 1. \tag{7.4.10}$$

In Fig. 7.12, which illustrates ACFs and values of n_c between 0.2 and 5, we show that this choise appears appropriate in practice.

It is left as an exercise for the reader to show that for a deterministically stable system driven by white noise the definition of coherence number given above is essentially equivalent to the definition used in Chapter 4, where we characterized an oscillatory return to equilibrium according to the number of cycles over which the amplitude of the transient decays by a factor e^{-1}.

Once a given fluctuation has been identified as quasi-cyclic we may turn to the problem of identifying the underlying mechanism. The possible candidates are as follows:

(a)   A deterministically stable system is driven by an external fluctuation with a strong periodic component. We call the phase-remembering quasi-cycles so generated *'periodically driven quasi-cycles'*.

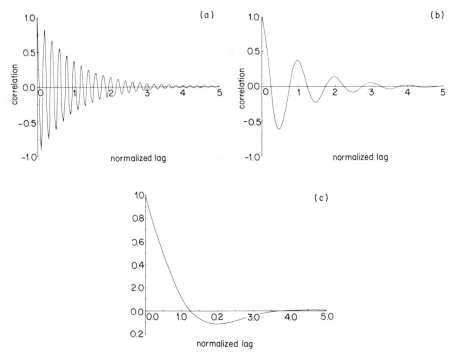

Fig. 7.12. Autocorrelation functions for phase-forgetting quasi-cycles obtained from equation (7.4.8). (a) $n_c = 5$, (b) $n_c = 1$, (c) $n_c = 0.2$.

(b) A deterministically stable but underdamped system is driven by an aperiodic external fluctuation. We call the phase-forgetting quasi-cycles so produced *'exogenous resonant quasi-cycles'*.

(c) A deterministically stable but underdamped system is perturbed by demographic stochasticity. We call these phase-forgetting quasi-cycles *'endogenous resonant quasi-cycles'*.

(d) A deterministically unstable system executes limit cycles perturbed by environmental or demographic stochasticity. We call such phase-forgetting cyles *'perturbed limit cycles'*.

Only one of these mechanisms can reliably be distinguished from the others by direct examination of the experimental data—periodically driven quasi-cycles are phase-remembering and can be identified by the presence of persisting cycles in the tail of the ACF. However, the required length of run (cf. equation (7.4.7)) may make even this identification ambiguous as we demonstrate in Fig. 7.13 for the well-worn data on oscillations in Canadian lynx populations. Bulmer (1974) has shown that in spite of the long run of these data, very similar goodness-of-fit statistics are obtained irrespective of whether the oscillations are modelled as phase-remembering or phase-forgetting cycles. Distinguishing the other mechanisms ((b), (c), (d)) is not

(a)

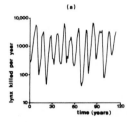

(b)

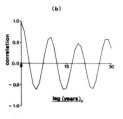

Fig. 7.13. Number of lynx trapped per year in the Mackenzie River district of Canada (graph (a)), and the autocorrelation function of these data (graph (b)). The original data are tabulated by Moran (1953).

even straightforward in principle and we conclude that in the majority of situations, the mechanisms for generating quasi-cycles can only be distinguished by the indirect (and philosophically vulnerable) route of constructing and testing specific models. This approach is followed in the case studies of Chapters 8 and 10.

B. Exogenous quasi-cycles in the damped Lotka–Volterra system

The analysis of models yielding periodically driven or exogenous resonant quasi-cycles is, at least in the locally linear approximation, a routine application of the transfer-function techniques emphasized in Sections 2.6, 4.3 and 7.3. However, the calculations themselves may be rather heavy and we have, therefore, chosen to illustrate the procedure by way of a worked example.

We consider again the damped Lotka–Volterra predator–prey model used as an example in Chapter 4. In this model we assume that in isolation the prey species grows logistically with intrinsic growth rate r and carrying capacity K. Additional losses due to predation are assumed to occur at a rate proportional to the product of the sizes of the predator population (C) and the prey population (F), so that

$$\dot{F} = rF(1 - F/K) - \theta FC. \qquad (7.4.11)$$

We then suppose that the predator population produces new recruits at a rate proportional to its total rate of food intake and that its members have a time—and density-independent per capita death rate ε. We thus describe the consumer dynamics by

$$\dot{C} = \gamma FC - \varepsilon C. \qquad (7.4.12)$$

We showed in Section 4.5B that the system defined by equations (7.4.11) and (7.4.12) has a single non-trivial stationary state

$$F^* = \varepsilon/\gamma, \qquad (7.4.13)$$

$$C^* = (r/\theta)\{1 - \varepsilon/K\gamma\}, \qquad (7.4.14)$$

and that provided $K > \varepsilon/\gamma$, so that the consumers have a positive net growth rate with the prey at or below saturation, this stationary state is both feasible (F^*, C^* both non-negative) and locally stable.

We also showed that if

$$r < 4K\gamma\left\{\frac{K\gamma}{\varepsilon} - 1\right\}, \tag{7.4.15}$$

the return to stable equilibrium is oscillatory. This is the context in which we might expect to be able to generate resonant quasi-cycles and to see if this indeed the case we shall now assume that the prey intrinsic growth rate r is somewhat influenced by time dependent external factors, so that

$$r = r_0(1 + \phi(t)), \tag{7.4.16}$$

where $\phi(t)$ is always small ($\ll 1$).

The analysis of this situation is a perfectly straightforward application of the techniques of Sections 4.3 and 7.3. We linearize about the stationary state (F^*, C^*) and hence show that in the locally linear approximation, the spectral densities of the fluctuations in F and C (S_f and S_c respectively) are related to the spectral density of the fluctuations in r (S_ϕ) by

$$S_f(\omega) = |T_f(\omega)|^2 S_\phi(\omega) \tag{7.4.17}$$

$$S_c(\omega) = |T_c(\omega)|^2 S_\phi(\omega) \tag{7.4.18}$$

where, by using equations (4.3.11) and (4.3.12) the square moduli of the transfer functions $T_f(\omega)$ and $T_c(\omega)$ can be shown to be

$$|T_f(\omega)|^2 = \frac{(\omega_0^2/\gamma)^2\omega^2}{(\omega_0^2 - \omega^2)^2 + \beta^2\omega^2}, \tag{7.4.19}$$

$$|T_c(\omega)|^2 = \frac{(\omega_0^4/\varepsilon\theta)^2}{(\omega_0^2 - \omega^2)^2 + \beta^2\omega^2}, \tag{7.4.20}$$

with

$$\beta = \frac{r_0\varepsilon}{\gamma K}, \tag{7.4.21}$$

$$\omega_0^2 = r_0\varepsilon\left(1 - \frac{\varepsilon}{\gamma K}\right). \tag{7.4.22}$$

To determine whether or not the fluctuations in F and C are quasi-cyclic we must evaluate their autocovariance functions which from equation (F18) are given by

$$C_f(\tau) = \frac{1}{2\pi}\int_{-\infty}^{\infty} |T_f(\omega)|^2 S_\phi(\omega)e^{i\omega\tau}\,d\omega, \tag{7.4.23}$$

$$C_c(\tau) = \frac{1}{2\pi} \int_{-\infty}^{\infty} |T_c(\omega)|^2 S_\phi(\omega) e^{i\omega\tau} \, d\omega. \qquad (7.4.24)$$

The evaluation of these expressions is only possible once we have made more detailed assumptions about the nature of the driving fluctuations, so as to be able to write down an explicit expression for their spectral density $S_\phi(\omega)$. We shall examine two distinct cases,

(a) $\phi(t)$ is purely aperiodic 'noise' whose spectrum can safely be regarded as 'white' over the frequency range in which either population exhibits any significant response. In this case we set S_ϕ equal to a constant

$$S_\phi(\omega) = S, \qquad (7.4.25)$$

(b) $\phi(t)$ consists of a periodic component of angular frequency ω_p superimposed on the same noise background, so that

$$S_\phi(\omega) = S + B[\delta_{\text{Dirac}}(\omega - \omega_p) + \delta_{\text{Dirac}}(\omega + \omega_p)]. \qquad (7.4.26)$$

To facilitate subsequent interpretation we shall further subdivide our analysis and consider separately the effects of these perturbations on over- and under-damped systems. We deal first with the case of model parameters chosen so that inequality (7.4.15) is not satisfied (i.e. $\beta > 2\omega_0$) and the return of the undriven system to its stable equilibrium is eventually monotonic (overdamped). We first define

$$\eta = [\beta^2/4 - \omega_0^2]^{1/2} \qquad (7.4.27)$$

$$\lambda_1 = \beta/2 + \eta \qquad (7.4.28)$$

$$\lambda_2 = \beta/2 - \eta \qquad (7.4.29)$$

and then evaluate the integrals in equations (7.4.23) and (7.4.24) to show that white noise driving (S_ϕ given by equation (7.4.25)) produces fluctuations with AC_oFs given by

$$C_f(\tau) = \left[\frac{S\omega_0^4}{2\beta\gamma^2\eta}\right][\lambda_1 e^{-\lambda_1|\tau|} - \lambda_2 e^{-\lambda_2|\tau|}], \qquad (7.4.30)$$

$$C_c(\tau) = \left[\frac{S\omega_0^6}{2\beta\varepsilon^2\theta^2\eta}\right][-\lambda_2 e^{-\lambda_1|\tau|} + \lambda_1 e^{-\lambda_2|\tau|}], \qquad (7.4.31)$$

while a driving fluctuation with a periodic component (S_ϕ given by equation (7.4.26)) yields population fluctuations whose AC_oFs are

$$C_f(\tau) = \left[\frac{S\omega_0^4}{2\beta\gamma^2\eta}\right][\lambda_1 e^{-\lambda_1|\tau|} - \lambda_2 e^{-\lambda_2|\tau|}] + \frac{B}{\pi}|T_f(\omega_p)|^2 \cos\omega_p\tau, \qquad (7.4.32)$$

$$C_c(\tau) = \left[\frac{S\omega_0^6}{2\beta\varepsilon^2\theta^2\eta}\right][-\lambda_2 e^{-\lambda_1|\tau|} + \lambda_1 e^{-\lambda_2|\tau|}] + \frac{B}{\pi}|T_c(\omega_p)|^2 \cos\omega_p\tau. \qquad (7.4.33)$$

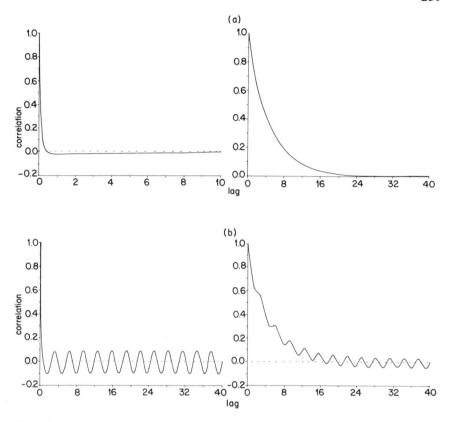

Fig. 7.14. Autocorrelation functions for the damped Lotka–Volterra model with a fluctuating prey intrinsic growth rate and parameters selected to give overdamping ($\beta > 2\omega_0$). The prey population results are shown on the left and the consumer on the right. (a) White noise driving fluctuations. (b) Quasi-periodic driving fluctuations.

These results, which are illustrated in Fig. 7.14, confirm our expectations. Aperiodic driving fluctuations applied to an overdamped system produce non-cyclic population fluctuations whose AC$_o$F approaches zero monotonically as $|\tau|$ becomes large (cf. Figs. 1.6(d) and 7.14(a)), while a driving fluctuation with a periodic component applied to such a system produces phase-remembering quasi-cycles whose AC$_o$F at large values of $|\tau|$ is a sinusoid of constant amplitude (cf. Figs. 1.6 and 7.14(b)).

When the model parameters are chosen so as to satisfy inequality (7.4.15) (i.e. $\beta < 2\omega_0$) so that the return of the undriven system to equilibrium is oscillatory (underdamped) the results are rather more interesting. In this case if we define

$$\omega_1 = \sqrt{(\omega_0^2 - \beta^2/4)} \qquad (7.4.34)$$

then we find that aperiodic driving (S_ϕ given by equation (7.4.25)) produces population fluctuations whose AC$_o$Fs are given by

$$C_f(\tau) = \left[\frac{S\omega_0^4}{2\beta\gamma^2}\right][e^{-\frac{1}{2}\beta|\tau|}]\left[\cos\omega_1\tau - \frac{\beta}{2\omega_1}\sin\omega_1|\tau|\right], \qquad (7.4.35)$$

$$C_c(\tau) = \left[\frac{S\omega_0^6}{2\beta\varepsilon^2\phi^2}\right][e^{-\frac{1}{2}\beta|\tau|}]\left[\cos\omega_1\tau + \frac{\beta}{2\omega_1}\sin\omega_1|\tau|\right], \qquad (7.4.36)$$

while a driving fluctuation with a periodic component (S_ϕ given by equation (7.4.26)) produces fluctuations characterized by

$$C_f(\tau) = \left[\frac{S\omega_0^4}{2\beta\gamma^2}\right][e^{-\frac{1}{2}\beta|\tau|}]\left[\cos\omega_1\tau - \frac{\beta}{2\omega_1}\sin\omega_1|\tau|\right] + \frac{B}{\pi}|T_f(\omega_p)|^2\cos\omega_p\tau,$$
$$(7.4.37)$$

$$C_c(\tau) = \left[\frac{S\omega_0^6}{2\beta\varepsilon^2\phi^2}\right][e^{-\frac{1}{2}\beta|\tau|}]\left[\cos\omega_1\tau + \frac{\beta}{2\omega_1}\sin\omega_1|\tau|\right] + \frac{B}{\pi}|T_c(\omega_p)|^2\cos\omega_p\tau.$$
$$(7.4.38)$$

Thus we see that when applied to an underdamped system, both quasi-periodic *and* aperiodic driving fluctuations give rise to population fluctuations whose AC$_o$Fs are oscillatory. Aperiodic driving produces phase-forgetting quasi-cycles whose AC$_o$F (see Fig. 7.15(a)) shows cycles whose angular frequency (ω_1) is close to the natural angular frequency of the system (ω_0) and whose amplitude goes to zero as τ becomes large (i.e. $\tau \gg 2/\beta$). A quasi-periodic driver now produces complex quasi-cycles with a phase-remembering component at frequency ω_p and a phase-forgetting component at ω_1, whose AC$_o$F (see Fig. 7.15(b)) thus exhibits a combination of damped oscillations at angular frequency ω_1 and persisting oscillations at frequency ω_p.

Our overall conclusion is thus that while in an overdamped system quasi-cyclic population fluctuations can only be produced by quasi-periodic driving, an underdamped system can in addition exhibit a resonant quasi-cyclic response to aperiodic driving. In practice the condition for the production of identifiable resonant quasi-cycles (equation (7.4.10)) is rather more stringent than the simple condition for underdamping ($\beta < 2\omega_0$). Phase-forgetting quasi-cycles are only distinguishable from aperiodic noise if their coherence number (i.e. the number of cycles during which the system memory persists) is greater than unity. Thus the condition for the production of observable quasi-cycles in this model is

$$n_c = \frac{\omega_1}{\pi\beta} \simeq \frac{\omega_0}{\pi\beta} > 1 \qquad (7.4.39)$$

which is guaranteed if and only if the model parameters are chosen so that

$$\frac{(K\gamma)(K\gamma - \varepsilon)}{r_0\varepsilon} > (\pi^2 + \tfrac{1}{4}) \simeq 10 \qquad (7.4.40)$$

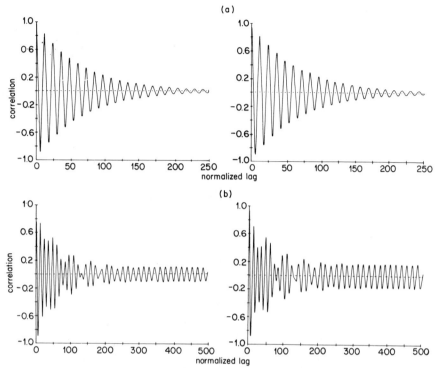

Fig. 7.15. Autocorrelation functions for the damped Lotka–Volterra model with a fluctuating prey intrinsic growth rate and parameters selected to give underdamping ($\beta < 2\omega_0$). The prey population results are shown on the left and the consumer population results on the right. (a) White noise driving fluctuations. (b) Quasi-periodic driving fluctuations

In Fig. 7.16 we illustrate the explicit (non-linear) solution of equations (7.4.11), (7.4.12) (7.4.16) and (7.4.25) with parameters chosen to give a range of coherence numbers. We see that when n_c is small the fluctuations appear essentially aperiodic, while when $n_c \geq 1$ the pattern is for bursts of essentially coherent fluctuations containing about 2–3 n_c cycles to be interspersed with short bursts of apparently incoherent noise. In Fig. 7.17 we illustrate for the purposes of contrast the effectively non-cyclic fluctuations obtained if the system is truly overdamped or is underdamped with a small coherence number.

7.5 SPATIALLY INHOMOGENEOUS ENVIRONMENTAL VARIABILITY

A. Characterization

In Section 7.4 we saw that questions about the qualitative nature of spatially homogeneous fluctuations would best be answered by constructing their time

(a) n_c = 1.1

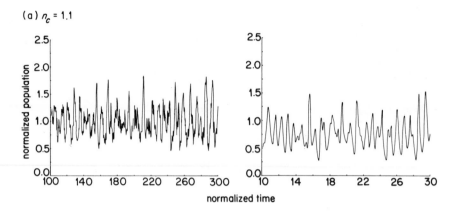

(b) n_c = 5.5

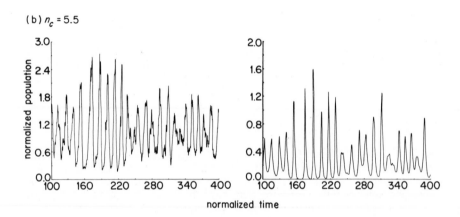

(c) n_c = 21.3

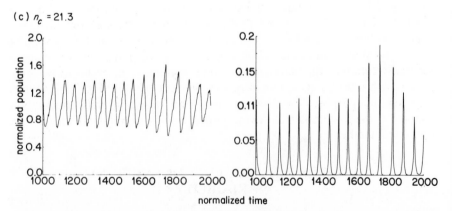

Fig. 7.16. Exogenous resonant quasi-cycles in the damped Lotka–Volterra system with a fluctuating prey intrinsic growth rate. The prey population results are shown on the left and the consumer population results on the right. (a) $n_c = 1.1$. (b) $n_c = 5.5$. (c) $n_c = 21.3$.

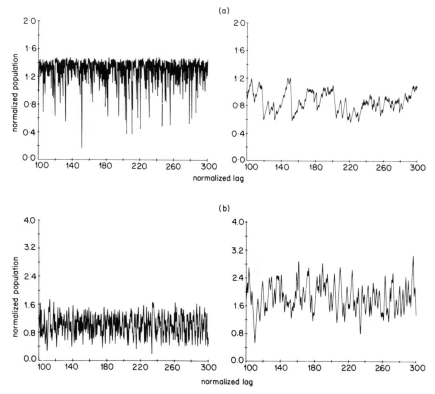

Fig. 7.17. Non-cyclic fluctuations in the damped Lotka–Volterra system with a fluctuating prey intrinsic growth rate. The prey population results are shown on the left and the consumer population results on the right. (a) Overdamped system. (b) Underdamped system with a small coherence numbers.

autocorrelation function, $\rho(\tau)$, which measures the correlation between the fluctuations at times separated by a lag τ. A similarly sensitive characterization of spatially inhomogeneous fluctuations can be attained by measuring the correlation between fluctuations occurring at places separated by a given distance, and times separated by a given lag. For a function of time and a single space variable (say $f(x, t)$) whose time and space average values (denoted by $\langle\ \rangle$ and $\langle\ \rangle_x$ respectively) satisfy

$$\langle f(x, t) \rangle = 0 \qquad \text{for all } x, \tag{7.5.1}$$

$$\langle f(x, t) \rangle_x = 0 \qquad \text{for all } t, \tag{7.5.2}$$

such a measurement is provided by the 'spatio-temporal' autocorrelation function,

$$\rho(\xi, \tau) = \frac{\langle \langle f(x + \xi, t + \tau)f(x, t) \rangle_x \rangle}{\langle \langle f(x, t)f(x, t) \rangle \rangle_x}. \tag{7.5.3}$$

It is clear that the experimental observation of this function requires such immense quantities of data that practical tests of theoretical evaluations are seldom possible. Fortunately, however, it is frequently possible to obtain a perfectly adequate characterization using the two 'partial' ACFs

$$\rho^t(\tau) = \rho(0, \tau),\tag{7.5.4}$$

and

$$\rho^x(\xi) = \rho(\xi, 0).\tag{7.5.5}$$

Although ρ^t and ρ^x are formally the expectation values of the time ACF of data at a given point and the space ACF of data taken at a given time, if we restrict attention to functions which are stationary in both space and time then they can safely be compared with the time ACF of data taken at a single point and the space ACF of data taken at a single time. Clearly these latter functions can be evaluated with more modest amounts of experimental effort.

If we classify the qualitative behaviour of each of the partial ACFs according to the scheme described in Section 7.4 then we can in principle recognize at least nine different regimes into which the behaviour of $f(x, t)$ might be classified. However, not all of these are at all likely to be observed in practice and thus we list below only those four possibilities which seem likely to occur frequently or to be of particular interest.

(a) No repetitive pattern of any kind; both partial ACFs flat or monotonically decreasing.
(b) Stationary spatial pattern; ρ^x quasi-cyclic, ρ^t flat or slowly decreasing.
(c) Homogeneous quasi-cycles; ρ^t quasi-cyclic, ρ^x flat or slowly decreasing.
(d) Quasi-waves; both partials cyclic or quasi-cyclic.

B. Modelling spatially inhomogeneous population fluctuations

Throughout this book we have repeatedly stressed the necessity for all population models to be firmly based on an unambiguous picture of the underlying birth and death processes. In spatially extended environments, however, even the basic formalism for describing birth and death processes is very imperfectly understood, and we therefore cannot follow our usual policy of setting up a formally correct (even if hopelesly cumbersome) formalism so as to develop tractable and well-defined approxiations based upon it. Until such a formalism and the accompanying approximations are developed we cannot obtain even the most approximate answers to questions about extinction is spatially inhomogeneous populations. Nevertheless we may still hope to make some progress in predicting the spatio-temporal pattern of environmentally driven fluctuations in cases where demographic stochasticity is negligible.

In Chapter 5 we discuss in some detail the circumstances in which it is possible to set up reasonably sanitary partial differential equation models of spatially extended populations, and show how such models can be used to derive a transfer function $T(k, \omega)$ relating the Fourier transform of the population fluctuations $(\tilde{\tilde{n}}(k, \omega)$ to the Fourier transform of the environmental fluctuations $(\tilde{\tilde{f}}(k, \omega))$ thus:

$$\tilde{\tilde{n}}(k, \omega) = T(k, \omega)f(k, \omega). \qquad (7.5.6)$$

An obvious extension of this relationship serves to show that if the spectral densities of the population and environmental fluctuations are $S_n(k, \omega)$ and $S_f(k, \omega)$ respectively, then

$$S_n(k, \omega) = |T(k, \omega)|^2 S_f(k, \omega). \qquad (7.5.7)$$

Once we know the spectral density of the fluctuations it is, in principle, straightforward to use the multi-dimensional analogues of equations (F18b) and (F19) to calculate their intensity (variance) and ACF. For the case of a population restricted to a single space dimension we find

$$\sigma^2 = \frac{1}{4\pi^2} \iint_{-\infty}^{\infty} S_n(k, \omega) \, dk \, d\omega, \qquad (7.5.8)$$

and

$$\rho(\xi, \tau) = \left(\frac{1}{2\pi\sigma}\right)^2 \iint_{-\infty}^{\infty} S_n(k, \omega) e^{i(k\xi + \omega\tau)} dk \, d\omega. \qquad (7.5.9)$$

In Sections 7.5C and D we illustrate this procedure by means of worked examples.

C. A single species worked example

As our first example we consider a single-species population distributed with density $\eta(x, t)$ over a one-dimensional space, which grows logistically to a space and time dependent carrying capacity $K(x, t)$, and which disperses by linear diffusion, so that

$$\frac{\partial \eta(x, t)}{\partial t} = r\eta(x, t)\left\{1 - \frac{\eta(x, t)}{K(x, t)}\right\} + D \frac{\partial^2 \eta(x, t)}{\partial x^2}. \qquad (7.5.10)$$

We assume that the carrying capacity variation can be rewritten as

$$K(x, t) = K^* + \phi(x, t) \qquad (7.5.11)$$

where $\phi(x, t)$ is a function with zero mean, and that the boundary conditions are selected so that when $\phi(x, t)$ is set everywhere equal to zero the system has a spatially uniform stationary state

$$\eta^* = K^*. \qquad (7.5.12)$$

Equation (5.6.9) now shows us that the spectral density of the fluctuations in population density (S_η) is related to the spectral density of the driving fluctuations (S_ϕ) by

$$S_\eta(k, \omega) = |T(k, \omega)|^2 S_\phi(k, \omega) \qquad (7.5.13)$$

where the transfer function $T(k, \omega)$ satisfies

$$|T(k, \omega)|^2 = \frac{r^2}{(r + Dk^2)^2 + \omega^2}. \qquad (7.5.14)$$

Thus, from equations (7.5.8) and (7.5.9), the intensity and ACF of the population density fluctuations are

$$\sigma_\eta^2 = \frac{1}{4\pi^2} \iint_{-\infty}^{\infty} \frac{S_\phi(k, \omega)r^2}{(r + Dk^2)^2 + \omega^2} \, dk \, d\omega, \qquad (7.5.15)$$

and

$$\rho_\eta(\xi, \omega) = \left(\frac{1}{2\pi\sigma_\eta}\right)^2 \iint_{-\infty}^{\infty} \frac{S_\phi(k, \omega)r^2 e^{i(k\xi + \omega t)}}{(r + Dk^2) + \omega^2} \, dk \, d\omega. \qquad (7.5.16)$$

We now consider driving fluctuations of two distinct types;

(a) a travelling wave of unit amplitude with angular frequency ω_p and wave-vector k_p, so that

$$S_\phi(k, \omega) = \pi^2 \{\delta_{\text{Dirac}}(k - k_p)\delta_{\text{Dirac}}(\omega - \omega_p) + \delta_{\text{Dirac}}(k + k_p)\delta_{\text{Dirac}}(\omega + \omega_p)\}, \qquad (7.5.17)$$

(b) white noise of unit spectral density, so that

$$S_\phi(k, \omega) = 1 \qquad \text{for all } k, \omega. \qquad (7.5.18)$$

When the driving fluctuation is a travelling wave (S_ϕ given by equation (7.5.17)) then it is easy to show from equations (7.5.15) and (7.5.16) that the intensity and ACF of the population density fluctuations are

$$\sigma_\eta^2 = \tfrac{1}{2} |T(k_p, \omega_p)|^2, \qquad (7.5.19)$$

and

$$\rho(\xi, \tau) = \cos(k_p\xi + \omega_p\tau) \qquad (7.5.20)$$

Thus we see that in this case (precisely as we would expect) the population fluctuation is itself a travelling wave of the same frequency and wave-vector as the driving function, but with an amplitude proportional to the magnitude of the transfer function at the appropriate frequency and wave-vector. When the driving fluctuation is white noise (S_ϕ given by equation (7.5.18)) it is easy to evaluate equation (7.5.15) to show that the intensity of the population density fluctuations is

$$\sigma_\eta^2 = \frac{r^{3/2}}{4D^{1/2}} \qquad (7.5.21)$$

and although we cannot obtain from equation (7.5.16) a simple analytic form for the global autocorrelation function $\rho(\varepsilon, \tau)$ it is relatively straightforward to evaluate the two partial ACFs ρ^t and ρ^t and p^x as

$$\rho^x(\xi) = \exp\{-\sqrt{(r/D)}\xi\},\tag{7.5.22}$$

and

$$\rho^t(\tau) = erfc(\sqrt{(r\tau)}) \equiv \frac{2}{\sqrt{\pi}} \int_{\sqrt{(r\tau)}}^{\infty} e^{-u^2}\,du,\tag{7.5.23}$$

The interpretation of these results is relatively straightforward. The partial ACFs are both monotonically decreasing so that the fluctuations show no pattern of any kind and are significantly correlated only over times less than r^{-1} and distances less than $\sqrt{(Dr^{-1})}$. The only other noteworthy feature can be observed from equation (7.5.21), which shows us that although the fluctuation intensity decreases as we might expect with increasingly effective dispersal (increasing D) it actually increases with increasing intrinsic growth rate (r). A straightforward explanation of this latter result is to be found in the fact that as r increases the population can respond more readily to high frequency components of the driving fluctuation.

D. A two-species worked example

As our final example we consider a general model of two interacting species distributed over a one-dimensional space with densities $\eta_1(x, t)$ and $\eta_2(x, t)$ respectively. Both species are assumed to have population growth rates G_1 and G_2 which depend only on the local population densities and a single environmental parameter $\phi(x, t)$, and to disperse by simple linear diffusion with diffusion coefficients D_1 and D_2 respectively. The dynamics of this system are described by

$$\frac{\partial \eta_m}{\partial t} = G_m(\eta_1, \eta_2, \phi) + D_m \frac{\partial^2 \eta_m}{\partial x^2} \qquad m = 1, 2,\tag{7.5.24}$$

and in Section 5.6B we show that if the spectral densities of the population fluctuations and the driving environmental fluctuations are S_{η_1}, S_{η_2}, and S_ϕ respectively then

$$S_{\eta_m}(k, \omega) = |T_m(k, \omega)|^2 S_\phi(k, \omega),\tag{7.5.25}$$

where if we define

$$A_{mn} = \left(\frac{\partial G_m}{\partial \eta_n}\right)^*,\tag{7.5.26}$$

and

$$\alpha_m = \left(\frac{\partial G_m}{\partial \phi}\right)^*,\tag{7.5.27}$$

then

$$|T_m(k, \omega)|^2 = \frac{[\alpha_n A_{mn} - \alpha_m A_{nn} + \alpha_m D_n k^2]^2 + (\omega \alpha_m)^2}{(\omega_0(k)^2 - \omega^2)^2 + (\omega \beta(k))^2} \quad \text{with} \begin{Bmatrix} m = 1, 2 \\ n = 3 - m \end{Bmatrix},$$

(7.5.28)

where

$$\omega_0^2(k) = (A_{11}A_{22} - A_{12}A_{21}) - (D_1 A_{22} + D_2 A_{11})k^2 + D_1 D_2 k^4, \quad (7.5.29)$$

and

$$\beta(k) = -A_{11} - A_{22} + (D_1 + D_2)k^2. \quad (7.5.30)$$

If we now assume that the driving fluctuations are white noise of unit spectral density then it is clear from equations (7.5.8) and (7.5.9) that the intensity and ACF of the population fluctuations are given by

$$\sigma_m^2 = \frac{1}{4\pi^2} \iint_{-\infty}^{\infty} |T_m(k, \omega)|^2 \, dk \, d\omega \quad (7.5.31)$$

and

$$\rho_m(\xi, \tau) = \left(\frac{1}{2\pi \sigma_m}\right)^2 \iint_{-\infty}^{\infty} |T_m(k, \omega)|^2 e^{i(k\xi + \omega \tau)} dk \, d\omega. \quad (7.5.32)$$

Substituting the explicit form for $|T_m(k, \omega)|^2$ from equation (7.5.28) and then integrating with respect to ω then tells us that

$$\rho_m(\xi, \tau) = \int_{-\infty}^{\infty} W_m(k) e^{-\frac{1}{2}\beta(k)|\tau|} \cos \omega_1(k)\tau \cos k\xi \, dk, \quad (7.5.33)$$

where

$$\omega_1(k) = \sqrt{(\omega_0(k)^2 - \beta^2(k)/4)}, \quad (7.5.34)$$

and

$$W_m(k) = \frac{1}{4\pi \sigma_m^2} \left[\frac{(\alpha_n A_{mn} - \alpha_m A_{nn} + \alpha_m D_n k^2)^2 + \alpha_m^2 \beta(k)}{\omega_0^2(k)\beta(k)} \right] \quad \text{with} \begin{Bmatrix} m = 1, 2 \\ n = 3 - m \end{Bmatrix}.$$

(7.5.35)

The integral in equation (7.5.33) can normally only be evaluated numerically. However, before expending the very considerable computational effort which is required even to evaluate only the four partial ACFs (ρ_m^t and ρ_m^x with $m = 1, 2$) it is wise to try and make an educated guess at the likely outcome. Such an educated guess can be made by examining the nature of the two weighting functions $W_m(k)$. It is immediately clear from equations (7.5.30) and (7.5.35) that for any deterministically stable system, $\beta(k)$ and hence the numerator of equation (7.5.35) are both monotonically increasing positive functions of k. Thus the qualitative behaviour of both weighting functions will be dominated by the variation of $\omega_0^2(k)$. Examination of equation (7.5.29) reveals that $\omega_0^2(k)$ can behave in two qualitatively different ways. If

$$D_1 A_{22} + D_2 A_{11} < 0 \qquad (7.5.36)$$

then ω_0^2 is a monotonically increasing function of k, while if this inequality is not satisfied, then ω_0^2 has a minimum value when $|k| = |k_{max}|$ where

$$k_{max}^2 = \frac{1}{2}\left\{ \frac{A_{11}}{D_1} + \frac{A_{22}}{D_2} \right\}. \qquad (7.5.37)$$

Thus we see that $W(k)$ either has a single maximum value when $k = 0$ or has two maxima at $\pm k_{max}$ respectively. We deal with these two cases in turn.

If inequality (7.5.36) is satisfied and in addition D_1 and D_2 are large so that both weighting functions have a sharply peaked maximum at $k = 0$, we can obtain an educated guess at the general form of $\rho(\xi, \tau)$ by evaluating equation (7.5.33) with $W_m(k)$ set equal to $\delta_{Dirac}(k)$. The result we obtain is

$$\rho(\xi, \tau) \sim e^{-(\beta(0)\tau)/2} \cos \omega_1(0)\tau \qquad (7.5.38)$$

which clearly shows that we should expect a careful evaluation of $\rho(\xi, \tau)$ to show that the fluctuations are homogeneous ($\rho^x(\xi)$ = constant) and that they will in addition be quasi-cyclic in time if $\omega_1(0)$ is real, i.e. if $\omega_0(0) < 2\beta(0)$.

If inequality (7.5.36) is not satisfied and in addition $\omega_0(k_{min})$ is small then $W_m(k)$ has sharp maxima at $k = \pm k_{max}$ and our educated guess can be obtained by setting $W(k) = \frac{1}{2}\{\delta_{Dirac}(k - k_{max}) + \delta_{Dirac}(k + k_{max})\}$ which yields

$$\rho(\xi, \tau) \sim \frac{1}{2}\{e^{-\lambda_1\tau} + e^{-\lambda_2\tau}\}\cos(k_{max}\xi) \qquad (7.5.39)$$

where

$$\lambda_1 = \frac{\beta(k_{max})}{2} + \sqrt{\left(\left[\frac{\beta(k_{max})}{2}\right]^2 - \omega_0^2(k_{max})\right)}, \qquad (7.5.40)$$

and

$$\lambda_2 = \frac{\beta(k_{max})}{2} - \sqrt{\left(\left[\frac{\beta(k_{max})}{2}\right]^2 - \omega_0^2(k_{max})\right)}. \qquad (7.5.41)$$

Thus in this case we expect that an accurate evaluation will show us that $\rho^t(\tau)$ is monotonically decreasing while $\rho^x(\xi)$ is cyclic or quasi-cyclic, which clearly indicates that the fluctuations in population density take the form of a stationary (i.e. non-propagating) spatial pattern.

7.6 INCORPORATING NON-LINEARITY

A. Non-linear stochastic differential equations

We have already demonstrated in Section (7.2) how to perform an exact numerical calculation of the development with time of a population probability distribution in circumstances where we know the functional dependence of the birth and death probabilities on a time-dependent quantity $\phi(t)$. We have also noted that once we elect to regard all or part of the environmental variability as random, we require new techniques to derive the statistical attributes (mean, variance, AC_oF, spectrum, extinction time etc.) of the population fluctuations from the corresponding properties of the driving noise. Our formal theory in Section (7.3) implies a 'brute-force' recipe for this problem: from a knowledge of the spectrum and PDF of the driving fluctuations we construct realizations of $\phi(t)$ and then, provided the spectral density of $\phi(t)$ 'rolls off' to zero at high frequencies, the individual realisations $\phi_i(t)$ are continuous permitting us to solve equations (7.2.1)–(7.2.3) for $P_i(N, t)$, the population PDF corresponding to $\phi_i(t)$. By considering a number of such realizations and averaging, we could obtain the overall PDF (and hence all the other described quantities) to any desired accuracy. However, this is a heavy-handed and somewhat impractical approach which is likely to yield a poor return in ecological insight for a heavy investment of computational effort.

It follows that approximations are required with an accuracy and range of applicability intermediate between the linear approximations already studied and the full numerical works. Ideally, approximation methods are derived by starting with a well-posed mathematical problem and introducing some precisely-defined, if formally unjustifiable assumptions. Very occasionally, the validity of such assumptions can be determined *a priori*, but more commonly they are verified by comparison with exact information obtained by numerical analysis. However, the starting-point for a conventional search for useful approximations is invariably a careful statement of the problem under investigation. To the best of our knowledge, no 'ideal' approximations of this type have been developed for non-linear population models with environmental stochasticity, but instead there have appeared a number of 'shot-in-the-dark' attempts to restate the model in a manner that leads directly to a singly stochastic process describable by a SDE of the form discussed in a different context in Chapter 6, namely

$$dN(t) = f(N)\, dt + g(N)\, d\omega(t), \qquad (7.6.1)$$

for which analytic techniques are available. There is no need to labour the philosophical limitations of this 'solution in search of a problem'; given its shaky foundations it stands or falls on what it delivers.

To see how a SDE of the form (7.6.1) might arise as an approximation to a birth and death process in a randomly varying environment, we first make the familiar discrete-to-continuous approximation and regard population as a continuous variable. With the additional assumption of a well-behaved driving function $\phi(t)$, the population is now described by the non-linear SDE

$$dN(t) = \{B(N, \phi(t)) - D(N, \phi(t))\}\, dt$$
$$+ \{B(N, \phi(t)) + D(N, \phi(t))\}^{1/2}\, d\omega(t). \quad (7.6.2)$$

We further assume that the 'wobble' $f(t)$ in the environmental variable $\phi(t)$

affects the birth and death probabilities additively, so that these take the special forms

$$B(N, \phi(t)) = B(N, \phi^*) + b(N)f(t), \qquad (7.6.3)$$

$$D(N, \phi(t)) = D(N, \phi^*) + d(N)f(t), \qquad (7.6.4)$$

which modifies the form of the non-linear SDE (7.6.2) to

$$dN(t) = \{B(N, \phi^*) - D(N, \phi^*)\}dt + \{b(N) - d(N)\}f(t)dt$$
$$+ \{B(N, \phi(t)) + D(N, \phi(t))\}^{1/2} d\omega(t). \quad (7.6.5)$$

The argument then goes that if the population fluctuations due to demographic stochasticity are small in comparison with the driven fluctuations, we can neglect the last term in equation (7.6.5) leaving us with the apparently simple form

$$dN(t) = \{B(N, \phi^*) - D(N, \phi^*)\} dt + \{b(N) - d(N)\}f(t) dt, \quad (7.6.6)$$

and that this equation can represent the effects of environmental stochasticity if we violate our previous assumption of a well-behaved driving function and let $f(t)$ be Gaussian white noise of spectral density S_ϕ. Since Gaussian white noise is formally the generalized derivative of a Wiener process, we can represent this assumption by

$$f(t) = S_\phi^{1/2} \frac{d\omega_\phi(t)}{dt}, \qquad (7.6.7)$$

where ω_ϕ represents a Wiener process. This yields the non-linear SDE

$$dN(t) = \{B(N, \phi^*) - D(N, \phi^*)\} dt + \{b(N) - d(N)\}S_\phi^{1/2} d\omega_\phi(t), \quad (7.6.8)$$

which is of the desired form (7.6.1) if we set

$$f(N) = B(N, \phi^*) - D(N, \phi^*), \qquad (7.6.9)$$

$$g(N) = \{b(N) - d(N)\}S_\phi^{1/2}. \qquad (7.6.10)$$

This reasoning is deceptively plausible, so it is worthwhile spelling out the assumptions involved and the limitations they imply. First and foremost, by dropping the demographic stochasticity term in equation (7.6.6) we have sacrificed any hope of accurately calculating extinction times. This is worth emphasizing as there exists a substantial quantity of rather difficult literature which purports to model extinction and persistence via equations of the form of (7.6.8). Most analyses of this type, however mathematically clever, are simply ecological nonsense—the unconvinced reader might consult Turelli (1977) who exposes the difficulties lucidly and mercilessly—and the best that can safely be done is to calculate the probability per unit time that N drops below a predetermined small value and to regard this as a measure of extinction probability. Secondly, the assumptions (7.6.3) and (7.6.4) amount to linearizing the effects of environmental variability on the birth and death probabilities, a procedure which is likely to be valid only when the driving fluctuations are small enough to permit the complete locally linear analysis of the previous section (involving linearization about $N = N^*$ and not a general N). Furthermore, once we allow $f(t)$ to be Gaussian white noise (which has infinite variance) the birth and death probabilities can become negative. We are thus forced to conclude that at best, non-linear SDEs of the type (7.6.8) are a marginal improvement on our prevous locally linear approximations.

When we proceed to analyse equation (7.6.8) we discover that this proposed marginal improvement in accuracy has been purchased at the price of mathematical ambiguity and that the final net gain from substantial effort is effectively nil. The reason for this is that white noise is sufficiently discontinuous to be unacceptable in differential equations without erecting a further mathematical edifice to take account of the fact that the processes of defining white noise and constructing differential equations both involve taking limits with $dt \to 0$. To illustrate this point, we recall that environmental white noise is only a convenient fiction used to describe pinkish noise with a large cut-off frequency ω_c implying that formulating the SDE (7.6.8) involves simultaneously taking the limits $dt \to 0$, $\omega_c \to \infty$. The formal solution of equation (7.6.8) involves integrals of the form

$$\int_0^t g(N(t'))\, d\omega(t'), \tag{7.6.11}$$

and integrals of course are themselves defined as limits of sums. It therefore follows that the expected value of the integral (7.6.11) is affected by the extent of correlation between successive terms in the summation which in turn depends on the magnitude of the product $\omega_c dt$. Two cases that have aroused considerable attention are the extremes

$$\omega_c\, dt \ll 1 \qquad \text{Stratanovich rule} \tag{7.6.12}$$

and

$$\omega_c\, dt \gg 1 \qquad \text{Ito rule.} \tag{7.6.13}$$

With the Stratanovich rule it can be shown that the integral (7.6.11) behaves rather like the elementary (Riemann) integrals discussed in introductory calculus texts, a feature which is intuitively plausible since over time intervals dt (which by equation (7.6.12) are much smaller than the correlation time ω_c^{-1} of the noise) the environmental variation is essentially continuous. On the other hand, with the Ito rule the elementary theory of integration is inapplicable and a new formalism is required. The detail of this formalism is beyond the scope of this book because of its doubtful relevance to population modelling, but the main conclusion is of interest. It is found on comparing the results of evaluating the integral (7.6.11) by the two rules that

$$\underset{\text{Stratanovich}}{\int_0^t g(N(t'))\, d\omega(t')} - \underset{\text{Ito}}{\int_0^t g(N(t'))\, d\omega(t')} = \int_0^t g(N(t')) \frac{dg(N(t'))}{dN}\, dt'. \tag{7.6.14}$$

Thus the two prescriptions, when applied to the SDE (7.6.8) lead to results which differ by an amount which is determined by the magnitude of the derivative with respect to N of $b(N) - d(N)$. In other words an SDE of the form (7.6.8) is mathematically ambiguous unless $b(N) - d(N)$ is a constant (as in our linear approximation) and the extent of the ambiguity is controlled by the degree of non-linearity. In effect, the sole advantage of the non-linear SDE over its linear counterpart is lost unless we can specify on *ecological*, rather than mathematical grounds, which integration rule to use.

It appears likely that any ecological arguments invoked to justify a particular choice of integration rule will be somewhat fragile. At best, a single-species non-linear birth and death model is an over-simple characterization of population growth, developed to capture the basic features of demographic fluctuations in regulated populations but (through neglect of age-structure, time-delays etc.) unlikely to be of much value when considering very short time scales. Similarly, the white noise approximation of environmental variation and the 'pseudo-linearization' implied by equations (7.6.3) and (7.6.4) are pretty crude characterizations of reality, unlikely to survive detailed scrutiny over short time intervals. Furthermore lurking in the background of any discussion of the limit $dt \to 0$ is the practical problem of estimating from experimental data the instantaneous (as opposed to time-averaged) values of birth and death probabilities, a procedure involving a number of replicate populations which grows to infinity as $dt \to 0$!

Why then have considerable efforts been expended in attempts to represent the effects of environmental stochasticity through the SDE (7.6.1)? The answer is the promise of a mathematical pay-off, since a population obeying this type of SDE has a probability density which is the solution of a diffusion equation of the form

$$\frac{\partial p(N, t)}{\partial t} = -\frac{\partial}{\partial N} \{M(N)p(N, t)\} + \frac{1}{2}\frac{\partial^2}{\partial N^2} \{V(N)p(N, t)\} \quad (7.6.15)$$

where the functions $M(N)$ and $V(N)$ (very loosely, M for mean rate and V for variance in population drift) can be determined from the SDE once an integration rule has been selected. In the 'birth and death' notation of equation (7.6.8), the results are

$$M(N) = \begin{cases} B(N, \phi^*) - D(N, \phi^*) & \text{Ito} \\ B(N, \phi^*) - D(N, \phi^*) + \frac{1}{2}S_\phi\{b(N) - d(N)\}\dfrac{d}{dN}\{b(N) - d(N)\} & \\ & \text{Stratanovich} \end{cases}$$

$$\hspace{10cm} (7.6.16)$$

$$V(N) = S_\phi\{b(N) - d(N)\}^2 \quad \text{Ito and Stratanovich} \quad\quad (7.6.17)$$

Armed with knowledge of $M(N)$ and $V(N)$ we can calculate a steady state probability density (if one exists) by setting $\partial p(N, t)/\partial t$ to zero to obtain

$$p^*(N) \propto [V(N)]^{-1} \exp 2 \left\{ \int_0^N \frac{M(x)}{V(x)} \, dx \right\} \qquad (7.6.18)$$

However, much of the value of such a probability density is lost by the assumptions used in its derivation and in particular it is very dangerous to base even the most speculative discussion of extinction on it. Again we refer the reader to Turelli's (1977) lucid paper for further detail concerning the mathematically strange and ecologically irrelevant phenomena that can be generated by this procedure.

B. Constructing realizations

In spite of the serious limitations of non-linear SDEs as *models*, there are situations where they can be used to add a little extra realism to a locally linear approximation (e.g. by stopping populations going negative!). The objective of such a study is more likely to be some additional 'feel' for the pattern of fluctuations than any improvement in statistical accuracy, and one route to such insight is the examination of explicit realizations of 'solutions' of the stochastic differential equations. With single-species models such realizations are a poor second best to realisations of the underlying birth and death model, but with more complex systems they appear to be the sole simple route to information on the effects of non-linearity.

The SDEs with which we are concerned contain a 'driving' white noise term

$$f(t) \equiv \frac{d\omega_\phi(t)}{dt}, \qquad (7.6.19)$$

with unit spectral density, and it is evident that integration of the SDE requires us to generate a sequence of values of $f(t)$ at time $t_s = s\Delta t$ (s an integer). From our earlier discussions of white noise we know that successive values of $f(t)$ should be statistically independent and drawn from a normal distribution with zero mean. The variance σ^2 of this distribution is obtained by noting that for a run of P values of t, the best approximation to the Fourier transform $\tilde{f}(\omega)$ is the summation

$$\tilde{f}(\omega) = \Delta t \sum_{s=1}^{P} f(t_s) e^{-i\omega t_s}. \qquad (7.6.20)$$

The spectral density $S(\omega)$ is then (cf. equations (F11) and (7.2.17))

$$S(\omega) = \frac{E\{|\tilde{f}(\omega)|^2\}}{P\Delta t} = \frac{\Delta t}{P} E\left\{ \sum_{s=1}^{P} \sum_{r=1}^{P} f(t_s) f(t_r) e^{-i\omega(t_r - t_s)} \right\}. \qquad (7.6.21)$$

However, since the values of $f(t_r)$ and $f(t_s)$ are independent unless $s = r$, the above expression simplifies to give

$$S(\omega) = \frac{\Delta t}{P} \sum_{s=1}^{P} |f(t_s)|^2 = \Delta t \sigma_f^2, \qquad (7.6.22)$$

from which we deduce that to represent white noise of unit spectral density we draw values from a normal distribution with mean zero and variance equal to $1/\Delta t$.

To generate a realization of pink noise there are two approaches. The most reliable is to evaluate the Fourier transform of sampled white noise generated by the above procedure, multiply the transform by $(1 + i\omega\tau_c)^{-1}$ where τ_c is the coherence time of the pink noise, and then perform an inverse Fourier transformation. (The reader can check by comparison with equation (7.3.21) that this produces pink noise.) This procedure is computationally practical for up to a few thousand data points if a program implementing the so-called 'fast Fourier transform' (FFT) is available (for example, Singleton, 1968, 1969). However, most realizations of SDEs are constructed with rather short time increments and this approach rapidly becomes time-consuming. The alternative approach is to recognize that pink noise itself can be generated by an SDE, namely

$$df(t) = -\tau_c^{-1}f(t)\,dt + d\omega(t) \tag{7.6.23}$$

and to solve this equation *simultaneously* with original SDE.

Once we have generated a realization of the driving noise (which in the following discussion we assume to be white) there remains the problem of integrating the SDE to produce a realization. With the Ito interpretation of an SDE, the simplest procedure is simply to choose a small time increment Δt and integrate step by step. This often requires a very small timestep and is excessively tedious but the results are normally meaningful (though the reader should beware of the computational booby traps triggered by the growth of $1/\Delta t$, the variance of the driving noise, as Δt becomes small). A Stratanovich SDE can be integrated in the same way by first using equation (7.6.14) to convert it to an Ito equation. However, the use of the more sophisticated algorithms which are strongly recommended with ordinary differential equations (Runge–Kutta, predictor–corrector etc.) is fraught with pitfalls.

C. Robustness

In spite of their limited value as population *models*, non-linear SDEs can be used in assessing the *mathematical* robustness of the locally linear approximations which we have been advocating in this chapter. We now outline the results of one such exercise (due to Pettipher and reported with other work in Nisbet, Gurney and Pettipher, 1977) involving yet again the damped Lotka–Volterra model (defined by equations (7.4.11) and (7.4.12)).

With this model, we have already (in Chapter 4) demonstrated the robustness of the locally linear approximation when applied to the special case of a deterministic sinusoidal driver. Since white noise is simply the superposition of many (strictly speaking, an infinite number of) such sinusoids, we should intuitively expect similar results with externally applied white noise, and Pettipher's results confirm this. He assumed the predator death rate in equation

(7.4.12) to be varying randomly and set

$$\varepsilon(t) = \varepsilon_0 + \xi(t), \tag{7.6.24}$$

where $\xi(t)$ was white noise of spectral density S. After local linearization and the use of the basic recipe, the fluctuation intensities for both populations were calculated as

$$\sigma_f^2 = \frac{SK}{2\gamma}\left(1 - \frac{\varepsilon}{\gamma K}\right), \tag{7.6.25}$$

$$\sigma_c^2 = \frac{Sr^2}{2\alpha^2\gamma K}\left(1 - \frac{\varepsilon}{\gamma K}\right)\left(\frac{\gamma^2 K^2}{\varepsilon r} - \frac{\gamma K}{r} + 1\right). \tag{7.6.26}$$

The effect of non-linearities on these approximations was tested by running realizations of the non-linear SDE with $\varepsilon(t)$ given by equation (7.6.24). The equation was interpreted as an Ito equation and integrated by the tedious step-by-step (Euler) algorithm described in Section 7.6B. For each of several values of S, a number (around 6) of realizations were run and the fluctuation intensity estimated. The results are shown in Fig. 7.18, and confirm the robustness of the linear approximation over the range of values of S studied, which ran right to the point where rapid extinction of realizations made estimation of the fluctuation statistics impractical.

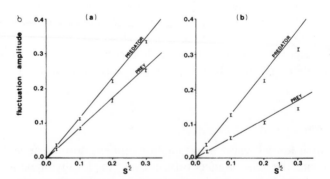

Fig. 7.18. A comparison of the standard deviations in prey and predator populations for a driven damped Lotka–Volterra model obtained from explicit realizations of the non-linear SDE (I) and from local linearization (——). The parameter values are: (a) $r = 1, K = 2, \theta = 1, \gamma = 1, \varepsilon = 0.5$ (an underdamped case), (b) $r = 1, K = 0.5, \theta = 1, \gamma = 1, \varepsilon = 0.35$ (an overdamped case). (Reproduced with permission from Nisbet, et al., *Journal of Theoretical Biology*, **68**, 143–160. Copyright by Academic Press Inc. (London) Ltd.)

7.7 OVERVIEW OF STOCHASTIC MODELLING

This chapter and its predecessor have contained heavy doses of both mathematical formalism and mathematical approximations. With the advantages of hindsight we now re-examine briefly the questions of how to select a type of model and how to decide which mathematical approximations may be invoked in its analysis.

The first question to consider is, 'When are stochastic models necessary'. Given that all the models we use are phenomenological and are thus (apart from the population balance equation $\Delta N = B - D + I - E$) based on equations which, unlike the fundamental equations in physics, cannot be regarded as articles of faith, the answer is determined by the return in ecological insight assessed against the input of personal effort. The amount of effort required for a particular piece of stochastic modelling is in turn determined by one's own background and in 'strategic' studies whose objective is 'feel' for possible types of dynamical behaviour the point at which to introduce stochastic models is thus in part a subjective matter. The only clear-cut objective criterion is that at least a superficial consideration of stochastic phenomena is unavoidable in all cases where demographic stochasticity is significant, and this includes *all* studies of extinction. With 'tactical' models and testable models of laboratory systems, the 'stochastic versus deterministic' decision is controlled by the magnitude of the demographic stochasticity. However, this is *not* a quantity which can be measured in advance of modelling, a point which we hope will become clear in the case studies. It is particularly well illustrated by the blowfly quasi-cycles in Fig. 8.1 in which we cannot decide *a priori* whether the characteristic 'jitter' at the top of the cycles is demographic noise or deterministically explicable structure; indeed one of the principal objectives of the modelling is to answer just that question.

Once we have chosen to use a stochastic model, there remains the task of selecting the mathematical approach to follow in its analysis. At the risk of providing fuel for May's now notorious on-line incinerator (May, 1974b, p. 10), we have decided to draw out the sequence of decisions involved in calculating fluctuation intensities on a flow diagram of the type favoured by systems analysts (Fig. 7.19) Most of the questions posed in the diagram have already been discussed in the text, but some points bear repeating. The first, and by far the most important, is that the starting point of any population model is the specification of birth and death probabilities over some (usually, but not invariably, small) time interval. The next is that the choice of representation of environmental variation is an exercise in modelling and not in mathematics; in particular 'random' environmental fluctuations are a fiction we invoke when ignorant of their detailed form. It follows that when faced with a situation involving large 'random' environmental variations, the likeliest way forward is to find out (or guess!) more about them, rather than to develop an elaborate (and new) mathematical formalism appropriate for 'truly' random phenomena. The final point is that at no less than four points in

278

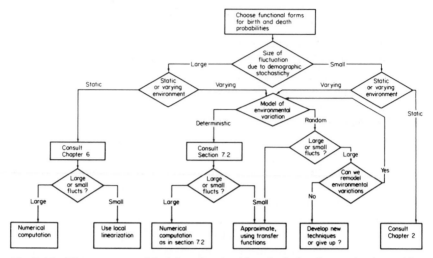

Fig. 7.19. The sequence of decisions involved in calculating fluctuation intensities from a stochastic model.

the diagram, we are asked to characterize fluctuations as 'large or small'. This leads us right back to the question of the robustness of approximations based on local linearization which we discussed in equation (7.6.). Given our broad conclusion that these approximations are more reliable than we have any right to expect, the default option here is to regard fluctuations as 'small' wherever this is remotely plausible, but this choice should normally be justified *a posteriori* by some numerical checks on the original non-linear model.

The decision sequence in calculating extinction times is closely related to that in Fig. 7.19. Either we use one of the exact methods outlined in Sections 6.6 and 7.2, or we rely on one of the more questionable simplifications in which the relative fluctuation intensity is used as an indicator of the expected time to extinction. In the first case, the difficulties are mathematical or computational and not conceptual, in the second they have already been discussed in the previous paragraph.

We conclude this overview by remarking on the number of points where decisions are made and then justified retrospectively. This is proof (if such is needed) that the various ecological, conceptual and mathematical questions involved in modelling population changes are never truly de-coupled, and 'modelling philosophies' such as we have outlined should be treated in the same way as models—retained only as long as they assist progress. Which is an appropriate point to cease philosophizing and start on the case studies.

SOURCES AND SUGGESTED FURTHER READING

Birth and death processes in varying environments: In spite of considerable interest in related problems in population genetics, there appears to be rather little applicable published work on birth and death processes in varying environments (deterministic or random). Keiding (1975) studies exponential growth and decline in random environments. Torrez (1979) derives recipes for extinction probabilities and extinction times in simple non-linear models, but the examples given are not ecologically relevant.

Environmental stochasticity: The basic strategy of modelling the effects of a varying environment by allowing random variation in one or more parameters has been used in a very wide range of applications. Areas where it has proved particularly effective include the evaluation of harvesting strategies (Beddington, and May, 1977, and modelling the 'ecological niche' (e.g. May, 1974a, Feldman and Roughgarden, 1975, Roughgarden, 1975, Turelli, 1978, Nisbet, Gurney, and Pettipher, 1978).

Stochastic differential and difference equations and diffusion approximations: Early work on population persistence and extinction using SDEs concentrated on demonstrating the existence of stationary solutions to diffusion equations (e.g. May, 1973b) and although it fortuitously led to many correct insights, this approach is now discredited, (see e.g. Turelli, 1977) in favour of the traditional procedure of carefully examining behaviour at the boundaries $N = 0$ and $N = \infty$ (Turelli 1977, Turelli and Gillespie, 1980). The reader who does not share our fear of the pitfalls associated with modelling extinction with the aid of continuous (diffusion or SDE) equations will find some useful mathematical techniques, clearly presented in Ludwig (1975) and Schuss (1980). The use of local linearization followed by Fourier analysis in the study of gross fluctuation characteristics has been advocated by Roughgarden (1975) and the reliability of results obtained in this way assessed by Nisbet, Gurney and Pettipher (1977). Platt and Denman (1975) survey situations where the spectral analysis of ecological data may aid modelling. Linear stochastic difference equation models are very commonly used in time series analysis (e.g. Chatfield, 1975; their use in population dynamics has been proposed by Poole (1976) in a paper which aroused some controversy (Anderson, 1978; Poole, 1978). A lucid introduction to the interpretation of non-linear SDEs, albeit in a physical context is given by Mortensen (1969).

Spatially distributed population: The literature on the effects of variable environments on the dynamics of spatially distributed population appears to be very sparse, largely we suspect because the *formulation* of non-linear birth and death models for mobile organisms is a difficult exercise (cf. Mollison 1977.)

PROBLEMS

(Those marked * are mathematically more demanding than the others.)

1. (Hassell, Lawton, and May, 1976). The difference equation model

$$N_{t+1} = (r + 1)N_t(1 + aN_t)^{-\beta}$$

was used by the above authors to model a large number of insect populations (cf. our discussion in Section 2.9). For the mosquito *Aedes aegypti*
they estimated (with large uncertainties)

$$r \simeq 10, \qquad \beta \simeq 2.$$

Show that with these parameters, a population of *Aedes aegypti* would in
an unchanging environment be stable and underdamped and estimate the
coherence number. Hence determine whether resonant quasi-cycles
might be expected in a variable environment.

2. Consider a birth and death model with

$$B(N) = \beta N; \qquad D(N) = \delta N \left\{ 1 - \frac{(\beta - \delta)N}{\delta K} \right\}.$$

(a) Show that the deterministic analogue of this model is a logistic
equation with carrying capacity K and intrinsic growth rate
$r = \beta - \delta$.

(b) Use the locally linear approximations of Chapter 6 to show that in a
static environment the intensity of the fluctuations due to demographic stochasticity is approximately

$$\sigma_N^2 = \frac{\beta K}{(\beta - \delta)},$$

and hence that with the crudest (Gaussian) approximation to the
population's CPDF, the mean time to extinction satisfies

$$\ln(\delta \tau_E) \simeq \frac{(\beta - \delta)K}{2\beta}$$

(c)* Use the approximation developed in Section 7.2C to derive an
approximation to the mean time to extinction when the carrying
capacity varies sinusoidally as

$$K = K_0(1 + b \cos \omega t).$$

3. (Nisbet, Gurney and Pettipher, 1977). The intensity of population fluctuations driven by environmental stochasticity can be greatly increased by
time-delays. To demonstrate this, consider the time-delayed logistic
parametrized in the peculiar form

$$\frac{dN}{dt} = rN(1 - \beta N_D) \qquad \text{with } N_D(t) \equiv N(t - T_D),$$

where β is the reciprocal of the carrying capacity. To model a fluctuating
carrying capacity, set

$$\beta = \beta_0(1 + \gamma(t)),$$

and scale the units of population so that $\beta_0 = 1$.

(a) Show that if $y(t)$ is white noise of spectral density S, then the intensity of the driven population fluctuations is approximately (in scaled units)

$$\sigma_N^2 = \frac{rS}{\pi} \int_0^\infty \frac{du}{1 + u^2 - 2u \sin(urT_D)}$$

which diverges to infinity as rT_D approaches $\pi/2$ (the point where deterministic instability occurs—see Section 2.7).

(b) Sketch the form of the spectral density function for a few values of the controlling parameter group rT_D in the underdamped region $(0.37 < r\tau < 1.57)$ and guess the minimum value of rT_D at which significant resonant quasi-cycles might arise.

4. (Roughgarden 1975). The logistic equation in discrete time can be written in the form

$$N_{t+\tau} = \left\{ 1 + r\tau - \frac{r\tau}{K_t} N_t \right\} N_t$$

where K_t is the carrying capacity at time t.

(a) Suppose the carrying capacity executed small fluctuations $k_t \, (\equiv k_t - K^*)$ about its mean value K^*, and show that to first order in n and k

$$n_{t+\tau} = (1 - r\tau)n_t + r\tau k_t. \tag{A}$$

(b) Hence show that if the values of k_t at successive times are uncorrelated and if k_t is normally distributed with zero mean and variance σ_k^2, then the intensity of the population fluctuations is

$$\sigma_N^2 = \frac{r\tau \sigma_k^2}{(2 - r\tau)},$$

provided $0 < r\tau < 2$.

(c)* Alternatively suppose that the fluctuations in carrying capacity are modelled as pink noise by way of a first-order autoregressive model

$$k_{t+\tau} = (1 - \tau/\tau_c)k_t + Z_t \tag{B}$$

where the Zs are independent, identically distributed random variables with mean zero and variance σ_z^2. By Fourier transforming equations (A) and (B) or by using the 'direct methods' of Section 6.6 show that the fluctuation intensity is now

$$\sigma_N^2 = \frac{r\tau}{2 - r\tau} \left\{ \frac{1 + (1 - r\tau)(1 - \tau/\tau_c)}{1 - (1 - r\tau)(1 - \tau/\tau_c)} \right\} \sigma_k^2.$$

5. A population has a density-dependent birth rate of the logistic form

$$B(N) = \begin{cases} aN(1 - N/K) & \text{if } N < K \\ 0 & \text{if } N \geq K, \end{cases}$$

and a death rate (incorporating natural deaths and harvesting)

$$D(N) = \delta N$$

(a) Calculate the expected time to extinction if the harvesting rate remains constant.

(b) Suppose that harvesting is restricted to 50 per cent of the year so that we can set

$$\delta(t) = \begin{cases} \delta_0 & \text{if } n < t < n + \frac{1}{2} \\ \delta_0 - \varepsilon & \text{if } n + \frac{1}{2} < t < n + 1 \end{cases}$$

where n is an integer. Suppose a is sufficiently large that we can use the approximation in Section 7.2C and estimate the new extinction time.

(c) Investigate whether a given fixed yield could more safely be obtained by constant effort harvesting or by seasonal harvesting.

Part III

Case Studies

Chapter 8

Oscillations in Laboratory Fly Populations

8.1 INTRODUCTION

Most elementary texts on population biology show, somewhere in the section on population oscillations, a picture of large, quasi-periodic fluctuations in the population of a laboratory culture in which some kind of fly is fed on a steadily replenished supply of inanimate food. The data most commonly used for this purpose, which is shown in Fig. 8.1, was obtained by Nicholson (1954, 1957) from cultures of the sheep blowfly *Lucillia cuprina*, in which the population was controlled by a single limiting factor: either the rate of food supply to the adult population ($N \# 1$) or the rate of food supply to the larvae ($N \# 2$, $N \# 3$). Fluctuations of a similar general type have also been observed in cultures of the housefly *Musca domestica* (Taylor and Sokal, 1976).

Despite their popularity as examples of oscillatory behaviour, there has been surprisingly little detailed theoretical analysis of these data sets. It is clear from the work of Maynard Smith (1974), which we described in Chapter 2, that almost any population dynamic in which high fertility is combined with a long development delay can, in principle, generate fluctuations of an appropriate type. However, despite a variety of more or less sophisticated attempts, no theoretical model has yet yielded a really satisfactory fit to even a single data set, still less provided a clear picture of the mechanism underlying the fluctuations so as to form a comprehensive framework within which the various, subtly different, experimental results can be systematically inter-related.

In this chapter we seek to formulate a model capable of providing such a framework, but as an initial (less ambitious) target we shall try to answer a number of specific questions concerning Nicholson's blowfly data:

(a) Are the fluctuations self sustaining limit cycles or driven quasi-cycles?
(b) What determines the period of the cycles and in particular its relationship to the development delay?

286

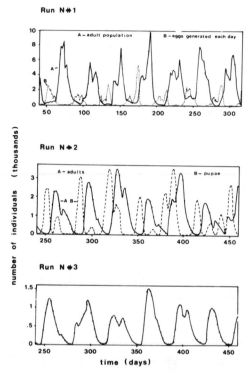

Fig. 8.1. Oscillations in laboratory cultures
of *Lucillia cuprina*. (From Nicholson, 1954,
1957.) (Reproduced by permission of CSIRO
and Cold Spring Harbor Laboratory)

(c)   What determines the amplitude of the cycles?
(d)   Why do the discrete generations observed in the larval-food limited
      cases ($N \# 2$, $N \# 3$) occur at uneven time intervals?
(e)   Why, in the adult-food limited case ($N \# 1$) do these discrete genera-
      tions merge into a single, almost continuous period of reproduction?

   If it is to be capable of answering the last two of these questions our model
clearly cannot simply *assume* that generations are discrete; rather it must
make the initial assumption of overlapping generations but its dynamics must
be such as to cause the spontaneous appearance of clearly marked discrete
generations under the appropriate conditions. In technical terms this implies
that we must formulate our model in terms of a differential rather than a
difference equation, and all the models which we shall discuss in this chapter
are therefore continuous-time models expressed in terms of differential
equations.

8.2   THE TIME-DELAYED LOGISTIC MODEL

Probably the simplest single-species continuous-time model capable of generating cyclic or quasi-cyclic fluctuations is the time-delayed logistic

$$\frac{dN(t)}{dt} = rN(t)\left\{1 - \frac{N(t - T_D)}{K}\right\} \tag{8.2.1}$$

which we discussed briefly in Chapter 2. Although this model violates one of the most fundamental rules of successful population modelling in that it is not based on clearly identified birth and death processes, it was, nevertheless, used by May (1974(b)) in the most successful previous attempt to fit a continuous time model to Nicholson's data. We shall therefore begin our deliberations by re-examining May's results, which relate to the adult food limited case $N \# 1$.

A. Analysis of the model

Since the analysis given in Section 2.7 is both brief and at the other end of the book, we shall reanalyse equation (8.2.1) from first principles. We begin by identifying those parameters which actually influence the qualitative features of the model's behaviour as distinct from those which can simply be thought of as 'scales'. To this end we restate equation (8.2.1) in terms of dimensionless variables

$$N' = N/K, \tag{8.2.2}$$

$$t' = t/T_D, \tag{8.2.3}$$

as

$$\frac{dN'}{dt'} = rT_D N'(t')\{1 - N'(t' - 1)\}, \tag{8.2.4}$$

thus showing that the qualitative behaviour of this model will be entirely determined by the value of the single free parameter rT_D.

Equation (8.2.4) has a single non-trivial stationary state

$$N'^* = 1 \tag{8.2.5}$$

and, following our standard procedure, we obtain a linear approximation to the properties of the system near this state by defining $n'(t')$ as the deviation of $N'(t')$ from N'^*, assuming that this deviation is small, and hence showing that to first order

$$\frac{dn'}{dt'} = -rT_D n'(t' - 1). \tag{8.2.6}$$

Following the procedure set out in Chapter 2, we assume that this equation has a solution of the general form

$$n'(t') = e^{-\mu't'}e^{i\omega't'} \tag{8.2.7}$$

and thus investigate the deterministic local stability of the system (i.e. whether a small perturbation from N'^* will grow or decay) by determining the values of the damping constant μ' for which such a solution is possible. On substituting the trial solution (8.2.7) back into the linearized dynamic equation (8.2.6) we find that the two are compatible if and only if

$$\mu' = + rT_D e^{\mu'} \cos \omega', \tag{8.2.8}$$

$$\omega' = + rT_D e^{\mu'} \sin \omega', \tag{8.2.9}$$

(cf. equations (2.7.5) and (2.7.6)).

Although these equations cannot be solved analytically they are extremely simple to solve numerically and in Fig. 8.2 we plot the allowed values of μ' and ω' against the controlling parameter rT_D. Figure 8.2 illustrates clearly the theoretical result (equation (2.7.8)) that if $rT_D < 1.57$, then μ' is positive, small perturbations from the steady state will decay and hence the stationary state is locally stable. When $rT_D < 0.37$ we see that the normalized natural

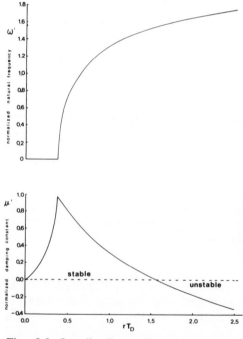

Fig. 8.2. Locally linear behaviour of the time-delayed logistic model. Numerical solutions of equations (8.2.8) and (8.2.9) plotted as a function of the controlling parameter rT_D.

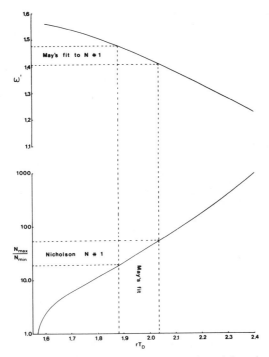

Fig. 8.3. The behaviour of the time-delayed
logistic model in the locally unstable region.

frequency ω' is zero, so that the return to equilibrium is monotonic (overdamped), while if $0.37 < rT_D < 1.57$ then ω' is finite and the return to
equilibrium is oscillatory (underdamped).

In the deterministically unstable region $rT_D > 1.57$ the exact solution of
the non-linear dynamic equation is a limit cycle, whose properties can only be
determined by direct numerical integration of equation (8.2.4). Fortunately
this investigation has already been performed for us by May (1974b) whose
results we quoted in Chapter 2. For ease of consultation we reproduce May's
results in Fig. 8.3, as a plot of normalized angular frequency ω' and maximum
to minimum population ratio (N_{max}/N_{min}) against rT_D.

B. Testing the model

The procedure used by May to fit the time delayed logistic model to the data
obtained by Nicholson in run $N\,\#\,1$, was to regard both the intrinsic growth
rate r and the development delay T_D as adjustable parameters whose values
he determined in the following way. We first observe the data has

$$\frac{N_{max}}{N_{min}} = 36 \pm 17, \tag{8.2.10}$$

which, if we assume that the fluctuations are of limit-cycle type, implies at once (see Fig. 8.3) that the controlling parameter rT_D must have a value in the range

$$1.880 < rT_D < 2.035. \tag{8.2.11}$$

We then choose the time scale of the model so as to produce the correct absolute value for the cycle period. From Fig. 8.3 it is clear that if rT_D is in the range given above then the normalized angular frequency of the cycles ω' must be in the range

$$1.405 < \omega' < 1.475 \tag{8.2.12}$$

or, equivalently, that the absolute cycle period T must be related to the development delay T_D by

$$4.26\, T_D < T < 4.47\, T_D. \tag{8.2.13}$$

Since the observed value of the absolute cycle period for run $N \# 1$ is

$$T = 38.1 \pm 1.5 \text{ days}, \tag{8.2.14}$$

this leads us to conclude that the development delay T_D must have an absolute value in the range

$$8.2 \text{ days} < T_D < 9.3 \text{ days}. \tag{8.2.15}$$

Thus we conclude that, by May's procedure, the parameters which provide the best fit of the time-delayed logistic model to Nicholson's run $N \# 1$ data are

$$r = 0.225 \pm 0.025 \text{ days}^{-1}, \tag{8.2.16}$$
$$T_D = 8.75 \pm 0.55 \text{ days}.$$

May evaluated the plausibility of this fit by comparing these parameter values with independent experimental observations. In particular he compared the best fit value of the delay time T_D with a value obtained from the life-history data for *Lucillia cuprina* in laboratory culture given by Nicholson (1957) and reproduced in Fig. 8.4.

By identifying $N(t)$ with the total population of both mature and immature adults May concluded that the appropriate value of the delay time was 12.1 days; a figure which he argued, compared acceptably with a best fit delay of around 9 days. Even accepting at face value the argument leading to a delay of 12.1 days the discrepancy between best fit and observed delay times remains worryingly large when compared with the confidence limits on the best fit value. However, an even more serious discrepancy becomes apparent when we realize that if we regard $N(t)$ as representing the total adult population (including reproductively inactive immatures) then there is no plausible reason for supposing that a simple relationship exists between the size of that population and the rate at which it reproduces. If we overcome this difficulty by defining $N(t)$ as the sexually mature adult population then examination of

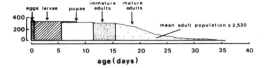

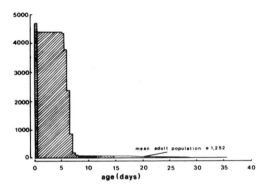

Fig. 8.4 Experimentally observed age-structure of *Lucillia cuprina* populations in
laboratory culture. (From Nicholson, 1957.)

Fig. 8.4 shows at once that the appropriate value of the delay time is somewhere between 14.3 and 15.6 days.

In fact we have an independent check on the value of the delay, since the
egg-laying data for run $N \# 1$ clearly shows bursts of reproduction preceding
each adult population peak. Since we know that in the adult food limited case,
egg to adult survival is both high and constant throughout the experiment, it
seems eminently reasonable to believe that the time lag between the peak rate
of egg laying and the subsequent adult population peak should be rather
precisely the delay time T_D. Examination of the data shows that this delay is
14.8 ± 0.4 days, and in view of the close correspondence between this value
and the life-history data we shall adopt the value

$$T_D = 14.8 \pm 0.4 \text{ days} \qquad (8.2.17)$$

in all our subsequent deliberations.

The fitting procedure we discussed above rests on the assumption that the
fluctuations observed by Nicholson are of limit-cycle type. Although the
plausibility of the fit thus obtained is highly questionalbe we cannot entirely
reject the time-delayed logistic model without first investigating the possibility that Nicholson was, in fact, observing resonant quasi-cycles (see Section
7.4). To evaluate this possibility we now make a second attempt to fit the
model to Nicholson's run $N \# 1$ data, this time plugging the measured value
for the delay time directly into the fitting procedure and using as our principal

input the observation that for this run the period to delay ratio is

$$T/T_D = 2.6 \pm 0.1. \qquad (8.2.18)$$

If the fluctuations are resonant quasi-cycles then their normalized angular frequency will be very close to that characterizing the oscillatory return to a stable equilibrium. They must therefore exhibit a period to delay ratio which is wholly determined by the value of rT_D and is related to the normalized natural angular frequency ω' plotted in Fig. 8.3 by

$$T/T_D = 2\pi/\omega'. \qquad (8.2.19)$$

If the fluctuations are of limit-cycle type then they will display a period to delay ratio which is similarly related to the normalized angular frequency plotted in Fig. 8.4, and which is thus also wholly determined by rT_D.

In Fig. 8.5 we plot the period to delay ratio predicted by the time-delayed logistic model over the entire range of rT_D for which it is capable of exhibiting any kind of cyclic or quasi-cyclic fluctuation. We see at once that there is no value of rT_D in either the limit-cycle or the quasi-cycle regime for which the discrepancy between the observed and predicted values of T/T_D is less than 53 per cent. We must thus conclude that the time-delayed logistic model is fundamentally incapable of explaining the fluctuations observed in Nicholson's experiments.

8.3   A MORE REALISTIC MODEL

We have clearly demonstrated the inability of the time-delayed logistic model to provide an acceptable fit to Nicholson's blowfly data. If we are to understand these experiments we therefore require a new and somewhat more

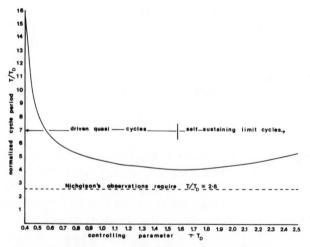

Fig. 8.5. Behaviour of the time-delayed logistic model.
Predicted cycle period as a function of rT_D.

realistic model. It will of necessity be a little more complex than the time-delayed logistic, but nevertheless if our efforts are to have any chance of success we must make strenuous efforts to minimize the number of adjustable parameters we introduce.

A. Formulation of the model

Nicholson's data consist primarily of observations of the time variation of adult population. We therefore begin by writing down a balance equation, similar to equation (2.1.1), for the population of sexually mature adults $N(t)$. The experimental conditions clearly rule out any possibility of immigration or emigration and the instantaneous rate of change of $N(t)$ must thus be simply the difference between the instantaneous rate of recruitment to the adult population $R(t)$ and the instantaneous total death rate $D(t)$, so that

$$\frac{dN}{dt} = R(t) - D(t). \tag{8.3.1}$$

The question of recruitment to the adult population should properly be dealt with by writing down balance equations analogous to equation (8.3.1) for the populations of all the various stages in the life-history of the species concerned. However, we shall evade the complexity which this would entail by means of three simplifying assumptions:

(a) all eggs take exactly T_D time units to develop into sexually mature adults,
(b) the rate at which the adult population produces eggs depends only on its current size,
(c) the probability of a given egg maturing into a viable adult depends only on the number of competitors of the same age.

Taken together, these imply that the rate of recruitment at time $t + T_D$ is a function (which we define formally as $\theta(N)$) only of the instantaneous size of the adult population at time t, so that

$$R(t + T_D) = \theta(N(t)). \tag{8.3.2}$$

The additional assumption that the total death rate $D(t)$ is a function (formally defined as $\phi(N)$) only of the instantaneous size of the adult population

$$D(t) = \phi(N(t)). \tag{8.3.3}$$

now enables the entire population dynamic to be expressed in the form of a single delay-differential equation of the general type analysed in Chapter 2, namely

$$\frac{dN(t)}{dt} = \theta(N(t - T_D)) - \phi(N(t)). \tag{8.3.4}$$

We now choose explicit forms for the density dependent recruitment- and death-rate functions θ and ϕ. In the case of the death-rate function we simply

assume that the *per capita* adult death rate has a time and density independent value δ, so that

$$\phi(N) = \delta N. \tag{8.3.5}$$

The construction of a suitable recruitment-rate function is much more
complex. We consider first the case of a system controlled by the rate at which
food is supplied to the adult population. In this situation survival from egg to
adult will have a constant value (say S) and the rate of recruitment at time
$t + T_D$ will simply be proportional to the rate at which eggs are being laid at
time t. It seems reasonable to suppose that in the presence of excess food an
adult population of N individuals would produce eggs at a rate proportional to
its size, the constant of proportionality (say Q) being determined by the
individual physiology of the females and the population sex ratio. However,
when food is supplied at a limited rate we would clearly expect intra-specific
competition to reduce average *per capita* fecundity below its saturation value.
Indeed, where there is no social hierarchy and competition is of the 'scramble'
type it seems probable that at very large populations a restricted food supply
will all be consumed in physical maintenance of the population, leaving no
surplus of any kind for the production of offspring. We shall, therefore,
assume that the average *per capita* fecundity drops exponentially with
increasing population and hence, combining the egg to adult survival S and
the saturation fecundity Q into a single constant $P = SQ$, write

$$R(t + T_D) = \theta(N(t)) = PN(t)\exp\{-N(t)/N_0\}. \tag{8.3.6}$$

In those experiments where the controlling factor is the rate at which food
is supplied to the larval population and the adults are always provided with
excess food, the situation is somewhat different. Here the average per capita
fecundity remains at its saturation value (Q) irrespective of the size of the
adult population, but egg to adult survival becomes density dependent since
the larvae must now compete for a limited food supply. In the interests of
mathematical tractability we now make the slightly dubious assumption that
this competition takes place only within a given age class, whose size will of
course be proportional to the instantaneous rate of egg laying, $QN(t)$. Within
the limitations of this assumption it seems eminently reasonable to assume
that if a given age class starts very small (i.e. if QN is very small) then egg to
adult survival will approach its 'excess food supply' value S. When an age class
starts out very large, the experimental evidence from batch cultures indicates
that few if any of its members survive to pupate successfully. We shall thus
choose to represent the probability that an egg laid at time t will survive to
become a sexually mature adult at time $t + T_D$ by the function
$S \exp\{-\alpha QN(t)\}$; the appropriate value of the constant α being determined
by the rate at which the larvae are supplied with food. The total density
dependence of the recruitment rate function appropriate to the larval food
supply limited case is thus given by

$$R(t + T_D) \equiv \theta(N(t)) = QNS \exp\{-\alpha QN\}, \tag{8.3.7}$$

which, by the simple expedient of writing $P = QS$ and $N_0 = (\alpha Q)^{-1}$ we can reduce to equation (8.3.6).

We thus see that in both the adult-food-limited and the larval-food-limited cases the dynamics of our system will be described by

$$\frac{dN}{dt} = PN(t - T_D)\exp\{-N(t - T_D)/N_0\} - \delta N(t), \qquad (8.3.8)$$

although the interpretation of the constants P and N_0 is clearly dependent upon the stage in the life history at which control is applied.

B. Analysis of the model

The analysis of equation (8.3.8) now proceeds along well-oiled tracks. We first identity the controlling parameters by moving to scaled variables

$$N' = N/N_0, \qquad (8.3.9)$$

$$t' = t/T_D, \qquad (8.3.10)$$

in terms of which the dynamic equation becomes

$$\frac{dN'}{dt'} = PT_DN'(t' - 1)\exp\{-N'(t' - 1)\} - \delta T_DN'(t'), \qquad (8.3.11)$$

which tells us immediately that the qualitative behaviour of the system must be determined by the values of the two products PT_D and δT_D.

Inspection of equation (8.3.11) shows clearly that this system has only one non-trivial stationary state

$$N'^* = \ln(P/\delta), \qquad (8.3.12)$$

which will have a positive value provided only that the parameters of the system are chosen so as to obey the elementary restriction that the maximum possible *per capita* reproduction rate shall be greater than the *per capita* death rate, so that

$$P > \delta. \qquad (8.3.13)$$

Defining $n'(t')$ as the (assumedly small) deviation of $N'(t')$ from this steady state now enables us to obtain a locally linear representation (exactly analogous to equation (2.7.12)) in which, to first order

$$\frac{dn'}{dt'} = -\delta T_Dn'(t') - \delta T_D\{\ln(P/\delta) - 1\}n'(t' - 1). \qquad (8.3.14)$$

Following precisely the procedure set out in Chapter 2, we now assume that this equation has a solution of the general form

$$n'(t') \propto e^{-\mu't'}e^{i\omega't'} \qquad (8.3.15)$$

and investigate the deterministic local stability of the system by determining

296

the values of the damping constant μ' for which such a solution is possible. On substituting our trial solution back into the linearized dynamic equation (8.3.14) we discover (cf. equations (2.7.14) and (2.7.15)) that the two are compatible if and only if

$$\mu' = \delta T_D\{1 + [\ln(P/\delta)-1]e^{\mu'} \cos \omega'\} \qquad (8.3.16)$$

and

$$\omega' = \delta T_D\{\ln(P/\delta)-1\}e^{\mu'} \sin \omega'. \qquad (8.3.17)$$

As in the case of the time-delayed logistic model, we cannot obtain general analytic solutions to these equations, and must therefore solve them numerically for a series of particular values of PT_D and δT_D. For each pair of parameter values we can tell whether or not the system is stable by examining the sign of the damping constant μ', and whether it is over- or under-damped by asking whether ω' is zero or non-zero. We can thus locate the regions of the $PT_D/\delta T_D$ plane in which the system behaves in various qualitatively different ways and in Fig. 8.6 we display a portion of that plane covering the biologically meaningful range of both parameters showing the disposition of the various regions.

In the deterministically stable region we can only seek an exploration of the quasi-periodic fluctuations observed by Nicholson in the hypothesis that the parameters of the system have values in the underdamped region, so that demographic or (less plausibly) environmental stochasticity will drive resonant quasi-cyclic population fluctuations with a normalized period (T/T_D) close to $2\pi/\omega'$. We recall from Chapter 7 that when quasi-cycles occur the pattern

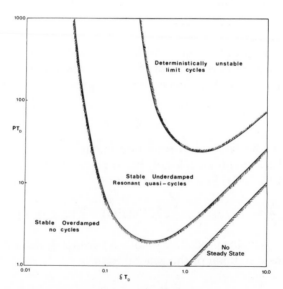

Fig. 8.6. Qualitative behaviour of the more realistic model.

of behaviour is for short periods of incoherent noise to separate long bursts of fairly coherent cycles; each burst containing a number of cycles corresponding to roughly twice the coherence number n_c which can (see Chapter 4) be inferred with acceptable accuracy from the expression

$$n_c = \frac{\omega'}{2\pi\mu'}. \tag{8.3.18}$$

We thus see that driven quasi-cycles can most conveniently be characterized by their normalized period T/T_D and their coherence number n_c, and in Fig. 8.7 we plot contours showing the variation of these quantities over the stable/underdamped region of the $PT_D/\delta T_D$ plane.

A plausible alternative to the driven quasi-cycle explanation of Nicholson's cycles is provided by those versions of this model whose parameters are in the deterministically unstable region. In this case the exact solution of equation (8.3.8), which can only be obtained by direct numerical integration, takes the form of a self-sustaining oscillation. For some parameter values this oscillation is a simple limit cycle very similar in form to that produced by the time-delayed logistic model discussed in Section 8.2. while for others the solution is either a more complex cycle or may even be formally aperiodic. In all cases, however, a spectral analysis of the solution reveals a single, clearly marked dominant period, which we again denote by T. We have therefore chosen to characterize each solution by the normalized dominant period T/T_D

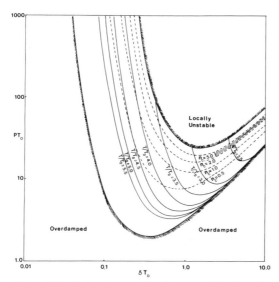

Fig. 8.7. Behaviour of the model in the stable/underdamped region. Contours of constant T/T_D (——) and n_c (————) in the $PT_D/\delta T_D$ plane. The shaded regions refer to experiments discussed in the text.

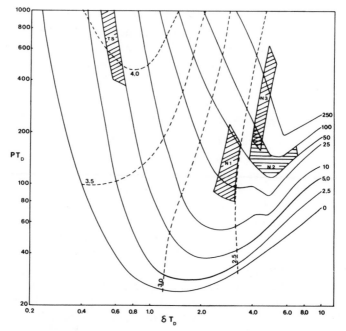

Fig. 8.8. Behaviour of the model in the locally unstable region. Contours of constant N_{max}/N_{min} (——) and T/T_D (----) in the $PT_D/\delta T_D$ plane. The shaded regimes refer to experiments discussed in the text.

and the ratio of maximum to minimum population N_{max}/N_{min} observed during the cycle. In Fig. 8.8 we plot contours of T/T_D and N_{max}/N_{min} on the part of the $PT_D/\delta T_D$ plane in which the model is deterministically unstable.

C. Testing the model

We now test the ability of our model to provide a satisfactory explanation of Nicholson's data. As before, our procedure is to determine the model parameter values which give the best fit to the experimental data and then compare these 'best fit' values with independent estimates of the same quantities.

Our model is capable of producing cycles of the general type observed by Nicholson by two, quite distinct, mechanisms: a locally unstable system yielding self-sustaining limit cycles or a locally stable but underdamped system in which demographic stochasticity gives rise to quasi-cyclic fluctuations. As there is no simple test of the experimental data which will distinguish between these two possibilities, we must clearly explore both. However, since it is evident from Fig. 8.6 that the values of the controlling parameters PT_D and δT_D which will produce a fit to the experimental data must differ dramatically under the two competing hypothesis, we may reasonably hope that our model will provide an *a posteriori* method of distinguishing which of the two is at work in this case.

In the previous section we characterized the limit-cycle solutions of equations (8.3.8) by their period to delay ratio T/T_D and their maximum to minimum population ratio N_{max}/N_{min}. We can easily make direct measurements of N_{max}/N_{min} for each of the three sets of experimental data shown in Fig. 8.1, and combining a direct measurement of the period T with our previous identification of the correct value of the delay T_D as 14.8 ± 0.4 days allows us to infer the appropriate value of T/T_D. We show the values obtained for N_{max}/N_{min} and T/T_D, together with their confidence limits, in Table 8.1.

For each experiment we now draw on the $PT_D/\delta T_D$ plane two pairs of contours corresponding to the upper and lower confidence limit of each measurement, and thus delineate the area of that plane in which the parameters must lie if the model behaviour is to mimic the experimental data. From these areas, which are shown shaded and marked with the appropriate run number in Fig. 8.8, we can infer the 'best fit' values of the controlling parameters which we show in Table 8.2. We must, however, take some care when interpreting the confidence limits shown in this table, since the complex shapes of the best fit areas mean that PT_D and δT_D cannot be allowed to vary independently over the whole of the quoted confidence interval.

We can also fit our model to Nicholson's data under the alternative hypothesis that we are looking at resonant quasi-cycles. Here we characterize the cycles by their period to delay ratio T/T_D and coherence number n_c. We have already measured T/T_D (see Table 8.1), but the small number of cycles observed in each data set makes an accurate measurement of n_c impossible. Fortunately the best fit values we obtain turn out to be remarkably insensitive to the exact value of n_c, and it is therefore quite sufficient to guess that for the general pattern of cycles observed by Nicholson we would expect $2 < n_c < 5$. On this basis we can delineate the best fit areas shown by the shading in Fig. 8.7, and hence derive the alternative set of best-fit parameters shown in Table 8.3.

Table 8.1. Characterization of Nicholson's experimental data.

Run	T/T_D	N_{max}/N_{min}
$N \# 1$	2.6 ± 0.1	36 ± 17
$N \# 2$	2.3 ± 0.1	77 ± 26
$N \# 3$	2.37 ± 0.03	240 ± 160

Table 8.2. Best fit values under the limit-cycle hypothesis.

Run	PT_D	δT_D
$N \# 1$	150 ± 70	2.9 ± 0.5
$N \# 2$	170 ± 50	5.5 ± 1.6
$N \# 3$	380 ± 250	4.7 ± 0.7

Table 8.3 Best fit values under the quasi-cycle hypothesis.

Run	PT_D	δT_D
$N \# 1$	23.5 ± 4.5	3.0 ± 0.7
$N \# 2$	45 ± 15	7.5 ± 3.0
$N \# 3$	32 ± 5	4.8 ± 0.8

We now seek to obtain independent estimates of the parameters P and δ, so as to assess the plausibility of these fits. It is immediately clear from a comparison of Tables 8.2 and 8.3 that the best fit values of δT_D required by the two hypotheses are essentially indistinguishable, while best fit values of PT_D are well grouped under each hypothesis and differ by a factor of between 4 and 10 between hypotheses. Thus our measurement of δ will provide a test of the self-consistency of the model in general, while the experimental value of P will provide a critical test of the mechanism which generates the observed cycles.

There are, unfortunately no entirely independent measurements on which to base an estimate of the death rate δ, but in both cases where Fig. 8.1 contains information from which we can make plausible guesses about the rate of recruitment to the adult population, close examination shows that during the portion of each cycle where the population size is approaching its minimum value the rate of adult recruitment is essentially zero. Equations (8.3.1), (8.3.3), and (8.3.5) tell us immediately that in such circumstances

$$N(t) \propto \exp\{-\delta t\}, \qquad (8.3.19)$$

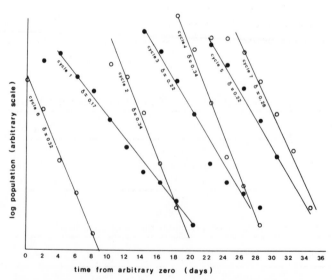

Fig. 8.9. Per-capita death rate estimation from Nicholson's experimental data ($N \# 1$). Data from cycles 1, 3, 5 and 7 are denoted by ● and data from cycles 2, 4 and 6 by ○.

Table 8.4 Independent death-rate measurements.

Run	δ	δT_D
$N \# 1$	0.27 ± 0.025 days^{-1}	4.0 ± 0.5
$N \# 2$	0.27 ± 0.03 days^{-1}	4.0 ± 0.6

so that a plot of ln N against t in these regions should yield a straight line of slope δ. Fig. 8.9 shows that for run $N \# 1$ the decline phase of each cycle can indeed be fitted satisfactorily by a single exponential, and we obtain a precisely similar result from run $N \# 2$. The values thus obtained for the death rate δ, and the corresponding values of the controlling parameter δT_D are shown in Table 8.4.

It is clear from a comparison of Tables 8.2–8.4 that while neither of the measured δT_D values agree exactly with their corresponding best fit values under either hypothesis both are firmly in the appropriate general region. This test thus confirms the general plausibility of our model, but provides no means of distinguishing between the two subsidiary hypotheses.

By contrast we may confidently expect a measurement of the fertility parameter P to allow us to distinguish unambiguously between limit cycles and quasi-cycles. It is therefore regrettable that only for one run ($N \# 1$) do we have data suitable for an accurate estimate of this parameter; the superficially appealing pupal population data for run $N \# 2$ being rendered useless in this respect since we have no reliable way of inferring from it a recruitment *rate*.

In the case of the adult food limited run $N \# 1$ we have details of the time variation of the rate of egg laying and since we know that in this case egg to adult survival is a constant 91 per cent it is clear that, with the addition of a trivial scale factor of 0.91, we can obtain from this data a curve of instantaneous future recruitment against time. There are several methods by which we

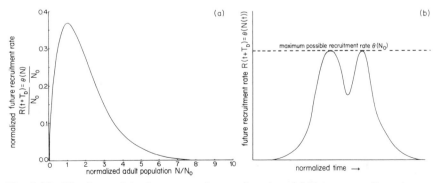

Fig. 8.10. The form of the future recruitment function. (a) Future recruitment as a function of present population. (b) Future recruitment as a function of time in the trough of large cycles.

could infer from this curve a value of the fertility parameter P. The most direct depends on the amplitude of the cycles being sufficient to produce a minimum population smaller than the value (N_0) at which the future recruitment function (shown in Fig. 8.10(a)) has its maximum value. The curve of future recruitment against time in the trough of each cycle then has the characteristic form shown in Fig. 8.10(b) and we can easily measure the appropriate value of P from

$$\frac{\text{Max rate of production of future recruitment}}{\text{Population at time of maximum production}} = \frac{\theta(N_0)}{N_0} = Pe^{-1} \quad (8.3.20)$$

Examination of the appropriate section of Fig. 8.1 shows clearly that the curve of future recruitment against time does indeed show the characteristic double peaked shape shown in Fig. 8.10(b), and hence we deduce that for run $N \# 1$

$$7.4 < P < 1.4 \quad (8.3.21)$$

and hence

$$100 < PT_D < 160. \quad (8.3.22)$$

This is clearly compatible with the value required under the limit-cycle hypothesis ($120 < PT_D < 220$) and absolutely incompatible with the value required under the resonant quasi-cycle hypothesis ($19 < PT_D < 28$). It is thus clear that, at least in the case of adult-food limitation, we have an unequivocal answer to the first question we posed in the introduction: *the fluctuations observed by Nicholson in this case are quite clearly of limit-cycle type.* In the case of the larval food limited systems no such clear answer can be obtained in the absence of data which can provide an accurate estimate of PT_D. However, the change in experimental conditions would have to change the value of this parameter by almost a factor of 10 to shift the system into the resonant quasi-cycle regime, and it therefore seems plausible to assume that these fluctuations, too, are limit-cycles. In the next section we shall introduce further circumstantial evidence to support this supposition.

8.4   THE QUALITATIVE BEHAVIOUR OF THE NEW MODEL

The new model discussed in Section 8.3 has clearly provided a much more satisfactory fit to the frequency and amplitude of the cycles observed by Nicholson than is possible with the time-delayed logistic, and has in the process enabled us to demonstrate that these fluctuations are of self-sustaining limit cycle type. However, this ability to mimic certain quantitative aspects of the fluctuations, while vitally important, is no guarantee that our model has truly captured the spirit of the system we seek to understand. An examination of Fig. 8.1 shows at once that there are several additional qualitative features of both the adult population fluctuations and, more significantly, the recruitment rate variations which any model making that claim must successfully predict. To assess whether our model also passes this test we show in Fig. 8.11 the time dependence of both adult population N and future recruitment rate $\theta(N)$ predicted by our model with parameters which match the frequency and amplitude of the adult population fluctuations to the data of runs $N \# 1$ to $N \# 3$.

Examination of the future recruitment rate curve shown in Fig. 8.11(a), shows that with the parameters appropriate to the adult food limited case $N \# 1$, our model predicts adult population oscillations with a slightly 'spiky' appearance and a pattern of breeding activity in which periods of essentially zero reproduction alternate with relatively long bursts of continuous reproductive activity each showing the incipient 'double hump' sketched in Fig. 8.10(b). Comparison of these predictions with the appropriate portion of Fig. 8.1 shows them to be very close indeed to what is observed experimentally.

With parameters appropriate to the larval-food limited case $N \# 2$ our model predicts considerably more complex behaviour. Here, although a spectral analysis of the adult population fluctuations (see Fig. 8.12) still shows a single, clearly defined, dominant frequency, the qualitative appearance of

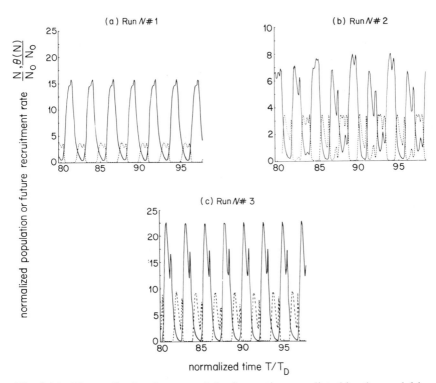

Fig. 8.11. The qualitative features of the fluctuations predicted by the model in the limit-cycle region. Adult population (——) and future recruitment (----) against time with model parameters giving 'best fit' to Nicholson's data. (a) Run $N \# 1$. (b) Run $N \# 2$. (c) Run $N \# 3$.

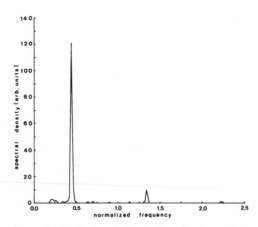

Fig. 8.12. Spectral analysis of the adult population fluctuations predicted by our model with the best-fit parameters from Nicholson's run $N \# 2$.

oscillations in both adult population and future recruitment rate is now rather complex. The future recruitment rate still shows well-separated bursts of reproduction, but now the quasi-continuous reproduction which characterized every burst in run $N \# 1$ is shown only in alternate cycles, each intervening burst showing two quite clearly marked 'discrete generations'. This pattern of reproduction is reflected, albeit more weakly, in the variation of adult populations where cycles with only a slight 'jitter' at the peak alternate with cycles with a pronounced 'double peak'. It is very clear from Fig. 8.1 that the adult-population cycles observed by Nicholson in run $N \# 2$ do indeed exhibit this pattern of alternating single and double peaks. Comparison of the predicted variation of future reproduction with the experimental observations is complicated in this case by the fact that Nicholson's data concerns pupal population size not pupal recruitment rate. However, even from the curves of pupal population we can see at once that our general qualitative prediction of pairs of almost discrete generations alternating with pairs of generations which merge into an almost continuous burst of reproduction is remarkably accurate. This success, although by no means as conclusive a proof as we constructed in the case of run $N \# 1$, is certainly strong circumstantial evidence of the correctness of our view that the fluctuations observed by Nicholson in the larval food limited case ($N \# 2$, $N \# 3$) are also limit-cycles.

Despite the fact that in the case of run $N \# 3$ we have no experimental data which even hints at the time variation of adult recruitment, it is still instructive to examine the appropriate model predictions (Fig. 8.11(c)). Here the change from the quasi-continuous reproduction of run $N \# 1$ to the quasi-discrete generations of run $N \# 2$ is even more marked and the pattern of 'generations' is much simpler. It is particularly easy to see the uneven spacing of the 'discrete' generations; pairs of closely spaced generations being quite widely separated by a long period of essentially zero reproduction.

Examination of Fig. 8.11 also gives us a strong clue that the discreteness of the generations depends quite simply on how low the minimum population is. The reason why this should be so is made crystal clear by Fig. 8.13 in which, for each of the three predicted fluctuation sets in Fig. 8.11, we have plotted the actual values of $\theta(N)$ against N. Although each of these curves is simply a part of the general future reproduction curve (equation (8.3.6)) underlying our whole model, the adult population variation 'scans' a different portion of the curve in each case. When the minimum population is pushed just below the maximum of the future reproduction curve the 'double hump' shape appears in the time variation of reproductive activity. As the fluctuations grow larger, forcing the minimum even further below N_0 (the maximum of the $\theta(N)$ curve) this double hump becomes steadily more marked and eventually turns into a pair of closely spaced but clearly discrete generations.

We can confirm this view with the aid of a further fitting exercise. We examine the data (Fig. 8.14(a)) of Taylor and Sokal (1976) showing cyclic fluctuations in the population of a laboratory culture of the housefly *Musca*

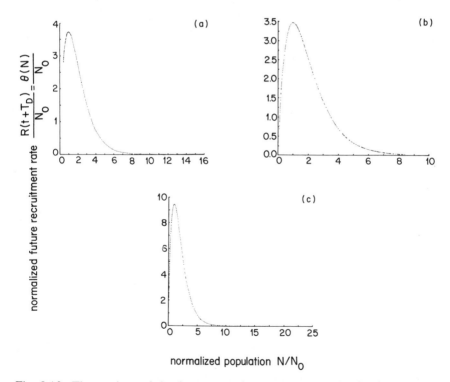

Fig. 8.13. The sections of the future recruitment curve sampled by the model during the cycles predicted with, (a) parameters of $N \# 1$, (b) parameters of $N \# 2$, (c) parameters of $N \# 3$.

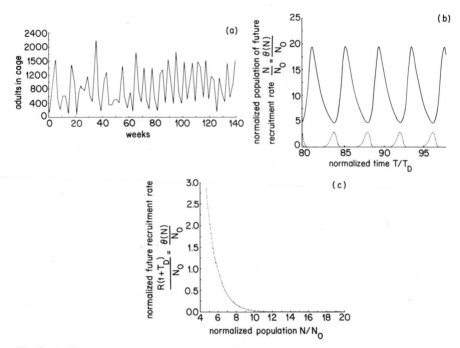

Fig. 8.14. Fit to the experimental data of Taylor and Sokal (1976). (a) Experimental results. (b) Predicted 'best fit' cycles in adult population (———) and future recruitment (————). (c) Portion of the future recruitment curve sampled during the predicted cycle.

domestica. Here (using the value of the delay $T_D = 10$ days, given by Taylor and Sokal) we measure

$$3.9 < T/T_D < 4.3 \tag{8.4.1}$$

$$3.6 < N_{max}/N_{min} < 5.0 \tag{8.4.2}$$

and hence, on the assumption that, here too, we are looking at a limit cycle, deduce that the controlling parameters must lie in the shaded region on Fig. 8.8 marked *TS*. This in turn yields 'best fit parameters' for this system in the ranges

$$350 < PT_D < 950, \tag{8.4.3}$$

$$0.5 < \delta T_D < 0.7. \tag{8.4.4}$$

With these parameters our model predicts the variations in adult population and future recruitment rate shown in Fig. 8.14(b). Since the amplitude of the adult population cycles in this case is rather small and has a minimum population well above the maximum of the recruitment curve (Fig. 8.14(c)) we see no separation of generations—simply a broad burst of reproduction in the trough of each cycle. Comparison of these qualitative predictions with the experimental results is less rewarding than it would be if there was data from which we could infer the adult recruitment rate. However, we can certainly say that there is no shred of evidence in the adult population record for the existence of the kind of double-humped peak shapes which are inevitable when the generations begin to separate.

We thus conclude that our model passes all the tests for qualitative plausibility to which we have subjected it.

8.5   CONCLUSIONS

We are now in a position to answer the specific questions posed in the introduction to this chapter, about the nature of the fluctuations observed by Nicholson.

(a)   *Are the fluctuations resonant auasi-cycles or self-sustaining limit-cycles?*

In the case of the adult food limited system $N \# 1$ we can say as unequivocally as is ever possible after a model-fitting exercise that the fluctuations are of limit-cycle type. For the larval food limited case ($N \# 2$ and $N \# 3$) we have no really hard evidence, but all the circumstantial evidence points to the correctness of the limit-cycle view here also.

(b)   *What determines the cycle period?*

Examination of Fig. 8.8 shows that the period to delay ratio of the limit cycles is determined principally by the value of the product δT_D. Thus the period of the cycles is set mainly by the delay and the adult death rate.

(c)   *What determines the cycle amplitude?*

From Fig. 8.8 we see that the ratio N_{max}/N_{min} is governed by all three main factors included in the model: delay T_D, fertility P, and mortality δ. The precise dependence on these quantities is complex and the only broad general conclusion is that high values of both PT_D and δT_D guarantee large amplitude cycles.

(d)   *Why are the separate generations observed in runs $N \# 2$ and $N \# 3$ unevenly spaced?*

The fundamental feature of our model which leads to the appearance of well-separated generations is the peaked shape of the future reproduction curve (Fig. 8.10). Given this feature the only further condition necessary for the generations to separate is that the cycle amplitude should be sufficient to force the minimum population well below the level at which the population has maximum reproductive potential. In these circumstances a new 'generation' will appear whenever the population size passes through the reproductively optimum level.

(e) *Why does run N # 1 not exhibit separate generations?*

In this experiment the controlling parameters PT_D and δT_D take on values which imply rather smaller cycles and higher population minima than those observed in the larval-food limited runs. In this case the minimum population level is only just below the reproductive optimum, and the curve of reproductive activity against time shows a small dip rather than a well-marked separation.

Our model has clearly been successful in its primary aim of elucidating the mechanism underlying Nicholson's observations of population fluctuations in laboratory cultures of *Lucillia cuprina*. Can it also be regarded as having succeeded in its more grandiose aim of providing a general framework for the discussion of quasi-periodic fluctuations in laboratory cultures of many different species. The evidence here is much less clear; being hardly changed one way or the other by our comparison with the extremely sparse data of Taylor and Sokal on the housefly *Musca domestica*. However, it seems likely that it at least provides the foundation on which such a framework may be erected, its most significant feature in this respect being the qualitative picture it provides of a mechanism by which a discrete or quasi-discrete pattern of generations can be maintained in the absence of external synchronization. In providing a clear understanding of the uneven timing of such generations, it indicates a possible avenue for the reconciliation of the 'discrete time' and 'continuous time' views of insect population dynamics.

SOURCES AND SUGGESTED FURTHER READING

A very comprehensive discussion of delay-differential models is given in MacDonald (1978). A delay-differential model with a 'humped' non-linearity leading to chaotic solutions is discussed in a physiological context by Mackey and Glass (1977); also Glass and Mackey (1978). The model which is the subject of the main discussion in this chapter is reported in the literature by Gurney, Blythe, and Nisbet (1980).

Several quantitative fits to Nicholson's data have been made using discrete-time models (for example, Hassell, Lawton, and May, 1976; Varley, Gradwell, and Hassell, 1973). Although discrete-time models are fundamentally incapable of explaining the uneven timing of the generation observed by Nicholson, it is interesting to note that the latter authors used a future recruitment curve of a very similar qualitative shape to ours, and concluded that the behaviour should be 'chaotic'.

Discussions of continuous-time models applicable to Nicholson's data have been given by Maynard Smith (1974), Taylor and Sokal (1976), May (1974b), Auslander, Oster, and Huffaker (1974), and Readshaw and Cuff (1980).

Chapter 9

Chemostat Populations of Unicellular Algae

9.1 INTRODUCTION

As our second case study we have chosen a series of experiments by Cunningham (1976; also Cunningham, and Maas, 1978) on transient growth of the unicellular alga *Chlamydomonas reinhardii* under nitrogen limitation. The growth of populations of microalgae under natural conditions frequently consists of 'bursts' of rapid increase against a background of slow growth or decline, and experiments on transient (as opposed to steady state) behaviour are thus a necessary step in elucidating the factors involved in the regulation of natural algal populations.

The simplest type of experiment involving transient population growth of algae (known as 'batch culture') involves inoculating a container of nutrient with a few algae; the population grows until cell division stops due to lack of limiting nutrient, and, apart from a very slow decline due to cell death, then remains constant. Fig. 9.1 contains data from a typical batch culture of chlamydomonas growing under nitrite limitation and illustrates both the characteristic sigmoidal (i.e. *S*-shaped) population growth curve and the simultaneous reduction of the level of residual nitrate in the culture vessel.

The only steady state that can be studied experimentally in batch culture experiments is the relatively uninteresting one in which all cell division has stopped. As an experimental trick to facilitate study of the dynamics of cell division without requiring excessively rapid measurements, microbiologists frequently study the steady states achieved by 'continuous cultures' growing in a *chemostat* to which medium containing limiting nutrient is supplied at a known rate and from which medium containing both cells and nutrient is washed out at the same rate (see Fig. 9.2). A chemostat population achieves a steady state by balancing recruitment through cell division with washout, thus 'freezing' the population at some point on the batch culture curve and permitting prolonged and precise study of the population's characteristics at different stages in its growth.

310

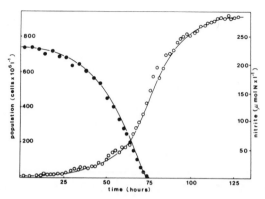

Fig. 9.1. A typical batch culture of *Chlamydomonas reinhardii*. Open circles denote cell numbers, closed circles residual nutrient concentration. (Reproduced by permission of Cambridge University Press from Cunningham, and Mass, 1978.)

Logically, batch culture and continuous culture experiments yield the same type of information on the population dynamics of the organism under investigation, but in practice batch culture data is normally too imprecise to be used to distinguish models of population growth. On the other hand, the nature of chemostat *transients* is remarkably sensitive to the detailed dynamics of cell division, and such transients may exhibit well-defined, reproducible features which can be used to elucidate the factors responsible for the control of cell numbers. Fig. 9.3 contains a striking example in which one of Cunningham's chlamydomonas cultures executed two well-defined oscillations in cell numbers before settling down to a new steady state.

Because of the sensitivity of chemostat transients to the underlying dynamics, they form an ideal testing ground for models of algal growth. Provided all the parameters in a model can be measured from batch culture studies, the model can be assessed through its ability to predict the form of the chemostat transients. In other words, a model of algal growth can be evaluated (and

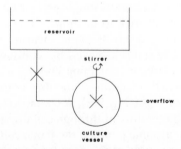

Fig. 9.2. A schematic representation of the chemostat.

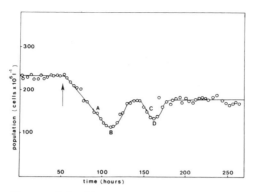

Fig. 9.3. Chemostat transient in *Chlamydomonas reinhardii* following a step in dilution rate from 0.023 hr^{-1} to 0.034 hr^{-1} at the arrow. (Reproduced by permission of Cambridge University Press from Cunningham, and Maas, 1978).

many simple models thus rejected) through the requirement that it fits *both* the batch culture and continuous culture data. In this chapter we construct and test several models of the growth of chlamydomonas under nitrite-limited conditions with the broad aim of determining what controls the rate of cell division. We approach this question via the narrower one of identifying a possible mechanism for the oscillations in Fig. 9.3. Our emphasis is on the *methods* of constructing and analysing the models; the reader interested in a discussion of the same models with greater concern for algal growth *per se* is referred to Cunningham and Nisbet (1980).

9.2 POPULATION AND NUTRIENT BALANCE IN THE CHEMOSTAT

We represent the chemostat as a culture vessel of volume $V(l)$ supplied with limiting nutrient of concentration S_R (mol l^{-1}) from a reservoir at a rate DV (l hr^{-1}) where the 'dilution rate' $D(hr^{-1})$ is the fraction of the volume of liquid in the culture vessel that is replaced in 1 hour. If N is the total number of cells in the vessel and μ the per capita growth rate (which may not equal the division rate as chlamydomonas cells appear to divide into more than two daughters), then dN/dt is obtained as always by balancing births $(= \mu N)$, deaths $(= 0)$, immigration $(= 0)$, and emigration $(= DN$ provided the vessel is well stirred), implying that

$$\frac{dN}{dt} = N(\mu - D). \tag{9.2.1}$$

We can also write down a balance equation for nutrient by considering supply from the reservoir, wash-out, and absorption by cells. If A

(mol hr^{-1} cell^{-1}) denotes the rate of uptake of nutrient by a single cell, and if this value is assumed at any particular instant to be constant for all cells (a point we discuss later in Section 9.3), then if S(mol l^{-1}) is the concentration of nutrient in the culture vessel,

$$\dot{S} = DS_R - DS - AV^{-1}N. \qquad (9.2.2)$$

A third quantity which proves useful in modelling is the *cell quota Q* (mol cell^{-1}) which is the average amount of stored nutrient in each cell in the culture vessel. This quantity increases due to absorption of nutrient and decreases because of cell division since the same amount of nutrient has then to be shared among more cells. If all cells are assumed to possess the average amount of nutrient at any particular instant, this implies

$$\dot{Q} = A - \mu Q, \qquad (9.2.3)$$

a result which enables us to consider the overall balance of nutrient in the system. If T denotes the total amount of nutrient in the culture vessel irrespective of whether it is free or stored then

$$T = SV + QN, \qquad (9.2.4)$$

and a few lines of algebra using equations (9.2.1)–(9.2.3) yields

$$\dot{T} = DVS_R - DT. \qquad (9.2.5)$$

As D is changed in the course of some of the experiments, we solve this equation for the general situation $D = D(t)$ and obtain

$$T = VS_R - (VS_R - T(0))\exp\left\{-\int_0^t D(x)\,dx\right\}, \qquad (9.2.6)$$

where $T(0)$ denotes the total amount of nutrient in the culture vessel at time $t = 0$. It follows that, irrespective of the initial conditions, provided the dilution rate is not zero a situation is approached where

$$T = SV + QN = VS_R = \text{constant}. \qquad (9.2.7)$$

The importance of this relation is that once constancy of the total nutrient content in the chemostat is established, it is maintained at all subsequent times even if the dilution rate is then altered. This is helpful mathematically as it implies that equation (9.2.7) is valid *throughout* the transient from one steady state to another following a step in dilution rate.

9.3   MODELLING THE CHEMOSTAT

Constructing a model of population growth in the chemostat involves specifying functional forms for the net growth rate μ and the nutrient absorption rate A. If μ and A simply depend on one or more of the 'bulk parameters' N, S, or Q, then equations (9.2.1)–(9.2.3) constitute a set of simultaneous, non-linear ordinary differential equations which can be analysed by the techniques of Chapter 4.

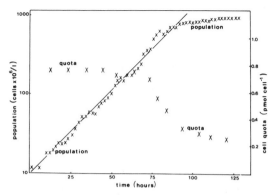

Fig. 9.4. Plots of cell quota and the logarithm of population against time for the batch culture of Fig. 9.1. (Superposition of two graphs in Cunningham, 1976; reproduced by permission.)

The most obvious feature of the batch culture shown in Fig. 9.1 is that cell division continues long after residual nitrite has dropped to undetectably small levels. This immediately precludes the possibility that the net growth rate μ is a function solely of S, an assumption which is frequently made in modelling bacterial chemostats (Monod, 1950). The most obvious alternative is that μ is a function of mean cell quota Q, a possibility which is readily tested by using equation (9.2.4) to calculate Q and then comparing the graphs of Q and the logarithm of N against time (Fig. 9.4). Presented in this way the data is very suggestive of the possibility that μ (which is proportional to the gradient of the log N graph) might depend on Q (though a delay in the relationship cannot be precluded). If μ does indeed depend on Q then the relationship must be that shown in Fig. 9.5.

The suggestion that division rate is determined by mean cell quota might appear rather implausible since in general we would expect considerable

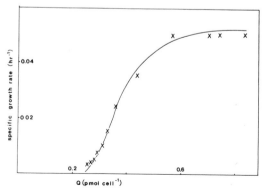

Fig. 9.5. Specific growth rate as a function of cell quota for the batch culture in Fig. 9.1. (Reproduced by permission from Cunningham, 1976.)

variation in the amount of stored nutrient among individuals in the population. Although it is unlikely that we could incorporate this variability in a testable model because of the difficulties in obtaining data, a brief qualitative investigation of its effects yields some insight into the approximations implied by letting μ depend only on Q. A complete description of the population would use the age-dependent formulation of Chapter 3 with $f(a,q,t,)\,\mathrm{d}a\mathrm{d}q$ representing the number of cells in the chemostat aged between a and $a + \mathrm{d}a$ containing between q and $q + \mathrm{d}q$ moles of limiting nutrient. Then (cf. equation (3.2.34))

$$\frac{\partial f}{\partial t} + \frac{\partial f}{\partial a} + \frac{\partial}{\partial q}(Af) + (D + b)f = 0, \qquad (9.3.1)$$

where $b(a,q)$ is the probability of division per unit time for an individual of age a with quota q. If each division yields n daughters, and (cf. equation (3.2.39)) if we assume for (relative) simplicity that the stored nutrient is shared equally among the daughters, then

$$f(0, q, t) = n^2 \int_0^\infty b(a, nq)f(a, nq)\,\mathrm{d}a. \qquad (9.3.2)$$

If we further assume that both A, the rate of nutrient absorption, and b, the probability of division depend on q but not on age, then integration of equation (9.3.1) yields

$$\dot{N} = (\mu - D)N, \qquad (9.3.3)$$

where

$$\mu = (n - 1)\int_0^\infty\!\!\int_0^\infty b(q)f(a, q)\,\mathrm{d}a\,\mathrm{d}q \bigg/ \int_0^\infty\!\!\int_0^\infty f(a, q)\,\mathrm{d}a\,\mathrm{d}q. \qquad (9.3.4)$$

By expanding $b(q)$ about the mean cell quota Q and retaining only zero- and first-order terms in $(q - Q)$ then we obtain after some manipulation

$$\mu = (n - 1)\,b(Q), \qquad (9.3.5)$$

which is a function of Q only. Thus a sufficient condition for the validity of an assumption that μ is a function of Q is that near the mean quota Q, $\mathrm{d}^2 b/\mathrm{d}q^2$ should be small; otherwise the variance in cell quota and possibly even higher moments are involved in setting the mean division rate.

The second major constituent of a bulk parameter model is the functional dependence of the nutrient absorption rate. We can calculate A from Fig. 9.1 using the relation

$$A = -VN^{-1}\frac{\mathrm{d}S}{\mathrm{d}t}, \qquad (9.3.6)$$

obtained by setting $D = 0$ in equation (9.2.2) and, as is evident from Fig. 9.6, it is virtually constant, at least until S becomes unmeasurably small. However, a model in which A was always constant would admit the possibility of cells

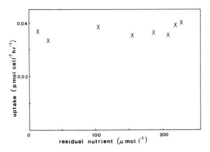

Fig. 9.6. Rate of uptake of limiting nutrient as a function of residual nutrient concentration for the batch culture of Fig. 9.1. (Reproduced by permission from Cunningham, 1976.)

absorbing nutrient when none was present and we therefore represent the rate of uptake by a function $A(S)$ which is virtually constant over the observed range of S and drops rapidly to zero with S. For the qualitative analysis in the present work there is no need to specify the precise form of $A(S)$; however, a biochemically plausible form would be a Michaelis–Menten relation

$$A(S) = \frac{A_{max}S}{K_s + S} \tag{9.3.7}$$

where for this culture $A_{max} = 0.03\ \mu\text{mol } N \text{ cell}^{-1} \text{ hr}^{-1}$, and K_s is a constant whose value is unknown but is certainly much smaller than $10\ \mu\text{mol l}^{-1}$, the smallest concentration in Fig. 9.6.

The batch-culture experiments thus suggest that we investigate the predictions of a model based on the balance equations ((9.2.1)–(9.2.3)), which on inserting the assumed functional dependence of A and μ become

$$\frac{dN}{dt} = N\{\mu(Q) - D\}, \tag{9.3.8}$$

$$\frac{dS}{dt} = DS_R - DS - A(S)V^{-1}N, \tag{9.3.9}$$

$$\frac{dQ}{dt} = A(S) - \mu(Q)Q. \tag{9.3.10}$$

9.4 ANALYSIS OF THE BASIC MODEL

We have just proposed that the batch culture experiments are compatible with the model embodied in the three equations (9.3.8)–(9.3.10). We can base our analysis of chemostat transients on any two of these equations since the variables S, N and Q are related by the conservation law (9.2.7). We choose N and Q as independent variables and obtain the pair of equations

$$\dot{Q} = A(S) - \mu(Q)Q \quad \text{with} \quad S \equiv S_R - V^{-1}QN, \qquad (9.4.1)$$

$$\dot{N} = N\{\mu(Q) - D\}, \qquad (9.4.2)$$

which are of the type investigated in detail in Section 4.2. These can be analysed by the routine procedure of identifying steady states and checking their stability.

In the interests of retaining maximum generality we do not specify the precise functional *forms* of μ and A, but argue that the derivatives $d\mu/dQ$ and dA/dS should plausibly be positive (otherwise the cells divide more slowly when they contain more nutrient and absorb nutrient more slowly when there is more in their environment). If this is the case, then provided the dilution rate D is chosen to balance a specific growth rate lying within the permissible range, there is only one value of cell quota (denoted by Q^*) for which $dN/dt = 0$. Similarly, there is only one value of A, and hence (from equation (9.4.1)) of N, for which $dQ/dt = 0$. We denote this steady state population by N^*.

To test the stability of the steady state (N^*, Q^*) we linearize and obtain

$$\dot{n} = N^* \left(\frac{d\mu}{dQ}\right)^* q, \qquad (9.4.3)$$

and

$$\dot{q} = -\left(\frac{dA}{dS}\right)^* \frac{Q^*}{V} n - \left[\frac{N^*}{V}\left(\frac{dA}{dS}\right)^* + Q^*\left(\frac{d\mu}{dQ}\right)^* + \mu(Q^*)\right] q, \quad (9.4.4)$$

where n, q are the perturbations of cell numbers and cell quota from their steady state values. For neighbourhood stability we require that the quantities a_1 and a_2 defined in equations (4.2.15) should be positive, i.e.

$$a_1 = \frac{N^*}{V}\left(\frac{dA}{dS}\right)^* + Q^*\left(\frac{d\mu}{dQ}\right)^* + \mu(Q^*) > 0 \qquad (9.4.5)$$

and

$$a_2 = \frac{N^*Q^*}{V}\left(\frac{dA}{dS}\right)^*\left(\frac{d\mu}{dQ}\right)^* > 0. \qquad (9.4.6)$$

Furthermore, for overdamping we require (cf. equation (4.2.16))

$$a_1^2 - 4a_2 > 0, \qquad (9.4.7)$$

which after a little regrouping of terms yields

$$\left\{ \frac{N^*}{V}\left(\frac{dA}{dS}\right)^* - Q^*\left(\frac{d\mu}{dQ}\right)^* \right\}^2 + \mu(Q^*)^2 + 2\mu(Q^*)\frac{N^*}{V}\left(\frac{dA}{dS}\right)^*$$

$$+ 2\mu(Q^*)Q^*\left(\frac{d\mu}{dQ}\right)^* > 0. \quad (9.4.8)$$

We have already argued that the derivatives $d\mu/dQ$ and dA/dS should be everywhere positive and the inequalities (9.4.5), (9.4.6), and (9.4.8) are thus always satisfied. This means that irrespective of the detailed forms of the μ/Q and A/S curves any feasible steady state is stable and the system is over-damped. We recall from Chapter 4 that in a two-variable (undelayed) differential equation model, overdamping implies that the approach to a steady state is either monotonic or involves a single 'overshoot'. It thus follows that we can immediately reject the entire class of models in which $\mu = \mu(Q)$ and $A = A(S)$, as models of *Chlamydomonas reinhardii*.

9.5 TIME-DELAY MODELS

A. Experimental evidence for a delay

The most obvious candidate as the source of the oscillations observed in continuous culture is a delay between changes in cell quota and in specific growth rate. The batch culture plot (Fig. 9.4) has too much scatter in the data for us to determine unambiguously whether there is a delay between the initial fall in quota and the flattening of the population curve. However, the continuous culture data is much more convincing and in Fig. 9.7 we show the variation with time of quota and specific growth rate calculated (using the

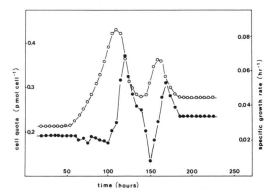

Fig. 9.7. Variation of cell quota (○) and specific growth rate (●) for the chemostat run in Fig. 9.3. (Reproduced by permission of Cambridge University Press from Cunningham, and Maas, 1978.)

balance equation (9.2.1) and the conservation equation (9.2.7)) for the continuous culture of Fig. 9.3. In spite of the obvious imprecision in the estimates of μ, the derivation of which requires numerical differentiation, it is clear from these graphs that *if* the specific growth rate is determined by the mean cell quota, then a time delay must be involved in the relationship. The data is too imprecise to reveal whether the delay is discrete or continuous, and in addition there is an apparent anomaly at the start of the transient where 40–50 hours elapses before there is any significant change in μ; however, over the bulk of the transient a delay of about 10 hours appears to be appropriate.

B. Discrete delay

A discrete delay is introduced by setting

$$\mu(t) = \mu(Q_D) \quad \text{where} \quad Q_D(t) \equiv Q(t - T_D), \qquad (9.5.1)$$

in equations (9.4.1) and (9.4.2) and thus obtaining a pair of differential-delay equations. The analysis of such equations is straightforward in principle but algebraically tedious in practice and is greatly simplified if we exploit Cunningham's observation that throughout the chemostat transients, residual nutrient concentrations were undetectably small and hence were very much less than S_R, the reservoir concentration. If we make the approximation $S = 0$ in the conservation equation (9.2.7) the result is

$$S_R = V^{-1}QN, \qquad (9.5.2)$$

and hence

$$Q_D = VS_R N_D^{-1}. \qquad (9.5.3)$$

Equation (9.2.1) can now be interpreted as a *single* delay-differential equation in N which we write in the form

$$\dot{N} = \{\mu(N_D) - D\}N, \qquad (9.5.4)$$

where

$$\mu(N_D) \equiv \mu(Q_D) \quad \text{with} \quad Q_D = VS_R N_D^{-1}. \qquad (9.5.5)$$

When we linearize this equation about the steady state N^* we obtain

$$\dot{n} = -bn_D, \qquad (9.5.6)$$

where

$$b = -N^* \left(\frac{d\mu}{dN_D}\right)^* = Q^* \left(\frac{d\mu}{dQ_D}\right)^* = \left(\frac{d\mu}{d(\ln Q_D)}\right)^*. \qquad (9.5.7)$$

Equation (9.5.6) was studied in Section 2.7 where it was seen that it represents a stable, overdamped system if $0 \leqslant bT_D \leqslant 0.37$ and an unstable (and with realistic non-linearity, probably limit cycling) system if $bT_D > 1.57$. Oscillations large enough to be readily observed only arise if the product $bT_D \gtrsim 1$ and for values between 1 and 1.57 we find that the period of the damped oscillations only varies from $4.65T_D$ ($bT_D = 1$) to $4.00T_D$ ($bT_D = 1.51$). Given the qualitative but non-quantitative reproducibility of the original experiments we can thus regard the main prediction of the discrete time-lag model as damped oscillations of period around four times the delay provided bT_D lies in the relevant narrow range of values.

C. Distributed delay

A possibly more realistic alternative to the discrete delay is the distributed version of Section 2.7C which results in the replacement of equation (9.5.6) by

$$\dot{n} = -b \int_0^\infty w(u)n(t - u)\,du \qquad (9.5.8)$$

where $w(u)$ is a normalized weighting function which might, for instance, take one of the forms shown in Fig. 2.9. The exponentially distributed delay (Fig. 2.9(b)) would appear inconsistent with the continuous culture data as with this type of delay, there would be some immediate response in division rate following the change in Q. However, a delay of the form (cf. Fig. 2.9(c))

$$w(u) = \frac{4u}{T_D^2} \exp\left\{-\frac{2u}{T_D}\right\} \qquad (9.5.9)$$

produces qualitatively similar behaviour to the discrete delay; the system is stable and overdamped if $0 \leqslant bT_D \leqslant 0.296$, and stable and underdamped if $0.296 < bT_D < 4$. The period of the oscillations increases from $3.14T_D$ ($bT_D = 4$) to $4.22T_D$ ($bT_D = 2$) by which point the coherence number is close to one and the oscillations are scarcely observable. Thus the main effect of this type of distributed delay is to produce oscillations qualitatively similar to the discrete case but occurring at somewhat larger values of bT_D and with a slightly shorter period (typically a little under $4T_D$).

D. Experimental tests

The one major constraint on the time-delay models, and indeed the feature which renders the assumption of a delay more than an empirical 'fix', is that they must explain *both* the overdamped behaviour in batch culture *and* the oscillations in continuous culture. The nature (exponential or oscillatory) of the transient behaviour in the delay models is determined by the product bT_D and for oscillations to appear in continuous culture but not in batch culture it is thus necessary that the quantity b increase as the dilution rate increases from zero (i.e. $db/dD > 0$). The delay T_D we are assuming to be a physiological attribute of the cells and as such be unaffected by dilution rate.

To evaluate db/dD we first note from equation (9.5.7) that

$$b \equiv -N^* \left(\frac{d\mu}{dN_D} \right)^* = -\left[\frac{d\mu}{d(\ln N_D)} \right]^* = \left[\frac{d\mu}{d(\ln Q_D)} \right]^*, \qquad (9.5.10)$$

and then that

$$\frac{db}{dD} = \frac{db}{dN^*} \cdot \frac{dN^*}{dD}. \qquad (9.5.11)$$

The second term on the right-hand side, dN^*/dD is evaluated by recalling that at a steady state

$$\mu(N^*) = D, \qquad (9.5.12)$$

differentiating both sides of this equation with respect to D, and obtaining

$$\frac{dN^*}{dD} = \left[\frac{d\mu}{dN_D} \right]^{*-1}. \qquad (9.5.13)$$

The first term on the right-hand side of equation (9.5.11) is more straightforward and is evaluated by differentiation of equation (9.5.10) with the result

$$\frac{db}{dN^*} = -\frac{1}{N^*} \left[\frac{d^2\mu}{d(\ln Q_D)^2} \right]^*. \qquad (9.5.14)$$

Thus

$$\frac{db}{dD} = -\frac{d^2\mu/d(\ln Q_D)^2}{N^*[d\mu/dN_D]^*} = \frac{[d^2\mu/d(\ln Q_D)^2]^*}{[d\mu/d(\ln Q_D)]^*} \qquad (9.5.15)$$

Since in all plausible models μ is an increasing function of Q_D (and hence of $\ln Q_D$), it is the sign of $d^2\mu/d(\ln Q_D)^2$ that determines whether b can increase as the dilution rate increases from zero in batch culture to finite values in continuous culture.

In Fig. 9.8 we plot the μ against $\ln Q_D$ graphs obtained from the batch culture of Fig. 9.1 with assumed delays of 0, 5, 10, and 15 hours. The maximum values of Q for which we have data apply to the exponential phase of growth where the rate of population increase is determined by the maximum rate of nutrient uptake, so that the approximation that $S = 0$ used in the present analysis is clearly invalid. However, away from the immediate neighbourhood of this maximum quota, the curves ought to be applicable to the present discussion and it is clear that for all the delays considered there is a tendency for the slope to increase initially with $\ln Q_D$. This is what we require for consistency.

The above qualitative reconciliation of the experiments on batch and continuous culture can be made quantitative by using Fig. 9.8 to estimate the parameter b. With a delay of 10 hours, the slope at $\mu = 0.034$ (the final dilution rate in the experiment of Fig. 9.3) is around $b \simeq 0.1$ hr^{-1} (though there is at least 30 per cent uncertainty in this estimate) giving

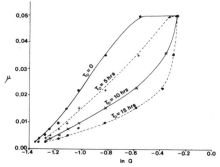

Fig. 9.8. Specific growth rate at time t against logarithm of cell quota at time $t - T_D$ with delays $T_D = 0, 5, 10, 15$ h for the batch culture of Fig. 9.1.

$bT_D \simeq 10 \times 0.1 = 1$, a value for which we would expect observable oscillations with a period of 40–50 hours. Near $\mu = 0$ (the batch culture steady state) b cannot be determined, but it is certainly less than 0.015 hr^{-1} giving $bT_D = 0.15$ which implies overdamping.

At this point a weakness of our model becomes apparent. The experimental oscillations are certainly not harmonic as is predicted by the linear analysis and because of this the 'period' is not well defined. We could reasonably define a period as the time interval AC (~60 hours) or BD (~ 45 hours) in Fig. 9.3, both of which are reasonably consistent with the model predictions, but there is no possibility of the present simple model explaining either the very long, slow decline that precedes the first minimum or the subsequent upward trend in population number that is superimposed on the oscillations. However, as the detailed shape of the oscillations was non-reproducible between experiments, more detailed modelling incorporating age structure and the distribution of nitrogen among the cells would at present appear unjustified given the current state of the experimental art.

9.6   MAIN CONCLUSIONS

Clearly the modelling in this chapter falls a long way short of meeting the broad objective of determining what controls cell division in *Chlamydomonas reinhardii* growing under conditions of nitrogen limitation. However, we have demonstrated unambiguously that no plausible model in which the cell division rate is determined solely by the instantaneous mean cell quota can explain the oscillations in cell numbers observed in continuous culture. The important feature of this result is its generality which was achieved by avoiding specifying functional forms for the assumed μ/Q and A/S relationships.

We were more successful in our narrower task of modelling the oscillations in Fig. 9.3 in a way compatible with the (non-oscillatory) batch culture results.

We managed to show:

(a)   A delayed dependence of division rate on cell quota can explain both the batch and continuous culture results if at values of cell quota corresponding to low dilution rates

$$\frac{d^2\mu}{d(\ln Q_D)^2} > 0 \qquad (9.5.16)$$

(b)   The $\mu - Q$ curve obtained by Cunningham from batch culture experiments satisfies condition (a) and a time lag of 10 hours is sufficient to produce observable oscillations in continuous culture with periods comparable with those observed.

The principal failure of the model is its inability to reproduce the detailed form of the chemostat oscillations which are not the damped sinusoids predicted by the present model. There is no problem in inventing time-lag models which will produce damped oscillations of almost any form (the reader might expect this after reading Chapter 8!) but this is a meaningless exercise in the absence of further experimental guidance on possible underlying mechanisms. In particular, the apparent time-lags suggested by the experiments may well be artefacts reflecting some underlying tendency to synchronization of individual cell cycles, or may simply reflect the elaborate biochemistry associated with cell division. The level of sophistication of the present model matches that of the experimental data available and fruitful elaboration must await a further round of experiments.

SOURCES AND SUGGESTED FURTHER READING

The growth dynamics of unicellular algae are reviewed in detail by Cunningham and Maas (1981). The experiments modelled in this chapter are reported by Cunningham (1976) and Cunningham and Maas (1978). Tentative evidence of damped oscillations in cell numbers in nitrogen-limited chemostat populations of Chlorella pyrenoidosa and Selenastrum gracile is given by Williams (1965, 1970) but the sampling interval is too long for unambiguous interpretation. Caperon (1969) reports overshoots in cell number but no oscillations for chemostat cultures of Isochrysis galbana. Nyholm (1978) may have obtained oscillations with Chlorella pyrenoidosa under phosphate limitation but the experiments were insufficiently long for this to be certain.

Much of the theoretical modelling of chemostat cultures has used a model originally proposed by Monod (1950) in which cell division rate depends on the residual substrate level. Burmaster (1979) shows that steady-state experiments alone cannot determine the validity of this assumption (as opposed to the assumption of dependence on cell quota) but the batch culture experiments reported in this chapter are clearly sufficient to preclude a Monod-type model of Cunningham's algae. The model in this chapter is a generalization of that formulated by Droop (1968) and by Caperon and Meyer (1972). The most useful analytic work relating to the present time-delay models is that of MacDonald (1976, 1978) which is particularly strong on methodology for distributed-delay models. The argument leading to equations (9.3.1) and (9.3.2) is based on Streifer (1974).

Chapter 10

Predator–Prey Quasi-Cycles in a Patchy Environment

10.1 HUFFAKER'S EXPERIMENTS

One of the best-known sets of laboratory experiments involving predator–prey interactions is that of Huffaker and co-workers (Huffaker 1958;
Huffaker, Shea, and Herman, 1963) who studied the population dynamics of
the predatory mite *Typhlodromus occidentalis* (Nesbitt) and the herbivorous
(orange-eating) six-spotted mite *Eototranychus sexmaculatus* (Riley). The
experiments were motivated by the apparent difficulty found by many workers in obtaining persistence of simple food–prey–predator systems in the
laboratory, and were intended to reveal whether the introduction of sufficient
spatial complexity into the system might induce persistence.

The basic experimental system was a tray on which oranges could be
arranged in a regular array as in Fig. 10.1. Oranges could have part of their
surfaces covered with paper (and thus inaccessible to mites) or could be
totally replaced by dummies, thereby permitting independent variation of
both the total availability of food and its distribution over the available space.

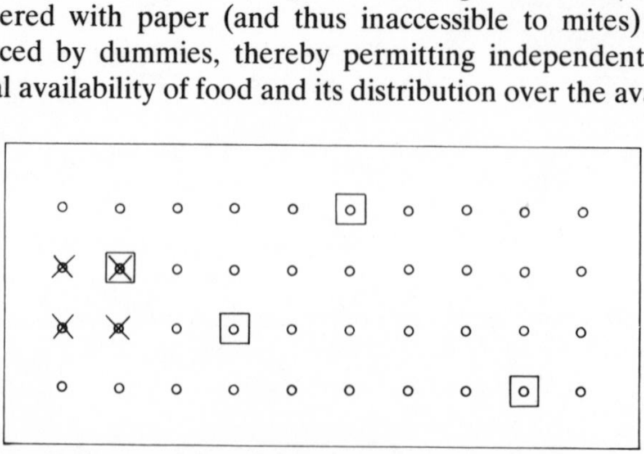

Fig. 10.1. The experimental 'arena'. Each position can
be occupied by an orange (with its surface wholly or
partly exposed) or a dummy, waxed, rubber ball.
(Reproduced from Huffaker, 1958.) Marked locations
refer to specific experiments described in the text.

In most of the experiments the schedule for replacement of oranges involved removing and replacing one quarter of the total every 11 days, the oldest or most overeaten oranges being given priority for replacement. Migration between oranges was possible for both species though this could be restricted by suitably placed vaseline barriers and wooden posts) but the rim of the tray was coated with petroleum jelly to prevent mites entering or leaving the complete experimental system.

A large number of experiments (described in detail in the original papers) were performed on this or similar systems with the following results.

(a)   Even with only a very small number of oranges exposed, the prey species could persist for long periods in the absence of predators. Figs. 10.2(a) and 10.2(b) illustrate results for four-orange systems in adjacent positions (marked × in Fig. 10.1) and in widely dispersed positions (marked □ in Fig. 10.1).

(b)   With the same amount of food as in (a) distributed over twenty oranges,

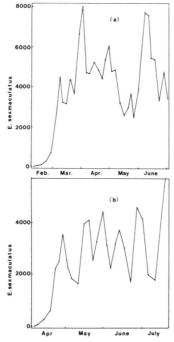

Fig.   10.2. Populations   of *Eototranychus sexmaculatus* in the absence of predators on a four-orange system with the oranges in, (a) adjacent positions, and (b) widely dispersed positions. (From Huffaker, 1958.)

326

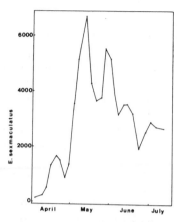

Fig. 10.3. A population of *Eototranychus sexmaculatus* in the absence of predators with twenty small patches of orange available for colonization (From Huffaker, 1958.)

population persistence was still achieved but this time with a series of violent rises and falls associated with the colonization of patches and their subsequent over-exploitation leading to local extinction (Fig. 10.3). The experiment was initiated by placing ten mites on each of two of the oranges. The first peak (April 19) was caused by population growth on these two patches, and the next two by the near-simultaneous colonization of several other patches. More of the synchronony induced by the initial conditions was by then lost, and the subsequent fluctuations were essentially non-cyclic.

(c) When both predators and prey were introduced to trays with only a small number of patches of orange exposed, the outcome was always either extinction of the prey and subsequent starvation of the predator (Fig. 10.4(a)) or predator extinction and prey recovery (Fig. 10.4(b)).

(d) In a few experiments involving very large numbers (hundreds) of patches, a small number of prey managed regularly to keep one step ahead of the predators and colonize a vacant orange before being consumed. The total population in the arena then persisted through a few predator–prey oscillations before extinction occurred and in Fig. 10.5(a) we illustrate an example of a 120-patch system. For this experiment Huffaker also published maps of the arena at regular intervals from which we can deduce the statistics of patch occupancy (Fig. 10.5(b)). Similar experiments were performed in some three-dimensional arrangements of oranges with the results illustrated in Fig. 10.6. In these experiments hazardous, vertical migration between trays

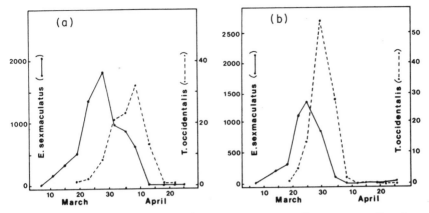

Fig. 10.4. Two of Huffaker's (1958) predator–prey experiments on small systems (Twenty small patches) illustrating, (a) extinction of both species, and (b) predator extinction followed by prey recovery.

was possible in addition to the horizontal migration within trays described above.

Broadly speaking, the picture that emerges from the set of experiments is that persistence of both prey and predator can be achieved if the prey can migrate sufficiently easily between oranges for a few to evade the attentions of the pursuing predators. Otherwise the system cannot survive beyond a single 'cycle' of the type illustrated in Fig. 10.4. The model to be developed in this chapter involves very simple representations of both migration and

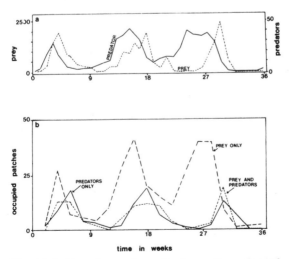

Fig. 10.5. Experimental results for a dispersion of 120 oranges in a two-dimensional arena. (a) Population densities. (b) Patch occupancy statistics.

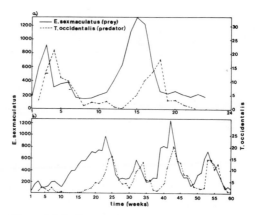

Fig. 10.6. Population densities in two three-dimensional systems. (From Huffaker, Shea, and Herman, 1968.)

local extinction but can be used to make both qualitative and quantitative predictions about the fluctuations in the number of oranges colonized at any particular instant. It also yields rough estimates of the likely number of 'cycles' before extinction in 'large' systems like those of Figs. 10.5 and 10.6.

10.2   A DISCRETE-STATE MODEL

Because of the spatial complexity of the experimental system, models (as opposed to simulations) of Huffaker's experiments are likely to be mathematically intractable without major simplifying assumptions. The inescapable minimum ingredients of a model purporting to represent the changes in population numbers would be some representation of the population dynamics on individual patches plus a representation of the processes of migration and colonization for each species. Even if the resulting doubly stochastic model were amenable to productive analysis (which it is not), the inevitable proliferation of unmeasured parameters would exclude use of the existing data to test its predictions. However, 'discrete-state' models of the type developed in Chapters 5 and 6, which are concerned only with the presence or absence of species on a particular patch and not with total population numbers, would appear ideally suited to this system, and this section is devoted to the construction of one such model.

We only recognize four possible states for a particular *patch*:

State 1—empty,
State 2—occupied by prey only,
State 3—occupied by prey and predators,
State 4—occupied by predators only.

The state of the entire *system* of M patches is specified by the set

$\{Q_i(t), i = 1, 2, 3, 4\}$ where $Q_i(t)$ denotes the number of patches in state i at time t. This choice of variable is the key to testing the model since the values of $Q_i(t)$ can be determined directly from Huffaker's published maps of the experimental arenas (cf. Figs. 10.5 and 10.6). The four Q_is are not independent since at any given time their sum is always equal to the total number of patches in the system, and the population dynamics can therefore be described completely in terms of any three of them; we thus choose the vector

$$\mathbf{Q}(t) \equiv \begin{bmatrix} Q_2(t) \\ Q_3(t) \\ Q_4(t) \end{bmatrix} \qquad (10.2.1)$$

to represent the state of the system.

Guided by the experiments described in the previous section (supplemented by a little speculation) we make the following assumptions.

(a)   Prey only successfully colonize empty patches.
(b)   Predators only successfully colonize patches already occupied by prey.
(c)   Prey extinction on a particular patch only occurs through over-exploitation by the predators.
(d)   Predator extinction on a particular patch can only arise through starvation.

The key word which makes assumptions (a) and (b) plausible is 'successfully'—we do not exclude the possibility of other types of colonization but merely regard them as of little significance in determining the global population dynamics (cf. Section 5.2C). Assumption (c) is speculative but is consistent with the observations (cf. Figs. 10.2, 10.3, 10.5, 10.6) that prey population densities (when converted to units of mites per orange area) are always heavily depressed by the presence of predators. Assumption (d) is made plausible by the experiments on small systems which showed clearly the tendency of predators to over exploit occupied patches, making it most implausible that all the predators would vacate a patch leaving behind a viable prey population.

The effect of these assumptions is that each patch progresses through its four states in strict cyclic order, and the model is completely specified by the four transition probabilities from each state to its successor in the cycle. Strictly speaking, these transition probabilities depend on the spatial distribution of the two populations, but to incorporate this feature in the model would involve formidable, and largely unresolved, mathematical problems (for a review see Bartlett, 1975). However, the experiment illustrated in Fig. 10.3 suggests that (at least for the prey) individual migrants can travel relatively long distances and initiate the colonization of patches some considerable distance from an occupied patch. If this migration is largely random, it follows that the probability that a potentially colonizable patch is successfully colonized is proportional to the number of patches which are potential sources of colonists. At time t, the proportion of patches occupied by prey is

$[Q_2(t) + Q_3(t)]/M$ and by predators is $[Q_3(t) + Q_4(t)]/M$. Thus writing the appropriate constants of proportionality (which have the dimensions of reciprocal time) as τ_1^{-1} and τ_2^{-1} we find that the probability $\alpha(\mathbf{Q})\, dt$ that during an infinitesimally small time interval dt one of the $Q_1(t)$ empty patches is colonized by prey is

$$\alpha(\mathbf{Q})\, dt = (M\tau_1)^{-1} Q_1(Q_2 + Q_3)\, dt$$

$$= (M\tau_1)^{-1}(M - Q_2 - Q_3 - Q_4)(Q_2 + Q_3)\, dt, \qquad (10.2.2)$$

and the probability $\beta(\mathbf{Q})\, dt$ that during dt one of the Q_2 patches occupied by prey only is colonized by predators is

$$\beta(\mathbf{Q})\, dt = (M\tau_2)^{-1}(Q_3 + Q_4)Q_2\, dt. \qquad (10.2.3)$$

The transitions from states 3–4 and 4–1 involve local extinction and as we saw in Chapter 6 the description of extinction is a rather delicate problem. Were the population on a particular site in a quasi-stationary state we could reasonably assume constant probabilities per unit time of extinction on that patch. However, as the most fundamental feature of the present model is that individual patches are undergoing rapid transients, an assumption of constant extinction probabilities is very dubious. We adopt the strategy of retaining the dubious assumption purely because it leads to substantial simplification of the mathematics although (in Section 6.8) we provide a measure of justification in the *a posteriori* demonstration that the global behaviour of similar single-species systems is in fact rather insensitive to the details of local extinction. We thus tentatively assume that a patch in state 3 has a constant probability τ_3^{-1} per unit time of prey extinction producing a transition to state 4 and that a patch in state 4 has a constant probability per unit time τ_4^{-1} of predator extinction causing a transition to state 1. The probability $\delta(\mathbf{Q})\, dt$ that during dt one of the Q_3 patches under dual occupation becomes a predator only site is thus

$$\delta(\mathbf{Q})\, dt = (Q_3/\tau_3)\, dt, \qquad (10.2.4)$$

while the probability $\varepsilon(\mathbf{Q})\, dt$ that during dt one of the Q_4 predator-only sites becomes empty and available for prey recolonization is

$$\varepsilon(\mathbf{Q}) = (Q_4/\tau_4)\, dt. \qquad (10.2.5)$$

We have now produced a representation of the system which is mathematically analogous to a set of three coupled birth and death processes, similar to, but more complex than, those of Chapter 6 and Section 6.8. We can thus describe the dynamics of the system by the discrete stochastic differential equations

$$dQ_2 = \{\alpha(\mathbf{Q}) - \beta(\mathbf{Q})\}\, dt + dz_1 - dz_2, \qquad (10.2.6)$$

$$dQ_3 = \{\beta(\mathbf{Q}) - \delta(\mathbf{Q})\}\, dt + dz_2 - dz_3, \qquad (10.2.7)$$

$$dQ_4 = \{\delta(\mathbf{Q}) - \varepsilon(\mathbf{Q})\}\, dt + dz_3 - dz_4. \qquad (10.2.8)$$

where the increments dz_1, dz_2, dz_3, dz_4 have mean zero and variance $\alpha(\mathbf{Q})\,dt$, $\beta(\mathbf{Q})\,dt$, $\delta(\mathbf{Q})\,dt$, and $\varepsilon(\mathbf{Q})\,dt$ respectively.

10.3 DETERMINISTIC STABILITY

The set of discrete SDEs (10.2.6)–(10.2.8) embody all the assumptions of the model without any additional mathematical approximations, and could in principle be used for *simulations* of the experiments. However, as we have at present no direct experimental route to values of the parameters τ_1 to τ_4, simulations of this type will serve only a limited purpose at this stage. Instead, we now make a series of mathematical simplifications and approximations which lead to testable interrelations between mean values of patch occupancy by prey predators or both, and the variance in these quantities.

Our first approximation is to replace the discrete SDEs by their continuous counterparts in which occupancies are no longer restricted to integer values. The result is

$$\frac{dQ_2}{dt} = \alpha(\mathbf{Q}) - \beta(\mathbf{Q}) + \sqrt{(\alpha(\mathbf{Q}))}\gamma_1(t) + \sqrt{(\beta(\mathbf{Q}))}\gamma_2(t), \qquad (10.3.1)$$

$$\frac{dQ_3}{dt} = \beta(\mathbf{Q}) - \delta(\mathbf{Q}) + \sqrt{(\beta(\mathbf{Q}))}\gamma_2(t) + \sqrt{(\delta(\mathbf{Q}))}\gamma_3(t), \qquad (10.3.2)$$

$$\frac{dQ_4}{dt} = \delta(\mathbf{Q}) - \varepsilon(\mathbf{Q}) + \sqrt{(\delta(\mathbf{Q}))}\gamma_3(t) + \sqrt{(\varepsilon(\mathbf{Q}))}\gamma_4(t), \qquad (10.3.3)$$

where $\gamma_1(t)$, $\gamma_2(t)$, $\gamma_3(t)$, $\gamma_4(t)$ are independent Gaussian white noise processes with unit spectral density.

In the absence of the noise terms these equations would have a deterministic steady state $\mathbf{Q}^*$ obtained by requiring that

$$\alpha(\mathbf{Q}^*) = \beta(\mathbf{Q}^*) = \delta(\mathbf{Q}^*) = \varepsilon(\mathbf{Q}^*), \qquad (10.3.4)$$

i.e. that

$$(M\tau_1)^{-1}(Q_2^* + Q_3^*)Q_1^* = (M\tau_2)^{-1}Q_2^*(Q_3^* + Q_4^*) = \tau_3^{-1}Q_3^* = \tau_4^{-1}Q_4^*. \tag{10.3.5}$$

The value of the deterministic steady-state patch occupancy is thus controlled by three dimensionless groups of parameters (τ_2/τ_1), (τ_3/τ_1), and (τ_4/τ_1). Conversely the values of each of these dimensionless ratios is uniquely defined by the steady-state occupancies, a feature we shall exploit when fitting the model to Huffaker's data. Thus

$$\frac{\tau_2}{\tau_1} = \frac{Q_2^*(Q_3^* + Q_4^*)}{Q_1^*(Q_2^* + Q_3^*)}; \qquad \frac{\tau_3}{\tau_1} = \frac{Q_3^* M}{Q_1^*(Q_2^* + Q_3^*)}; \qquad \frac{\tau_4}{\tau_1} = \frac{Q_4^* M}{Q_1^*(Q_2^* + Q_3^*)}.$$

$$(10.3.6)$$

Neighbourhood stability of the deterministic steady state is investigated with the aid of the standard techniques from Chapter 4. If $\mathbf{q}(t)$ represents the deviation of $\mathbf{Q}(t)$ from the deterministic steady state $\mathbf{Q}^*$ then to first order in $\mathbf{q}$

$$\dot{\mathbf{q}} = \tau_1^{-1} \mathbf{A} \, \mathbf{q}, \tag{10.3.7}$$

where after a few lines of algebra involving equation (10.3.6) it can be shown that the stability matrix is

$\mathbf{A} =$

$$x_1(x_2 + x_3)\begin{bmatrix} -\left\{\dfrac{x_2^2 + x_2 x_3 + x_3 x_1}{x_1 x_2 (x_2 + x_3)}\right\} & \left\{-\dfrac{1}{x_1} + \dfrac{(x_4 - x_2)}{(x_2 + x_3)(x_3 + x_4)}\right\} & \left\{-\dfrac{x_1 + x_3 + x_4}{x_1(x_3 + x_4)}\right\} \\[2ex] \dfrac{1}{x_2} & -\left\{\dfrac{x_4}{x_3(x_3 + x_4)}\right\} & \left\{\dfrac{1}{x_3 + x_4}\right\} \\[2ex] 0 & \dfrac{1}{x_3} & -\dfrac{1}{x_4} \end{bmatrix}$$

with

$$\tag{10.3.8}$$

$$x_1 \equiv Q_1^*/M, \qquad x_2 \equiv Q_2^*/M, \qquad x_3 \equiv Q_3^*/M, \qquad x_4 \equiv Q_4^*/M. \tag{10.3.9}$$

Demonstrating neighbourhood stability now involves verifying four Routh–Hurwitz inequalities (see Table 4.1), namely

$$a_1 = - \, \text{Trace } \mathbf{A} > 0, \tag{10.3.10}$$

$$a_2 = \Sigma \, (\text{principal minors of } \mathbf{A}) > 0, \tag{10.3.11}$$

$$a_3 = - \, \text{Det } \mathbf{A} > 0, \tag{10.3.12}$$

$$a_1 a_2 - a_3 > 0. \tag{10.3.13}$$

Calculating the trace of $\mathbf{A}$ (and hence a_1) is simply a matter of adding the diagonal elements of the matrix. The quantities a_2 and a_3 are harder to evaluate, but much laborious algebra can be saved by noting that the 2×2 determinant at the bottom right of $\mathbf{A}$ is zero. After a fair amount of effort we obtain

$$a_1 = x_1(x_2 + x_3)\left\{\frac{1}{x_1} + \frac{1}{x_4} + \frac{x_3}{x_2 x_4 (x_2 + x_3)} + \frac{x_4}{x_3 (x_3 + x_4)}\right\} \tag{10.3.14}$$

$$a_2 = x_1(x_2 + x_3)\left\{\frac{1}{x_1 x_4} + \frac{x_3}{x_2 x_4 (x_2 + x_3)} + \frac{x_4}{x_1 x_3 (x_2 + x_3)}\right.$$

$$\left. + \frac{1}{x_1 x_2} + \frac{1}{(x_2 + x_3)(x_3 + x_4)}\right\}, \tag{10.3.15}$$

$$a_3 = x_1(x_2 + x_3)\left\{\frac{(x_3 + x_4)}{x_1 x_2 x_3 x_4} + \frac{1}{x_3 x_4 (x_2 + x_3)}\right\}, \tag{10.3.16}$$

all of which are clearly positive. The final condition (inequality (10.3.13)) is much more troublesome and we exhausted our algebraic stamina without successfully simplifying the obscenity that results from using equations (10.3.14)–(10.3.16) to evaluate $a_1 a_2 - a_3$ in terms of the x's. This type of algebraic impasse is commonly encountered with differential equations involving three or more variables, and it is seldom possible to justify the investment of man-weeks required to resolve the difficulty. Fortunately, in this model our earlier insistence on minimizing the number of free parameters means that the inequality can readily be checked numerically by way of an exhaustive scan of positive values of x_2, x_3 and x_4, chosen so as to ensure that x_1 is also positive. One such scan involving 10^6 combinations of parameters showed no violation of inequality (10.3.13), and this result, together with the rigorous demonstration of inequalities (10.3.10–(10.3.12), establishes 'beyond reasonable doubt' the local stability of any steady state with positive patch occupancies.

The importance of the above argument is twofold. First, since any positive steady state is deterministically stable, the present model cannot explain the oscillations in patch occupancy as limit cycles (which require a deterministically *unstable* steady state) but only in terms of the mechanism discussed in Section 7.4 involving the filtering of white noise by an apparently deterministically stable, but underdamped system. Secondly, it permits us to use the locally linear approximations of Chapters 6 and 7 (which involve expansions around a stable steady state) to predict the intensity of fluctuations in patch occupancy. This is done in the next section.

10.4   GROSS FLUCTUATION CHARACTERISTICS

A. Theory

The gross characteristics of the fluctuations in patch occupancy can now be investigated with the aid of the locally linear approximations introduced in Chapters 6 and 7. This (hopefully) by now routine procedure involves identifying deterministic steady states and linearizing in terms of the q_i's (the fluctuations in patch occupancy) and the γ_i's (the noise terms in equation (10.3.1)–(10.3.3)). The expansion with respect to the q_i's merely involves a repeat of the algebra in Section 10.3, while that in the γ_i's simply involves replacing $\mathbf{Q}$ by $\mathbf{Q}^*$ in the original equation. If we recognize that at a deterministic steady state $\alpha(\mathbf{Q}^*) = \beta(\mathbf{Q}^*) = \gamma(\mathbf{Q}^*) = \varepsilon(\mathbf{Q}^*)$, the final result is a linear SDE which can be written in the shorthand form

$$\frac{d\mathbf{q}}{dt} = \tau_1^{-1}\mathbf{A}\mathbf{q} + \sqrt{(\alpha(\mathbf{Q}^*))}\mathbf{v}(t), \tag{10.4.1}$$

where the 'noise term' $\mathbf{v}(t)$ is defined by

$$\mathbf{v}(t) \equiv \begin{bmatrix} \gamma_1(t) - \gamma_2(t) \\ \gamma_2(t) - \gamma_3(t) \\ \gamma_3(t) - \gamma_4(t) \end{bmatrix}. \tag{10.4.2}$$

To recast equation (10.4.1) in terms of dimensionless quantities, we first note that although in our analysis we pretend that $\mathbf{q}(t)$ is a continuous variable, this is solely a device for simplifying calculations; in the real world patch occupancy is an integer and hence is dimensionless. We further note that since white noise is defined (loosely) as the 'time-derivative' of a Wiener increment which has the dimensions of $(\text{time})^{1/2}$, (cf. equations (6.2.31) and (6.2.36)), it must have the dimensions $(\text{time})^{1/2}/\text{time}$, i.e. $(\text{time})^{-1/2}$. We arbitrarily chose to let the constant τ_1 define the units of time, and finally introduce the notation

$$\mathbf{q}'(t') = \mathbf{q}(\tau_1 t), \tag{10.4.3}$$

and

$$\gamma_i'(t') = \tau_1^{1/2}\gamma_i(\tau_1 t'); \qquad \mathbf{v}'(t') = \tau_1^{1/2}\mathbf{v}(\tau_1 t'). \tag{10.4.4}$$

The effect of equation (10.4.4) is that in terms of normalized frequencies, the constituent white noise terms $\gamma_i'(t')$ (associated with the discreteness of colonization and extinction events) of the normalized noise vector $\mathbf{v}'(t')$ still have unit spectral density. Moreover, when the original linear SDE (10.4.1) is rewritten in dimensionless form the result is

$$\frac{d\mathbf{q}'(t')}{dt'} = \mathbf{A}\mathbf{q}'(t') + \left\{\frac{Q_1^*(Q_2^* + Q_3^*)}{M}\right\}^{1/2} \mathbf{v}'(t'). \tag{10.4.5}$$

Since $\mathbf{A}$ depends (see equations (10.3.8) and (10.3.9)) only on the steady-state patch occupancies, it follows that the fluctuations in patch occupancy can be characterized in all features except their time scale by the steady-state patch occupancies. This is the feature of the model which makes it experimentally testable and is a consequence of the requirement that each site must progress cyclically through its possible states.

It is a straightforward, but rather tedious, exercise in the techniques of Chapter 7 to evaluate the Fourier transforms $\tilde{\mathbf{q}}'(\omega')$ of the deviations in patch occupancy from their steady state values. Still using the dimensionless form of the SDE and defining ω' as the angular frequency in our dimensionless units ($\omega' = \omega\tau_1$) we obtain

$$i\omega\tilde{\mathbf{q}}'(\omega') = \mathbf{A}\tilde{\mathbf{q}}'(\omega') + \left\{\frac{Q_1^*(Q_2^* + Q_3^*)}{M}\right\}^{1/2} \tilde{\mathbf{v}}'(\omega'), \tag{10.4.6}$$

from which it follows that

$$\tilde{\mathbf{q}}'(\omega') = (i\omega'\mathbf{I} - \mathbf{A})^{-1}\left\{\frac{Q_1^*(Q_2^* + Q_3^*)}{M}\right\}^{1/2} \tilde{\mathbf{v}}'(\omega'). \tag{10.4.7}$$

The individual expressions for the components of $\tilde{\mathbf{q}}'(\omega')$ are too lengthy to be usefully displayed explicitly, principally because of the complexity of the terms introduced by matrix inversion. However, if we define a matrix

$$\mathbf{Y} = \left\{ \frac{Q_1^*(Q_2^* + Q_3^*)}{M} \right\}^{1/2} (i\omega'\mathbf{I} - \mathbf{A})^{-1}, \qquad (10.4.8)$$

and recognize that the elements of $\mathbf{Y}$ can be calculated from the recipe for matrix inversion in Appendix M, we can illustrate the remaining steps in the calculation of gross fluctuation characteristics without excessively cumbersome algebra. Since equation (10.4.7) written out in full now becomes

$$\begin{bmatrix} \tilde{q}_2'(\omega') \\ \tilde{q}_3'(\omega') \\ \tilde{q}_4'(\omega') \end{bmatrix} = \begin{bmatrix} Y_{22} & Y_{23} & Y_{24} \\ Y_{32} & Y_{33} & Y_{34} \\ Y_{42} & Y_{43} & Y_{44} \end{bmatrix} \begin{bmatrix} \tilde{\gamma}_1'(\omega') - \tilde{\gamma}_2'(\omega') \\ \tilde{\gamma}_2'(\omega') - \tilde{\gamma}_3'(\omega') \\ \tilde{\gamma}_3'(\omega') - \tilde{\gamma}_4'(\omega') \end{bmatrix}, \qquad (10.4.9)$$

it follows that

$$\tilde{q}_2'(\omega') = Y_{22}\tilde{\gamma}_1'(\omega') + (Y_{23} - Y_{22})\tilde{\gamma}_2'(\omega') + (Y_{24} - Y_{23})\tilde{\gamma}_3'(\omega') - Y_{24}\tilde{\gamma}_4'(\omega'),$$
$$(10.4.10)$$

with similar equations for $\tilde{q}_3'(\omega')$ and $\tilde{q}_4'(\omega')$. The gross characteristics of the fluctuations in Q_2 are obtained via the spectral density $S_2'(\omega')$ defined by (cf. equation (6.5.28))

$$S_2'(\omega') = \lim_{T \to \infty} \frac{1}{T} E\{|\tilde{q}_2(\omega')|^2\}, \qquad (10.4.11)$$

evaluation of which involves recognizing that each white-noise term represents totally independent processes (γ_1 prey colonization, γ_2 predator colonization, γ_3 prey extinction, γ_4 predator extinction) and hence

$$\lim_{T \to \infty} \frac{1}{T} E\{|\tilde{\gamma}_i'(\omega')\tilde{\gamma}_j'^*(\omega')|\} = \begin{cases} 1 & \text{if } i = j \\ 0 & \text{if } i \neq j \end{cases} \qquad (10.4.12)$$

Thus

$$S_2'(\omega') = |Y_{22}|^2 + |(Y_{23} - Y_{22})|^2 + |(Y_{24} - Y_{23})|^2 + |Y_{24}|^2, \quad (10.4.13)$$

the frequency dependence of course deriving from the dependence of the individual Ys (through equation (10.4.8)) on ω'. Similar expressions can be derived for $S_3'(\omega')$ and $S_4'(\omega')$. The intensity of the fluctuations in patch occupance strictly $\sigma_{tim,i}^2$ as in equation (6.5.38) but for compactness denoted by σ_i^2) is now evaluated from the integrals

$$\sigma_i^2 = \frac{1}{2\pi} \int_{-\infty}^{\infty} S_i'(\omega') \, d\omega' = \frac{1}{\pi} \int_0^{\infty} S_i'(\omega') \, d\omega' \qquad (10.4.14)$$

which are most conveniently evaluated numerically. As $S_i'(\omega')$ involves the steady state occupancies Q_i^* (through the Y matrix), we now have a prediction of σ_i^2 involving solely these patch occupancies. This is the basis of our experimental tests on the model.

B. Experimental tests

The application of the above theory to Huffaker's experiments involves one very fundamental assumption *additional* to those involved in the formulation of the model. Our analysis predicts relationships among quantities (means and variances in patch occupancy) which are formally defined in terms of expectation values and as such, cannot be measured without either a large number of replicate experiments or a single, very long (theoretically infinite) experiment. The latter possibility involves the use of the 'ergodic theorems' mentioned in Chapter 6 which guarantee equality of long-time averages and expectation values in the *model*, but which give us little practical guidance as to how long a time may be rigorously regarded as 'long' when estimating means and variances from time averages in a single *experiment*. Plausibly, this time should substantially exceed both the time lag required for the ACF to become insignificantly different from zero, and the time required for any transients to decay; however, in the present experiments extinction probably occurs before this condition is satisfied. Nevertheless, in the absence of experimental values of the 'microscopic' parameters τ_1 to τ_4 we have no practical alternative but to assume that transient effects are relatively unimportant and to use short-time averages over one complete experiment to make experimental estimates of means and variances. The probity of this procedure is established *a posteriori* by comparing the statistics of whole- and half-runs.

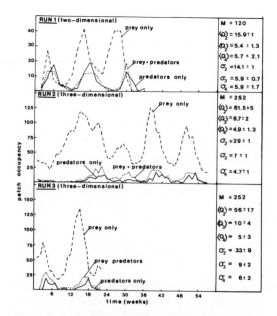

Fig. 10.7. Statistics of patch occupancy for the 'long' experimental runs illustrated in Figs. 10.5 and 10.6.

We confine our tests to those experiments for which there are published maps of the state of the arena at regular intervals. These are the 120-patch, two-dimensional arena of Fig. 10.5 (referred to as 'Run 1') and the two, 252-patch, three-dimensional arenas of Fig. 10.6 (referred to as 'Runs 2 and 3'). From the maps we can measure the patch occupancies $\{Q_i(t)\}$ as functions of time, the results being shown in Fig. 10.7 where we also display the statistics of patch occupancy obtained through 'short-time averages' as described in the previous paragraph. The uncertainties quoted in Fig. 10.7 are 'guesstimates' which were arrived at by comparing results for a whole run with those for half-runs.

Runs 2 and 3 were effectively replicates of each other (though there were a few differences—the prey growth at the start of Run 2 was apparently impeded by air pollutants while the end of the same run was caused by a viral disease of the prey) and the patch occupancy statistics might reasonably be expected to be comparable. We show in Table 10.1 that this is the case, and in view of the higher uncertainties in measurements from Run 3 (due to its more rapid extinction) we regard this run solely as evidence of the reliability of the measurements in Run 2 and restrict our quantitative tests of the model to Run 1 (for which there was no replicate) and Run 2.

Our strategy for testing the model relies on the fact that, in the model, the fluctuation amplitudes, σ_2, σ_3, and σ_4, can be calculated from a knowledge of the deterministic steady-state occupancies which in the linear approximation are equal to the mean patch occupancies. We therefore use the *measured* values of $\langle Q_2 \rangle$, $\langle Q_3 \rangle$, and $\langle Q_4 \rangle$ to *predict* (via equations (10.4.8), (10.4.13), (10.4.14) and analogous equations) the fluctuation amplitudes σ_2, σ_3, and σ_4 and then compare these predictions with the measured time average values quoted in Fig. 10.7. Because of the uncertainties in the measured mean occupancies (the input to the calculation) there is of course uncertainty in the predictions, but this is easily estimated by repeating the calculations for a selection of values of mean occupancies at the extremes of the experimentally permitted ranges. Table 10.2 contains the results of the calculations and we see that in all but one case (σ_3 in Run 2) the predicted and observed fluctuation amplitudes agree to within the quoted confidence limits. The one exceptional case is little cause for concern given the very restricted data set on which the predictions were based, the necessarily crude procedure for guessing the experimental uncertainties, and the mathematical approximations involved in the analysis of the fluctuations.

Table 10.1. Comparison of patch occupancy statistics for the two replicate experiments in three-dimensional arrays of oranges.

Run	$\langle Q_2 \rangle$	$\langle Q_3 \rangle$	$\langle Q_4 \rangle$	σ_2	σ_3	σ_4
2	61.5 ± 5	8.7 ± 2	4.9 ± 1.3	29 ± 1	7 ± 1	4.7 ± 1
3	56 ± 17	10 ± 4	5 ± 3	33 ± 9	9 ± 2	6 ± 2

Table 10.2. Comparison of predicted and measured fluctuation amplitudes for Runs 1 and 2.

	Run 1			Run 2		
	σ_2	σ_3	σ_4	σ_2	σ_3	σ_4
Experimental measurements	14 ± 1	5.9 ± 0.7	5.9 ± 1.7	29 ± 1	7 ± 1	4.7 ± 1
Model predictions	10 ± 3	5.9 ± 0.5	5 ± 1	31 ± 4	9.9 ± 0.6	5.6 ± 1.4

10.5 EXTINCTION TIMES

We cannot rigorously apply the procedures of Chapters 6 and 7 for estimating extinction times without considerable labour which appears unjustified in the present investigation in view of the lack of data against which to test any predictions (two genuine extinctions plus one extinction associated with disease and thus outwith the scope of the model). However 'ballpark estimates' of the order of magnitude of the mean time to extinction combined with an estimate of the period of the quasi-cycles should permit us to predict whether extinction is virtually certain after one cycle (as in the small systems), a few cycles, or many cycles.

The simplest fate of the system to consider is predator extinction followed by prey recovery. The only way in which this can occur is through a single, local predator extinction in a system with $Q_2 \neq 0$, $Q_3 = 0$, $Q_4 = 1$. Rigorous calculation of the mean time for such an event is difficult, but we can approach the problem heuristically by treating it as analogous to that of estimating the mean time to extinction of a single-species population in a quasi-stationary state. This was covered in Chapter 6 where we showed that (cf. equation (6.5.8))

$$\tau_E = [D(1)P_c^*(1)]^{-1} \tag{10.5.1}$$

where $D(1)$ was the probability of a single death in a population consisting of exactly one individual. A similar argument applied to the present model would yield

$$\tau_E = \tau_4 \times \{\text{Probability that } Q_2 \neq 0, Q_3 = 0, Q_4 = 1\}^{-1}, \tag{10.5.2}$$

though care is required in rigorously defining the probability in this equation. This expression is the basis of our guess at τ_E. If we define $E(t)$ (E = eater) to be the total number of patches occupied by predators, i.e.

$$E(t) = Q_3(t) + Q_4(t), \tag{10.5.3}$$

then the mean (E^*) and variance (σ_E^2) of $E(t)$ can be calculated by methods similar to those used in the previous section (but note that since $Q_3(t)$ and $Q_4(t)$ are in general correlated, the calculation of fluctuation amplitude has to proceed *ab initio*). For the two experimental runs under investigation we obtain

$$E^* = \begin{cases} 14 \pm 3 & \text{Run 1} \\ 15 \pm 5 & \text{Run 2} \end{cases} \qquad \sigma_E = \begin{cases} 11 \pm 2 & \text{Run 1} \\ 15 \pm 2 & \text{Run 2} \end{cases} \qquad (10.5.4)$$

from which it seems safe to deduce that $\sigma_E/E^* \sim 1$. If $E(t)$ were normally distributed about its mean value and *if* prey extinction followed by predator starvation can be regarded as improbable then equation (10.5.2) gives us the estimate

$$\tau_E \sim \tau_4 \sqrt{(2\pi)} \, \sigma_E \exp\{E^{*2}/2\sigma_E^2\}, \qquad (10.5.5)$$

which since we know the value of the ratio τ_4/τ_1 (cf. equation (10.3.6)) can be used to determine τ_E in terms of our base unit of time, τ_1. The result is

$$\tau_E = \begin{cases} 15\tau_1 & \text{Run 1} \\ 7\tau_1 & \text{Run 2}. \end{cases} \qquad (10.5.6)$$

To comment on these guesses at τ_E, we now evaluate the period of the quasi-cycles. This is most easily done by examination of the spectral density functions which were calculated en route to σ_E. For both runs these had sharp peaks at frequencies corresponding to periods given by

$$\text{period} = \begin{cases} 5\tau_1 & \text{Run 1} \\ 3\tau_1 & \text{Run 2} \end{cases} \qquad (10.5.7)$$

Comparing these results with our crude estimates of extinction time suggests that for both runs extinction might be expected after a few cycles.

We have carried out a similar analysis for the case where the system's ultimate fate is assumed to be prey extinction followed by predator starvation. The results are much the same—persistence for a few cycles—and thus we cannot meaningfully determine which species is likely to go extinct first. However, we feel confident that the order of magnitude of our estimates of extinction time is reliable and we thus conclude that while the detailed fate of either 'long' experiment is unpredictable, extinction of one or both species could be expected after a few cycles, again in agreement with experiment.

10.6 CONCLUSIONS

Huffaker's experiments had the rather special feature that population changes were studied on an arena containing a large number of *near-identical* small patches. Our model, therefore, diverts attention away from the intra-patch dynamics and on to the simpler question of the presence or absence of mites on particular patches. The central feature of the model is the assumption that patches progress *in order* through their four states (empty, containing prey only, containing both prey and predators, containing predators only) and that we can specify transition probabilities between each state and its successor in the cycle. The fluctuations in patch occupancy can then be shown to be centred on a deterministically stable steady state and thus are unambiguously *not* limit cycles.

The alternative possibility is that the fluctuations are resonant quasi-cycles 'driven' by a mechanism rather similar to demographic stochasticity in homogeneous populations, the 'discrete' processes in this case being colonization and local extinction which change the number of patches in a particular state by ± 1. We show that the amplitude of such fluctuations would be controlled solely by the mean patch occupancies and use this result to predict fluctuation amplitudes in three of Huffaker's experiments. Predicted and measured fluctuation amplitudes agree well.

The data available does not justify an extensive investigation of extinction times, but we can perform an order-of-magnitude calculation of the ratio of the expected extinction time to the period of the quasi-cycles. We are unable to determine which species is likely to suffer extinction first, but we can predict that the systems used by Huffaker are likely to persist for only a few cycles, again in agreement with experiment.

SOURCES AND SUGGESTED FURTHER READING

Gurney and Nisbet (1978b) contains an analysis of the model in this chapter with more emphasis on the qualitative dynamics and less on the comparison with Huffaker's experiments. Computer simulation of similar models but taking account of the detailed spatial distribution of occupied patches have been published by Maynard Smith (1974), Hilborn (1975), and Zeigler (1976).

Appendix C

Calculus with Functions of Two or More Variables

In this book, we are assuming familiarity with basic calculus as applied to functions of a single variable. In particular, we assume understanding of the concepts of differentiation and integration and the ability to perform these operations mechanically on simple functions (powers of x, exponential and logarithm, trigonometric functions). The reader wishing to review these topics may consult any one of the myriads of texts on basic calculus—books with a biological bias include Causton (1977) and Eason, Coles and, Gettingby (1980).

We also assume familiarity with the idea of *series expansions* in which approximations to the value of a function are calculated at points in the vicinity of a point at which its value is known. For example if the curve in Fig. C1 represents the equation

$$y = f(x), \tag{C1}$$

then in the vicinity of a point $x = a$ we have

$$y = f(a + \xi) = f(a) + \xi \left(\frac{\mathrm{d}f}{\mathrm{d}x} \right)_{x=a} + R(\xi) \tag{C2}$$

where the remainder term $R(\xi)$ is 'of order ξ^2', i.e. as $\xi \to 0$

$$\lim_{\xi \to 0} \frac{1}{\xi^2} |R(\xi)| = \text{some finite number,} \tag{C3}$$

This implies that for x sufficiently close to a, we can satisfactorily approximate $f(x)$ by the *locally linear approximation*

$$f(a + \xi) = f(a) + \xi \left(\frac{\mathrm{d}f}{\mathrm{d}x} \right)_{x=a}, \tag{C4}$$

the interpretation of which is shown in Fig. C1.

341

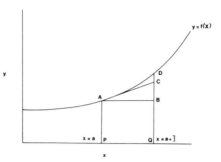

Fig. C1. Illustration of the approximation inherent in local linearization. AC is the tangent to the curve $y = f(x)$ at $x = a$. The line QD represents $f(a + \xi)$ and QC the linear approximation to this quantity (equation C4). CD represents the remainder term $R(\xi)$ which approaches zero rapidly as $\xi \to 0$.

Our aim in this appendix is to present the key results in the extension of these concepts to functions of more than one variable. Our target is the less mathematically experienced reader who is following the 'short route' (chapters 1, 2, 4, 8, and 9) through the book. The results quoted will give him sufficient background to master the material in these chapters (for which many-variable calculus is of peripheral importance) and, we hope, to capture the 'flavour' of the argument in the more mathematical chapters.

The key concept in the differential calculus of functions of many variables is the *partial derivative*. Given a function $f(x_1, x_2)$ of two variables we define

$$\frac{\partial f}{\partial x_1} = \lim_{\xi \to 0} \frac{f(x_1 + \xi, x_2) - f(x_1, x_2)}{\xi} \tag{C5}$$

i.e. it is the 'ordinary' derivative of f with respect to x_1 calculated in the situation where x_2 is held constant. Similarly, given a function $f(x_1, x_2, \ldots x_M)$ of M variables, we define

$$\frac{\partial f}{\partial x_i} = \lim_{\xi \to 0} \left\{ \frac{f(x_1, x_2, \ldots, x_i + \xi \ldots x_M) - f(x_1, x_2, \ldots x_M)}{\xi} \right\} \tag{C6}$$

To construct series expansions (sometimes known as Taylor expansions) of functions of two variables we use the result

$$f(a_1 + \xi_1, a_2 + \xi_2) = f(a_1, a_2) + \xi_1 \left(\frac{\partial f}{\partial x_1} \right)_{\substack{x_1 = a_1 \\ x_2 = a_2}} + \xi_2 \left(\frac{\partial f}{\partial x_2} \right)_{\substack{x_1 = a_1 \\ x_2 = a_2}} + R, \tag{C7}$$

where R is of order ξ^2, which for a function of M variables, generalizes to

$$f(a_1 + \xi_1, a_2 + \xi_2, \ldots a_M + \xi_M) = f(a_1, a_2, \ldots a_M) + \sum_{i=1}^{M} \xi_i \left(\frac{\partial f}{\partial \xi_i}\right)_{\substack{\xi_1 = a_1 \\ \xi_2 = a_2}} + R$$

$$\text{etc.} \qquad \text{(C8)}$$

where R is of order ξ^2.

The key concept in multi-variable integral calculus is the multi-dimensional integral which we use at several points in Chapter 5 and also in Section 7.5. We are only concerned with definite integrals whose interpretation as limits of sums is relatively straightforward. Given a function $f(x_1, x_2)$ and an area A of the (x_1, x_2) plane divided into small squares as in Fig. 5.4, we define

$$\int_A f(x_1, x_2) \, dx_1 \, dx_2 = \lim_{a \to 0} \frac{1}{a^2} \sum_i f(x_{1i}, x_{2i}) \qquad \text{(C9)}$$

where (x_{1i}, x_{2i}) are the coordinates of the centre of the ith square and the sum runs over all squares totally included in the area. Obviously this definition can be readily extended to larger numbers of variables, even where the simple geometrical analogy fails but there is little point in writing down the summation explicitly.

Appendix D

The Dirac δ-Function

In our discussion of the theory of Fourier transforms, we shall make frequent use of the so called Dirac δ-function, which we write $\delta_{\text{Dirac}}(x)$ and whose crucial property is that if $F(x)$ is any reasonably well-behaved function of x then

$$\int_{-\infty}^{\infty} F(x)\delta_{\text{Dirac}}(x)\,dx = F(0). \tag{D1}$$

The δ-function, which is technically a 'generalized function' (Lighthill, 1958), is usually defined as the limiting case of a sequence of well-behaved functions. Various sequences can be used for this purpose, and in our case the most suitable is

$$D(x, a) \equiv \frac{1}{\pi}\frac{\sin ax}{x} = \frac{1}{2\pi}\int_{-a}^{a} e^{ixy}\,dy, \tag{D2}$$

from which we define

$$\delta_{\text{Dirac}}(x) = \lim_{a \to \infty} D(x, a). \tag{D3}$$

In Fig. D1 we show $D(x, a)$ as a function of x for several values of a, and it is evident that as a increases $D(x, a)$ becomes steadily more sharply peaked about $x = 0$. These changes take place without any accompanying change in the area under the curve since it can be shown that

$$\int_{-\infty}^{\infty} D(x, a)\,dx = 1 \qquad \text{for all } a. \tag{D4}$$

We also note from equation D2 that

$$D(0, a) = \frac{a}{\pi}, \tag{D5}$$

so that as a becomes very large (Fig. D2) $D(x, a)$ becomes in essence a single very narrow spike at $x = 0$ with 'wings' on each side consisting of oscillations so rapid as to contribute essentially nothing to the area under the curve. It is now rather easy to see how the vital property of the δ-function (equation D1)

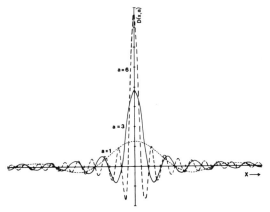

Fig. D1. $D(x, a)$ as a function of x for three values
of $a = a = 1$ (----), $a = 3$ (----), $a = 6$
(----).

arises. If $F(x)$ is any reasonably well-behaved function of x, then it is clear
from equation D4 that

$$\int_{-\infty}^{\infty} F(x)D(x, a)\, dx - F(0) = \int_{-\infty}^{\infty} \{F(x) - F(0)\}D(x, a)\, dx. \qquad (D6)$$

But with the aid of a few sketches it is easy to convince oneself that

$$|F(x) - F(0)| \leqslant x \max\left|\frac{dF}{dx}\right| \qquad (D7)$$

and hence that

$$\left|\int_{-\infty}^{\infty} \{F(x) - F(0)\}D(x, a)\, dx\right| \leqslant \max\left|\frac{dF}{dx}\right|\int_{-\infty}^{\infty} xD(x, a)\, dx. \qquad (D8)$$

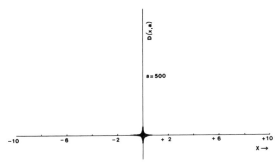

Fig. D2. $D(x, a)$ as a function of x for $a = 500$.

But

$$\int_{-\infty}^{\infty} xD(x, a) \, dx = \int_{-\infty}^{\infty} \frac{1}{\pi} \sin ax \, dx = \frac{1}{a\pi} \int_{-\infty}^{\infty} \sin y \, dy \qquad \text{(D9)}$$

which formally goes to zero as $a \to \infty$. Thus we can infer that, provided $\max |\, dF/dx \,|$ is finite,

$$\lim_{a \to \infty} \left| \int_{-\infty}^{\infty} \{F(x) - F(0)\}D(x, a) \, dx \right| = 0 \qquad \text{(D10)}$$

so that

$$\int_{-\infty}^{\infty} \{F(x) - F(0)\}\delta_{\text{Dirac}}(x) \, dx = 0 \qquad \text{(D11)}$$

hence proving equation D1.

Appendix F

Fourier Analysis

F1 CONTINUOUS AND DISCRETE FOURIER TRANSFORMS

Fourier analysis consists, in essence, of representing a function of one or more variables as a superposition of sinusoidal components. The discussion which follows is couched entirely in terms of functions of a single variable, and moreover ignores or circumvents a number of the more troublesome subtleties of the technique. The reader who wishes to explore these subtleties or generalize the treatment to include multiple variables is advised to consult one of the many texts covering the subject (e.g. Hobbie 1978, Chapter 9, Champeney 1973, or Bendat and Piersol, 1971). A useful table of standard Fourier Transforms can be found in Oberhettinger, 1973.

We consider first a continuous function $X(t)$ which is known over the interval $-T/2 \leqslant t \leqslant T/2$, and define a new function $\tilde{X}(\omega)$ which is related to it by

$$\tilde{X}(\omega) = \int_{-T/2}^{T/2} X(t)e^{-i\omega t}\, dt. \tag{F1}$$

The nature of the relationship between X and $\tilde{X}$ is illuminated by evaluating a second new quantity

$$X_R(t) = \frac{1}{2\pi}\int_{-\infty}^{\infty} \tilde{X}(\omega)e^{i\omega t}\, d\omega. \tag{F2}$$

On substituting from equation (F1) into (F2) we find

$$X_R(t) = \frac{1}{2\pi}\int_{-\infty}^{\infty} \left[\int_{-T/2}^{T/2} X(t')e^{-i\omega t'}\, dt'\right]e^{i\omega t}\, d\omega, \tag{F3}$$

which, if we rearrange the terms a little and reverse the order of integration, becomes

$$X_R(t) = \int_{-T/2}^{T/2} X(t')\left[\frac{1}{2\pi}\int_{-\infty}^{\infty} e^{i\omega(t-t')}\, d\omega\right] dt'. \tag{F4}$$

Consultation of Appendix D now allows us to identify the term in square brackets as a Dirac delta function, so that

$$X_R(t) = \int_{-T/2}^{T/2} X(t')\delta_{\text{Dirac}}(t - t')\,dt' = X(t), \tag{F5}$$

from which we conclude that X_R is simply the original function X.

We can thus summarize the relationship between the quantity $X(t)$ and its *Fourier transform* $\tilde{X}(\omega)$ as follows:

$$\tilde{X}(\omega) = \int_{-T/2}^{T/2} X(t)e^{-i\omega t}\,dt, \tag{F6a}$$

$$X(t) = \frac{1}{2\pi}\int_{-\infty}^{\infty} \tilde{X}(\omega)e^{i\omega t}\,d\omega; \tag{F6b}$$

the operation by which $X(t)$ is retrived from $\tilde{X}(\omega)$ being known as *inverse Fourier transformation*. We also note in passing that the zero frequency ($\omega = 0$) value of $\tilde{X}$ is related to the average value of $X(t)$ thus

$$\tilde{X}(0) = \int_{-T/2}^{T/2} X(t)\,dt = T\langle X(t)\rangle \tag{F7}$$

A feeling for the behaviour of the Fourier transform can be obtained if we realize that equation (F6b) implies that $(1/2\pi)\,\tilde{X}(\omega)$ is the amplitude density of the components of $X(t)$ in the angular frequency interval ω to $\omega + d\omega$. That is to say $(1/2\pi)\,\tilde{X}(\omega)\,d\omega$ is, very roughly, the 'amplitude of the component of $X(t)$ with angular frequency ω'. This interpretation is less clouded with mathematical technicalities in the case of the *discrete Fourier transform*, which we define by considering a function $X(q\Delta t)$ whose instantaneous value is known at a series of N times spaced at equal intervals (Δt) over the time period $-T/2 \leqslant q\Delta t \leqslant T/2$. Now if we define

$$\tilde{X}_D(s\omega_0) = \frac{1}{N}\sum_{q=-N/2}^{+N/2} X(q\Delta t)e^{isq\omega_0\Delta t} \quad \text{(integer } s, q) \tag{F8}$$

where

$$\omega_0 = 2\pi/T, \quad N = T/\Delta T. \tag{F9}$$

then an exactly parallel argument to that given above shows that

$$X(q\Delta t) = \sum_{s=-N/2}^{+N/2} \tilde{X}_D(s\omega_0)e^{isq\omega_0\Delta t} \quad \text{(integer } q, s) \tag{F10}$$

Thus $\tilde{X}_D(s\omega_0)$ is precisely interpretable as the amplitude of the component of $X(q\Delta t)$ with angular frequency $s\omega_0$.

F2 SPECTRAL DENSITY AND AUTOCOVARIANCE FUNCTION

If a function $X(t)$ has zero mean value then the fluctuation intensity (variance) of its components in the frequency band ω to $\omega + d\omega$ is $S_x(\omega)\,d\omega$ where the *spectral density* $S_x(\omega)$ is formally defined as

$$S_x(\omega) = \lim_{T \to \infty} \frac{|\tilde{X}(\omega)|^2}{T}. \tag{F11}$$

There are some technical problems about the existence of this function where $X(t)$ is white noise, but these can usually be solved by the insertion of an appropriate statistical expectation in place of $|\tilde{X}(\omega)|^2$.

Now consider the inverse transform of S_x

$$C_x(\tau) = \frac{1}{2\pi} \int_{-\infty}^{\infty} S_x(\omega) e^{i\omega\tau}\, d\omega. \tag{F12}$$

Substituting in turn from equations (F11) and (F6a) and interchanging the order of integration and limit taking, we find

$$C_x(\tau) = \lim_{T \to \infty} \frac{1}{2\pi T} \int_{-\infty}^{\infty} \left[\int_{-T/2}^{T/2} X(t) e^{+i\omega t}\, dt \right] \left[\int_{-T/2}^{T/2} X(t') e^{-i\omega t'}\, dt' \right] e^{i\omega\tau}\, d\omega \tag{F13}$$

which, on collecting terms and interchanging the order of integration, becomes

$$C_x(\tau) = \lim_{T \to \infty} \frac{1}{2\pi T} \int_{-T/2}^{T/2} \int_{-T/2}^{T/2} \int_{-\infty}^{\infty} X(t)X(t') e^{i\omega(t+\tau-t')}\, d\omega\, dt'\, dt, \tag{F14}$$

$$= \lim_{T \to \infty} \frac{1}{T} \int_{-T/2}^{T/2} \int_{-T/2}^{-T/2} X(t)X(t') \left[\frac{1}{2\pi} \int_{-\infty}^{\infty} e^{i\omega(t+\tau-t')}\, d\omega \right] dt'\, dt. \tag{F15}$$

Reference to Appendix D now shows that

$$C_x(\tau) = \lim_{T \to \infty} \frac{1}{T} \int_{-T/2}^{T/2} \int_{-T/2}^{T/2} X(t)X(t')\delta_{\text{Dirac}}(t + \tau - t')\, dt'\, dt \tag{F16}$$

$$= \lim_{T \to \infty} \frac{1}{T} \int_{-T/2}^{T/2} X(t)X(t + \tau)\, dt. \tag{F17}$$

Thus, since $\langle X(t) \rangle = 0$, we see that the inverse transform of $S_x(\omega)$ is just the autocovariance function, $C(\tau)$, defined in Chapter 1, so that this function and the spectral density function form a Fourier transform pair

$$S_x(\omega) = \int_{-\infty}^{\infty} C(\tau) e^{-i\omega\tau}\, d\tau, \tag{F18a}$$

$$C(\tau) = \frac{1}{2\pi} \int_{-\infty}^{\infty} S_x(\omega) e^{i\omega\tau}\, d\omega; \tag{F18b}$$

a result which is often referred to as the Wiener–Khinchin Theorem. It is, of course, an obvious corollary of equation (F18(b)), that the variance of the fluctuations in X is

$$\sigma^2_{\text{tim}} = C(0) = \frac{1}{2\pi} \int_{-\infty}^{\infty} S_x(\omega) \, d\omega. \tag{F19}$$

F3   CROSS-SPECTRAL DENSITY AND CROSS-COVARIANCE

If we have two processes $X(t)$ and $Y(t)$ both with zero mean and defined in the time interval $-T/2 \leq t \leq T/2$, then by analogy with equation (F11) we can define their *cross spectral density* $S_{xy}(\omega)$ as

$$S_{xy}(\omega) = \lim_{T \to \infty} \frac{\tilde{X}^*(\omega)\tilde{Y}(\omega)}{T} \tag{F20}$$

where $\tilde{X}^*(\omega)$ is the complex conjugate of the transform of X. An exactly parallel argument to that given in Section F2 now shows us that this function forms a Fourier transform pair with the cross-covariance function

$$C_{xy}(\tau) = \lim_{T \to \infty} \frac{1}{T} \int_{-T/2}^{T/2} X(t)Y(t + \tau) \, dt \tag{F21}$$

so that

$$S_{xy}(\omega) = \int_{-\infty}^{\infty} C_{xy}(\tau)e^{-i\omega\tau} \, d\tau, \tag{F22}$$

$$C_{xy}(\tau) = \frac{1}{2\pi} \int_{-\infty}^{\infty} S_{xy}(\omega)e^{i\omega\tau} \, d\omega. \tag{F23}$$

F4   FOURIER TRANSFORM OF A DERIVATIVE

The utility of Fourier transform techniques in solving certain kinds of differential equation, arises primarily from the fact that a very simple relationship exists between the transform of any given function and the transform of any of its derivatives. We consider two functions $X(t)$ and $Y(t)$, both known over the time interval $-T/2 \leq t \leq T/2$, and related by

$$Y(t) = \frac{d^n}{dt^n} \{X(t)\}. \tag{F24}$$

By definition equation (F6a) the Fourier transform of $Y(t)$ is

$$\tilde{Y}(\omega) = \int_{-T/2}^{T/2} Y(t)e^{-i\omega t} \, dt \tag{F25}$$

and on substituting from equation (F24) we find that this becomes

$$\tilde{Y}(\omega) = \int_{-T/2}^{T/2} \left[\frac{d^n}{dt^n} \{X(t)\} \right] e^{-i\omega t} \, dt. \tag{F26}$$

If we now use equation (F6b) to substitute for $X(t)$ in terms of $\tilde{X}(\omega)$ we find

$$\tilde{Y}(\omega) = \int_{-T/2}^{T/2} \left[\frac{d^n}{dt^n} \left\{ \frac{1}{2\pi} \int_{-\infty}^{\infty} \tilde{X}(\omega') e^{i\omega' t}\, d\omega' \right\} \right] e^{-i\omega t}\, dt \qquad (F27)$$

which, on interchanging the order of integration and differentiation, becomes

$$\tilde{Y}(\omega) = \int_{-T/2}^{T/2} \left[\frac{1}{2\pi} \int_{-\infty}^{\infty} \tilde{X}(\omega')(i\omega')^n e^{i\omega' t}\, d\omega' \right] e^{-i\omega t}\, dt. \qquad (F28)$$

If we now interchange the order of integration with respect to time and frequency then we obtain

$$\tilde{Y}(\omega) = \int_{\infty}^{\infty} (i\omega')^n \tilde{X}(\omega') \left[\frac{1}{2\pi} \int_{-T/2}^{T/2} e^{i(\omega'-\omega)t}\, dt \right] d\omega' \qquad (F29)$$

and hence show (cf. Appendix D) that since in the limit $T \to \infty$ the term in square brackets is a δ-function, then

$$\tilde{Y}(\omega) = \int_{\infty}^{\infty} (i\omega')^n \tilde{X}(\omega') \delta_{\text{Dirac}}(\omega' - \omega)\, d\omega'. \qquad (F30)$$

Thus, if

$$Y(t) = \frac{d^n}{dt^n} \{X(t)\}, \qquad (F31)$$

and the time (T) over which X is known is very long $(T \to \infty)$

$$\tilde{Y}(\omega) = (i\omega)^n \tilde{X}(\omega). \qquad (F32)$$

In practice, although this relation is only formally exact in the limit $T \to \infty$, it is normally acceptably accurate provided only that T is long enough to submerge the effects of the endpoints.

F5   FOURIER TRANSFORM OF A TIME-LAGGED FUNCTION

We consider now two functions $X(t)$ and $Y(t)$ which are simply the same function plotted on graphs whose time scales have been displaced by an amount T_D relative to one another, so that

$$Y(t) = X(t - T_D). \qquad (F33)$$

For convenience we assume both X and Y to be known at all times (i.e. $T \to \infty$) so that

$$\tilde{Y}(\omega) = \int_{-\infty}^{\infty} Y(t) e^{-i\omega t}\, dt \qquad (F34)$$

or, from equation (F33)

$$\tilde{Y}(\omega) = \int_{-\infty}^{\infty} X(t - T_D) e^{-i\omega t}\, dt. \qquad (F35)$$

A change of variable to $z = t - T_D$ now shows that

$$\tilde{Y}(\omega) = \int_{-\infty}^{\infty} X(z)e^{-i\omega(z+T_D)}\,dz \qquad \text{(F36)}$$

$$= e^{-i\omega T_D}\int_{-\infty}^{\infty} X(z)e^{-i\omega z}\,dz \qquad \text{(F37)}$$

But the integral on the right-hand side of equation (F37) is just the Fourier transform of $X(t)$, $\tilde{X}(\omega)$. Thus if

$$Y(t) = X(t - T_D) \qquad \text{(F38)}$$

and the time (T) over which $X(t)$ is known is very large, then

$$\tilde{Y}(\omega) = e^{-i\omega T_D}\tilde{X}(\omega) \qquad \text{(F39)}$$

F6   FOURIER TRANSFORM OF A CONVOLUTION

We now consider the case of a function $X(t)$, known over $-\infty < t < \infty$, which is a *convolution* of two other functions $A(t)$ and $B(t)$, thus

$$X(t) = \int_{-\infty}^{\infty} A(\tau)B(t - \tau)\,d\tau. \qquad \text{(F40)}$$

The Fourier transform of X is now

$$\tilde{X}(\omega) = \int_{-\infty}^{\infty}\left[\int_{-\infty}^{\infty} A(\tau)B(t - \tau)\,d\tau\right]e^{-i\omega t}\,dt \qquad \text{(F41)}$$

which can be rewritten

$$\tilde{X}(\omega) = \int_{-\infty}^{\infty}\int_{-\infty}^{\infty} A(\tau)e^{-i\omega\tau}B(t - \tau)e^{-i\omega(t-\tau)}\,d\tau\,dt. \qquad \text{(F42)}$$

Interchanging the order of integration with respect to t and τ and introducing a new variable $z = t - \tau$ changes this to

$$\tilde{X}(\omega) = \int_{-\infty}^{\infty} A(\tau)e^{-i\omega\tau}\left[\int_{-\infty}^{\infty} B(z)e^{-i\omega z}\,dz\right]d\tau. \qquad \text{(F43)}$$

But the term in square brackets is just $\tilde{B}(\omega)$, the Fourier transform of B, and is hence independent of τ so that

$$\tilde{X}(\omega) = \tilde{B}(\omega)\int_{-\infty}^{\infty} A(\tau)e^{-i\omega\tau}\,d\tau = \tilde{B}(\omega)\tilde{A}(\omega). \qquad \text{(F44)}$$

Thus, to summarize, if

$$X(t) = \int_{-\infty}^{\infty} A(\tau)B(t - \tau)\,d\tau \qquad \text{(F45)}$$

then

$$\tilde{X}(\omega) = \tilde{A}(\omega)\tilde{B}(\omega). \tag{F46}$$

F7 TRANSFORMS OF CERTAIN SPECIAL FUNCTIONS

A. A constant

Suppose that $X(t)$ has a constant value, say Q. In this case

$$\tilde{X}(\omega) = \int_{-T/2}^{T/2} Qe^{-i\omega t}\,dt \tag{F47}$$

i.e.

$$\tilde{X}(\omega) = \frac{2Q\,\sin(\omega T/2)}{\omega} \tag{F48}$$

In the special case of $T \to \infty$, reference to Appendix D shows that the transform becomes a δ-function at the origin

$$\tilde{X}(\omega) = 2\pi Q\delta_{\text{Dirac}}(\omega). \tag{F49}$$

This is clearly reasonable since a constant has a finite average value (cf. equation (F7)) but has no components at any finite frequency.

B. A sinusoid

Suppose $X(t)$ is a sinusoid of frequency ω_0 and amplitude Q, so that

$$X(t) = Q\,\cos\omega_0 t. \tag{F50}$$

In this case

$$\tilde{X}(\omega) = \int_{-T/2}^{T/2} Q\,\cos(\omega_0 t)e^{-i\omega t}\,dt \tag{F51}$$

i.e.

$$\tilde{X}(\omega) = Q\left[\frac{\sin[(\omega - \omega_0)T/2]}{\omega - \omega_0} + \frac{\sin[(\omega + \omega_0)T/2]}{\omega + \omega_0}\right] \tag{F52}$$

so that in the special case $T \to \infty$, X becomes two δ-functions, one at $\omega = \omega_0$ and the other at $\omega = -\omega_0$;

$$X(\omega) = \pi Q\delta_{\text{Dirac}}(\omega - \omega_0) + \pi Q\delta_{\text{Dirac}}(\omega + \omega_0). \tag{F53}$$

Appendix M

Matrices

M1 BASIC CONCEPTS

Matrix theory is used in this book solely as a kind of mathematical shorthand to avoid writing down and manipulating large sets of linear algebraic equations. None of the subtle properties (especially those relating to special symmetries) which yield a rich pay-off in physics and engineering are used, and this appendix therefore has the restricted aim of defining and justifying (without overmuch attention to mathematical rigour) the small number of commonly used operations involving matrices. There is an elementary introduction to matrix manipulations (including examples from population dynamics) in Eason, Coles, and Gettingby (1980).

We start by defining a *column vector* $\mathbf{x}$ which is simply a set of M numbers $x_1, x_2, \ldots x_M$ arranged in a vertical column, i.e.

$$\mathbf{x} = \begin{bmatrix} x_1 \\ x_2 \\ \cdot \\ \cdot \\ \cdot \\ x_M \end{bmatrix}. \tag{M1}$$

We then suppose we have P linear equations relating the xs, i.e.

$$\begin{aligned}
A_{11}x_1 + A_{12}x_2 &+ \ldots + A_{1M}x_M = b_1 \\
A_{21}x_1 + A_{22}x_2 &+ \ldots + A_{2M}x_M = b_2 \\
&\vdots \\
A_{P1}x_1 + A_{P2}x_2 &+ \ldots + A_{PM}x_M = b_P
\end{aligned} \tag{M2}$$

As a prelude to developing a shorthand notation for this complete system of linear equations we define a *matrix* $\mathbf{A}$ to be simply the coefficients of the x's arranged in a rectangular array of P rows and M columns, the coefficient A_{ij} occupying the position jth from the left on the ith row down, i.e.

$$\mathbf{A} = \begin{bmatrix} A_{11} & A_{12} & \cdots & A_{1M} \\ A_{21} & A_{22} & \cdots & A_{2M} \\ \vdots & \vdots & & \\ A_{P1} & A_{P2} & \cdots & A_{PM} \end{bmatrix} \qquad \text{(M3)}$$

(Note that in this notation a column vector is simply a $(P \times 1)$ matrix).We now define *multiplication* of two matrices. If $\mathbf{A}$ is a $(P \times M)$ matrix and $\mathbf{B}$ is a $(M \times Q)$ matrix, then the product $\mathbf{AB}$ is a $(P \times Q)$ matrix whose i, jth element is

$$(\mathbf{A}\,\mathbf{B})_{ij} = \sum_{k=1}^{M} A_{ik} B_{kj}, \qquad i = 1, 2, \ldots P; \quad j = 1, 2, \ldots Q, \qquad \text{(M4)}$$

the product of two matrices being only defined for the case where the number of columns of the first is equal to the number of rows of the second. The set of linear equations $(M2)$ can now be written in the very simple form

$$\mathbf{Ax} = \mathbf{b}, \qquad \text{(M5)}$$

which we used in Chapters 3 and 4.

M2   DETERMINANT AND INVERSE

Consider again the set of linear equations (M2). If $M = P$, this represents M simultaneous, linear equations in M unknowns, and experience with elementary algebra suggests that (provided at least one of the bs is non-zero) there should 'normally' be a unique solution for all the xs. If there is, then it can easily be shown (e.g. by imagining the elementary method of solution through successive elimination of the variables) that the general form of the solution has each x as a linear combination of bs, i.e.

$$x_i = \sum_{k=1}^{M} C_{ik} b_k, \qquad \text{(M6)}$$

or in a matrix notation

$$\mathbf{x} = \mathbf{Cb}. \qquad \text{(M7)}$$

If we substitute equation (M7) for $\mathbf{x}$ in equation (M5) we obtain

$$\mathbf{ACb} = \mathbf{b} \qquad \text{(M8)}$$

which, since $\mathbf{b}$ has already been assumed to a non-zero vector, implies

$$\mathbf{AC} = \mathbf{I}. \qquad \text{(M9)}$$

which $\mathbf{I}$ is the *unit matrix* whose diagonal elements (I_{11}, I_{22} etc.) are equal to one, with all other elements zero, i.e.

$$\mathbf{I} = \begin{bmatrix} 1 & 0 & 0 & \ldots & 0 \\ 0 & 1 & 0 & \ldots & 0 \\ \cdot & \cdot & \cdot & & \\ \vdots & \vdots & \vdots & & \\ 0 & 0 & 0 & \ldots & 1 \end{bmatrix}. \tag{M10}$$

It can similarly be shown by premultiplying both sides of equation (M5) by $\mathbf{C}$ that $\mathbf{CA} = \mathbf{I}$ and thus $\mathbf{C}$ is a matrix with the special property that

$$\mathbf{AC} = \mathbf{CA} = \mathbf{I}. \tag{M11}$$

The matrix $\mathbf{C}$ satisfying equation (M11) is called the *inverse* of $\mathbf{A}$ and is normally written $\mathbf{A}^{-1}$.

We must now specify the 'normal' conditions for which a set of M linear equations in M unknowns has a unique solution. An algebraic equation of the form $Ax = b$ (where A, x, and b are simply real numbers) has a solution $x = b/A$ provided $A \neq 0$. We require an analogous result for sets of simultaneous linear equations, which leads us to the concept of the *determinant* of a square matrix. Intuitively (and this can be proved rigorously) the set of equations (M2) (with $M = P$) has a unique solution provided the equations are independent of each other. For example, if $M = 2$, each equation represents a line on a graph with axes x_1, x_2, and these lines will intersect at a point (the solution) unless they are parallel. The gradients of the two lines are $-A_{11}/A_{12}$ and $-A_{21}/A_{22}$, so we can argue that the inverse matrix (and a solution of the equations) exists provided

$$A_{11}A_{22} - A_{12}A_{21} \neq 0. \tag{M12}$$

If $M = 3$, each equation represents a plane in a coordinate system with axes x_1, x_2, x_3. The three planes intersect at a point provided no two of them are parallel and provided the lines of intersection of any two of them with the third are not parallel. With some tedious and rather uninstructive labour, it can be shown that this requirement amounts to

$$A_{11}A_{22}A_{33} + A_{12}A_{23}A_{31} + A_{13}A_{21}A_{32} - A_{11}A_{32}A_{23} - A_{12}A_{21}A_{33}$$

$$-A_{13}A_{22}A_{31} \neq 0. \tag{M13}$$

The expressions in equations (M12) and (M13) are particular cases (for $M = 2, 3$) of the determinant of a matrix and the general condition for the existence of the inverse of a matrix is that its determinant should not be zero. Formally we define

$$\det \mathbf{A} = \sum_{i=1}^{M} \sum_{j=1}^{M} \ldots \sum_{k=1}^{M} \varepsilon_{ij\ldots k} A_{1i} A_{2j} \ldots A_{Mk}, \tag{M14}$$

where

$$\varepsilon_{ij\ldots k} = \begin{cases} +1 & \text{if } i, j, \ldots k \text{ is an even permutation of the numbers } 1, 2, \ldots M \\ -1 & \text{if } i, j, \ldots k \text{ is an odd permutation of the numbers } 1, 2, \ldots M \\ 0 & \text{if } i, j, \ldots k \text{ is not a permutation of the numbers } 1, 2, \ldots M. \end{cases}$$
(M15)

An even (odd) permutation of the numbers $1, 2, \ldots M$ is one which is achieved by an even (odd) number of pairwise changes of position of the numbers (e.g. $1234 \to 2143$ is even; $1234 \to 4312$ is odd). In practice determinants are seldom evaluated directly from equation (M14) since there is a much simpler and more memorable recursive procedure. It can be shown from equation (M14) that

$$\det \mathbf{A} = A_{11}M_{11} - A_{12}M_{12} + A_{13}M_{13} - \ldots + (-1)^{M+1}A_{1M}M_{1M} \quad \text{(M16)}$$

where M_{ij} (called the *minor* of A_{ij}) is the determinant of the $(M-1) \times (M-1)$ matrix obtained by blocking out the ith row and the jth column of $\mathbf{A}$. This process is known as expanding the determinant along its first row, and can obviously be generalized to any row or column (preferably one containing many zero elements!). For example with $M = 3$,

$$\det \mathbf{A} = \det \begin{bmatrix} A_{11} & A_{12} & A_{13} \\ A_{21} & A_{22} & A_{23} \\ A_{31} & A_{32} & A_{33} \end{bmatrix}$$
(M17)

$$= A_{11}(A_{22}A_{33} - A_{32}A_{23}) - A_{12}(A_{21}A_{33} - A_{31}A_{23}) + A_{13}(A_{21}A_{32} - A_{31}A_{22})$$
(M18)

which is of course equation (M13) in disguise.

There remains the need to give an explicit formula for the inverse of a matrix. The general form of the (i,j)th element of $\mathbf{A}^{-1}$ is

$$(\mathbf{A}^{-1})_{ij} = \frac{(-1)^{i+j}M_{ji}}{\det \mathbf{A}}$$
(M19)

a result proved in most texts on matrix theory. In practice this formula is seldom used except when $M = 2$ for which it simplifies to yield

$$\mathbf{A}^{-1} = \frac{1}{A_{11}A_{22} - A_{21}A_{12}} \begin{bmatrix} A_{22} & -A_{12} \\ -A_{21} & A_{11} \end{bmatrix},$$
(M20)

a result we use several times in the text. At one point (in Chapter 10) we invert a 3×3 matrix; this is simply a matter of slogging out the nine minors and substituting in equation (M19). With $M \geqslant 4$, matrix inversion is normally performed numerically and there is a wide range of well-tested procedures available in most computer libraries. Discussion of these is beyond the scope of this appendix except to warn the reader that direct evaluation of equation (M19) is a potentially inaccurate method that is not recommended.

M3   HOMOGENEOUS LINEAR EQUATIONS

Occasionally we are faced with a set of linear equations of the form (known as a homogeneous system)

$$\mathbf{Ax} = \mathbf{0}, \tag{M21}$$

where $\mathbf{0}$ is a column vector containing M zeros. If $\det \mathbf{A} \neq 0$, then $\mathbf{A}^{-1}$ exists and the only $\mathbf{x}$ satisfying this equation is the uninteresting solution

$$\mathbf{x} = \mathbf{A}^{-1}\mathbf{0} = \mathbf{0} \tag{M22}$$

This is because the individual equations that make up equation (M21) represent lines, planes or hyperplanes (the analogues of planes in four or more dimensions) passing through the origin $(\mathbf{x} = \mathbf{0})$ which is normally the only point at which they all intersect. However, if the equations are *not* independent, then there may be a set of non-zero values of $\mathbf{x}$ (a line, plane or hyperplane depending on the dimensionality) which satisfy equation (M21). For example the equations

$$\left. \begin{array}{r} x_1 - 2x_2 + 5x_3 = 0 \\ 2x_1 - 4x_2 + 8x_3 = 0 \\ -3x_1 + 6x_2 + 7x_3 = 0 \end{array} \right\} \tag{M23}$$

are satisfied if

$$x_1 = 2x_2 \quad \text{and} \quad x_3 = 0, \tag{M24}$$

i.e. if

$$\mathbf{x} = \mu \begin{bmatrix} 2 \\ 1 \\ 0 \end{bmatrix}, \tag{M25}$$

where μ is an arbitrary constant. The general conditions for the existence of a non-zero solution of equation (M21) is that

$$\det \mathbf{A} = 0. \tag{M26}$$

where μ is an arbitrary constant.

M4   EIGENVALUES AND EIGENVECTORS

At two points in the text (age-structure models and many-species differential equation models) we encounter equations of the form

$$\mathbf{Ax} = \lambda\mathbf{x}, \tag{M27}$$

where $\mathbf{A}$ is a square matrix, $\mathbf{x}$ a (real or complex) column vector, and λ a (real or complex) number. This equation can obviously be recast in the form

$$(\mathbf{A} - \lambda\mathbf{I})\mathbf{x} = 0, \tag{M28}$$

which by the argument just presented can only have a non-trivial solution for **x** if

$$\det(\mathbf{A} - \lambda\mathbf{I}) = 0. \tag{M29}$$

Writing out the matrix in full this becomes

$$\det \begin{bmatrix} A_{11}-\lambda & A_{12} & A_{13} & \cdots & A_{1M} \\ A_{21} & A_{22}-\lambda & A_{23} & \cdots & A_{2M} \\ \vdots & \vdots & \vdots & & \\ A_{M1} & \cdot & \cdot & \cdot & A_{MM}-\lambda \end{bmatrix} = 0, \tag{M30}$$

and if we recall that each term in the determinant is a product of M matrix elements with *exactly* one element from each row then it becomes obvious that the determinant is a polynomial of degree M in λ. This polynomial is called the *characteristic polynomial* of **A** and its roots are the *eigenvalues* of **A**. We derive the polynomial explicitly in Section 4.2A for $M = 2$, the result being

$$\lambda^2 + a_1\lambda + a_2 = 0, \tag{M31}$$

where

$$a_1 = -(A_{11} + A_{22}) = -\text{Trace } \mathbf{A}, \tag{M32}$$

and

$$a_2 = A_{11}A_{22} - A_{21}A_{12} = \det \mathbf{A}. \tag{M33}$$

(The *trace* of a matrix is a name given to the sum of the diagonal elements (A_{11}, A_{22} etc.) of the matrix). When $M = 3$, the characteristic polynomial is

$$\lambda^3 + a_1\lambda^2 + a_2\lambda + a_3 = 0, \tag{M34}$$

where $a_1 = -\text{Trace } \mathbf{A}$

$$a_2 = \det\begin{bmatrix} A_{22} & A_{23} \\ A_{32} & A_{33} \end{bmatrix} + \det\begin{bmatrix} A_{11} & A_{13} \\ A_{31} & A_{33} \end{bmatrix} + \det\begin{bmatrix} A_{11} & A_{12} \\ A_{21} & A_{22} \end{bmatrix} \tag{M35}$$

$$a_3 = -\det \mathbf{A}. \tag{M36}$$

The three determinants in a_2 are sometimes called the *principal minors* of **A**.) When $M > 3$, the coefficients in the characteristic polynomial become tedious to write down in general, but if required the determinant (M29) can readily (if tediously) be evaluated by the recursive procedure described in the previous section. Although explicit calculation of the characteristic polynomial is a very useful tool in analytic work, especially in demonstrations of stability by the Routh–Hurwitz criteria, derivation of the characteristic polynomial followed by numerical root finding is *not* a safe numerical technique for finding the eigenvalues of any but the smallest matrices (frightening examples of possible numerical snags can be found in many numerical analysis texts). However, a prodigious number of stable, rapid algorithms for computing eigenvalues exist and most computer centres have library programs implementing one or more of these.

In general, there are M eigenvalues for a $M \times M$ matrix and if these are distinct (i.e. no two equal), then the solutions of the homogeneous equation (M27) corresponding to each eigenvalue are distinct and are known as *eigenvectors* of **A**. Considerable complication occurs in identifying the eigenvectors when the eigenvalues are not all distinct, but resolution of this problem is never required in the present work.

References

Abramowitz, M. and Segun, I. A. (1965), *Handbook of Mathematical Functions*, Dover Publications Inc., New York.

Abrams, P. A. (1975), Limiting similarity and the form of the competition coefficients, *Theoretical Population Biology*, **8**, 356–375.

Abrams, P. A. (1976), Niche overlap and environmental variability, *Mathematical Biosciences*, **28**, 357–372.

Allee, W. C., Emerson, A. E., Park, O., Park, T., and Schmidt, K. P. (1949), *Principles of Animal Ecology*, W. B. Saunders, Philadelphia.

Allwright, D. J. (1978), Hypergraphic functions and bifurcations in recurrence relations, *SIAM Journal of Applied Mathematics*, **34**, 687–691.

Anderson, O. D. (1978), On sorting out Poole's paper 'Stochastic difference equation predictions of population fluctuations' about the Box–Jenkins analysis and forecasting of ecological time series. *Theoretical Population Biology*, **13**, 179–189.

Anderson, R. M., and May, R. M. (1978), Regulation and stability of host–parasite population interactions, I: regulatory processes, *Journal of Animal Ecology*, **47**, 219–247.

de Angelis, D. L. (1975), Global asymptotic stability criteria for models of density-dependent population growth, *Journal of Theoretical Biology*, **50**, 35–43.

de Angelis, D. L. (1976), Application of stochastic models to a wildlife population, *Mathematical Biosciences*, **31**, 227–236.

Auslander, D. M., Oster, G. F., and Huffaker, C. B. (1974), Dynamics of interacting populations, *Journal of the Franklin Institute*, **297**, 345–376.

Baltensweiler, W. (1968), The cyclic population dynamics of the grey larch tortrix *Zeiraphera* Hubrner (=*Semasia diniana* Quenec) (Lepidoptera: Tortricidae), in *Insect Abundance* (Ed. T. R. E., Southwood), Symposium of the Royal Entomological Society, London, **4**, 88–97.

Barnet, S., and Storey, C. (1970). *Matrix Methods in Stability Theory*, Nelson, London.

Barrett, G. W. (1968), The effects of acute insecticide stress on a semi-enclosed grassland ecosystem, *Ecology*, **49**, 1019–1035.

Bartlett, M. S. (1957), On theoretical models for competitive and predatory biological systems, *Biometrika*, **44**, 27–42.

Bartlett, M. S. (1960), *Stochastic Population Models*, Spottiswoode, Ballantyne & Co. Ltd., London and Colchester.

Bartlett, M. S. (1966), *An Introduction to Stochastic Processes* (2nd Edition, 1966), Cambridge University Press.

Bartlett, M. S. (1975), *The Statistical Analysis of Spatial Pattern*, Chapman and Hall, London.

362

Bartlett, M. S., Gower, J. C., and Leslie, P. H. (1960), A comparison of theoretical and empirical results for some stochastic population models, *Biometrika*, **47**, 1–11.

Beddington, J. (1974), Age distribution and the stability of simple discrete-time population models, *Journal of Theoretical Biology*, **47**, 65–74.

Beddington, J. R., Free, C. A., and Lawton, J. H. (1976), Concepts of stability and resilience in predator-prey models, *Journal of Animal Ecology*, **45**, 791–816.

Beddington, J. R., Free, C. A., and Lawton, J. H. (1978), Characteristics of successful natural enemies in models of biological control of insect pests, *Nature, London*, **273**, 513–519.

Beddington, J. R., Hassell, M. P., and Lawton, J. H. (1976), The components of arthropod predation. II: The predator rate of increase, *Journal of Animal Ecology*, **45**, 165–185.

Beddington, J. R., and May, R. M. (1975), Time delays are not necessarily destabilizing, *Mathematical Biosciences*, **27**, 109–118.

Beddington, J. R., and May, R. M. (1977), Harvesting natural populations in a randomly fluctuating environment, *Science*, **197**, 463–465.

Bellman, R., and Cooke, K. L. (1963), *Differential Difference Equations*, Academic Press, New York.

Bendat, J. S., and Piersol, A. G. (1971), *Random Data: Analysis and Measurement Procedures*, Wiley–Interscience., New York.

Bernardelli, H. (1974), Population waves, *Journal of the Burma Research Society*, **31**, 1–18.

Betts, J. A. (1970), *Signal Processing, Modulation, and Noise*, Hodder and Stoughton, London.

Bigger, M. (1976), Oscillations of tropical insect populations, *Nature, London*, **259**, 207–209.

Bigger, M., and Tapley, R. E. (1969). Predictions of outbreaks of coffee leaf miners on Kilimanjaro, *Bulletin of Entomological Research*, **58**, 601–617

Box, G. F., and Jenkins, G. M. (1970), *Time Series Analysis: Forecasting and Control*, Holden-Day, San Francisco.

Boyarsky, A. (1980), Randomness implies order, *Journal of Mathematical Analysis and Applications*, **76**, 483–497.

Boyce, M. S., and Daley, D. J. (1980), Population tracking of fluctuating environments and natural selection for tracking ability, *American Naturalist*, **115**, 480–491.

Brauer, F. (1977), Stability of some population models with delay, *Mathematical Biosciences*, **33**, 345–358.

Brauer, F. (1979), Boundedness of solutions of predator prey systems, *Theoretical Population Biology*, **15**, 268–273.

Brauer, F., and Sanchez, D. A. (1975), Constant rate population harvesting: equilibrium and stability, *Theoretical Population Biology*, **8**, 12–30.

Brauer, F., Soudack, A. C., and Jarosch, H. S. (1976), Stabilization and destabilization of predator-prey systems under harvesting and nutrient enrichment, *International Journal of Control*, **23**, 553–573.

Buckingham, E. (1914), On physically similar systems: illustrations of the use of dimensional equations, *Physical Review*, **4**, 345.

Bulmer, M. G. (1974), A statistical analysis of the 10-year cycle in Canada, *Journal of Animal Ecology*, **43**, 701–718.

Bulmer, M. G. (1976), The theory of prey-predator oscillations, *Theoretical Population Biology*, **9**, 137–150.

Burmaster, D. E. (1979), The continuous culture of phytoplankton: mathematical equivalence among three steady state models, *American Naturalist*, **113**, 123–134.

Caperon, J. (1969), Time lag in population growth response of *Isochrysis galbana* to a variable nitrate environment, *Ecology*, **50**, 188–192.

Caperon, J., and Meyer, J. (1972), Nitrogen limited growth of marine phytoplankton,

II: Uptake kinetics and their role in nutrient limited growth of phytoplankton, *Deep Sea Research*, **19**, 619–632.

Causton, D. R. (1977), *A Biologist's Mathematics*, Edward Arnold, London.

Champeney, D. C. (1973), *Fourier Transforms and their Physical Applications*, Academic Press., London.

Charlesworth, B. (1980), *Evolution in Age-Structured Populations*, Cambridge Studies in Mathematical Biology, Cambridge University Press.

Chatfield, C. (1975), *Analysis of Time Series: Theory and Practice*, Chapman and Hall, London.

Coffman, C. V., and Coleman, B. D. (1978). On the growth of populations with narrow spread in reproductive age, II: Conditions of convexity, *Journal of Mathematical Biology*, **6**, 285–303.

Coffman, C. V., and Coleman, B. D. (1979), On the growth of populations with narrow spread in reproductive age, III: Periodic variations in the environment, *Journal of Mathematical Biology*, **7**, 281–301.

Coleman, B. D. (1978), On the growth of populations with narrow spread in reproductive age, I: General theory and examples, *Journal of Mathematical Biology*, **6**, 1–19.

Coleman, B. D. (1979), Nonautonomous logistic equations as models of the adjustment of populations to environmental change, *Mathematical Biosciences*, **45**, 159–173.

Coleman, B. D., and Hsieh, Y-H. (1979), Theory of the dependence of population levels on environmental history for semelparous species with short reproductive seasons, *Proceedings of the National Academy of Sciences*, U.S.A. **76**, 5407–5410.

Coleman, B. D., Hsieh, Y-H., and Knowles, G. P. (1979), On the optimal choice of r for a population in a periodic environment *Mathematical Biosciences*, **46**, 71–85.

Copson, E. T. (1962), *An Introduction to the Theory of Functions of a Complex Variable*, Clarendon Press, Oxford.

Cunningham, A. (1976), *Transient Growth Dynamics of* Chlamydomonas reinhardii *populations in nitrite-limited continuous culture*, PhD. Thesis, University of Strathclyde, Glasgow, UK.

Cunningham, A., and Maas, P. (1978), Time lag and nutrient storage effects in the transient growth response of *Chlamydomonas reinhardii* in nitrogen limited batch and continuous culture, *Journal of General Microbiology*, **104**, 227–231.

Cunningham, A., and Maas, P. (1981), The growth dynamics of unicellular algae, in *Mathematical Models in Microbiology* (Ed. M. Bazin), Vol. 1: *Microbial Population Dynamics*, CRC Press Inc., Bora Raton, Florida.

Cunningham, A., and Nisbet, R. M. (1980), Time lag and cooperativity in the transient growth dynamics of microalgae, *Journal of Theoretical Biology*, **84**, 189–203.

Cushing, J. M. (1977), *Integrodifferential Equations and Delay Models in Population Dynamics*, Springer-Verlag: Lecture Notes in Biomathematics, Vol. 20.

Davidson, J. (1938), On the growth of the sheep population in Tasmania, *Transactions of the Royal Society of South Australia*, **62**, 342–346.

DeBenedictis, P. A. (1977), The meaning and measurement of frequency-dependent competition, *Ecology*, **58**, 158–166.

Doebelin, E. O. (1972), *System Dynamics*, Charles E. Merrill Publishing Co., Columbus, Ohio.

Droop, M. R. (1968), Vitamin B_{12} and marine ecology, IV: The kinetics of uptake, growth and inhibition in *Monochrysis lutheri*, *Journal of the Marine Biological Association of the United Kingdom*, **54**, 825–855.

Eason, G., Coles, C., and Gettingby, G. (1980), *Mathematics and Statistics for Biosciences*, Ellis Horwood, Chichester.

Elton, C. (1927), *Animal Ecology*, Sidgwick and Jackson, London.

Falk, H. (1980), Remarks on nonlinear birth and death models, *Physica*, **100A**, 615–624.

364

Feldman, M. W., and Roughgarden, J. (1975), A population's stationary distribution and chance of extinction in a stochastic environment with remarks on the theory of species packing, *Theoretical Population Biology*, **7**, 197–207.

Fisher, M. E., and Goh, B. S. (1977), Stability in a class of discrete-time models of interacting populations, *Journal of Mathematical Biology*, **4**, 265–274.

Von Foerster, H. (1959), Some remarks on changing populations, in *The Kinetics of Cellular Proliferation*. (Ed. F. Stohlman, Jr.) pp. 382–407, Grune & Stratton, New York.

Fujii, K. (1967), Studies on interspecies competition between the azuki bean weevil *Callosobruchus chinensis* and the southern cowpea weevil *C. maculatus*, II: Competition under different environmental conditions, *Research in Population Ecology*, **9**, 192–200.

Fujii, K. (1968), Studies on interspecies competition between the azuki bean weevil and the southern cowpea weevil, III: Some characteristics of strains of two species, *Research in Population Ecology*, **10**, 87–98.

Gilpin, M. E. (1974), A Liapunov function for competition communities, *Journal of Theoretical Biology*, **44**, 35–48.

Gilpin, M. E. (1975), *Group Selection in Predator-Prey Communities*, Princeton University Press, Princeton.

Glass, L., and Mackey, M. (1978), Pathological conditions resulting from instabilities in physiological control mechanisms, in *Bifurcation Theory and Application in Scientific Disciplines* (Eds. O. Gurel and O. E. Rössler), Annals of the New York Academy of Sciences, Vol. 316.

Goel, N. S., Maitra, S. C., and Montroll, E. W. (1971), On the Volterra and other nonlinear models of interacting populations, *Reviews of Modern Physics*, **43**, 231–276.

Goel, N. S., and Richter-Dyn, N. (1974), *Stochastic Models in Biology*, Academic Press, London.

Goh, B. S. (1977), Global stability in many-species systems, *American Naturalist*, **111**, 135–143.

Goodman, L. W. (1967), On the reconciliation of mathematical theories of population growth, *Journal of the Royal Statistical Society, Series A*, **130**, 541–553.

Gradshteyn, I. S., and Ryzhik, I. W. (1965), *Tables of Integrals, Series and Products*, Academic Press, London.

Gurney, W. S. C., Blythe, S. P., and Nisbet, R. M. (1980), Nicholson's blowflies revisited, *Nature, London*, **287**, 17–21.

Gurney, W. S. C., and Nisbet, R. M. (1975), The regulation of inhomogeneous populations, *Journal of Theoretical Biology*, **52**, 441–457.

Gurney, W. S. C., and Nisbet, R. M. (1976a), A note on nonlinear population transport, *Journal of Theoretical Biology*, **56**, 249–251.

Gurney, W. S. C., and Nisbet, R. M. (1976b), Spatial pattern and the mechanism of population regulation, *Journal of Theoretical Biology*, **59**, 361–370.

Gurney, W. S. C., and Nisbet, R. M. (1978a), Single species population fluctuations in patchy environments, *American Naturalist*, **112**, 1075–1090.

Gurney, W. S. C., and Nisbet, R. M. (1978b), Predator-prey fluctuations in patchy environments, *Journal of Animal Ecology*, **47**, 85–102.

Gurney, W. S. C., and Nisbet, R. M. (1979), Ecological stability and social hierarchy, *Theoretical Population Biology*, **16**, 48–80.

Gurney, W. S. C., and Nisbet, R. M. (1980), Age-dependent population dynamics in static and variable environments, *Theoretical Population Biology*, **17**, 321–344.

Gurtin, M. E., and MacCamy, R. C. (1974), Non-linear age-dependent population dynamics, *Archive for Rational Mechanics and Analysis*, **54**, 281–300.

Gurtin, M. E., and MacCamy, R. C. (1977), On the diffusion of biological populations, *Mathematical Biosciences*, **33**, 35–49.

Gurtin, M. E., and MacCamy, R. C. (1978), Population dynamics with age dependence, in *Nonlinear Analysis and Mechanics*, Heriot-Watt Symposium, Pitman Lecture Note Series, London.

Gurtin, M. E., and MacCamy, R. C. (1979), Some simple models for nonlinear age-dependent population dynamics, *Mathematical Biosciences*, **43**, 199–211.

Hasegawa, M., and Tanemura, M. (1976), On the pattern of space division by territories, *Annals of the Institute of Statistical Mathematics*, Part B, **28**, 509–519.

Hassell, M. P., Lawton, J. H., and Beddington, J. R. (1976), The components of arthropod predation. I: The prey death rate, *Journal of Animal Ecology*, **45**, 135–164.

Hassell, M. P., Lawton, J. H., and Beddington, J. R. (1977), Sigmoid functional responses by invertebrate predators and parasitoids, *Journal of Animal Ecology*, **46**, 249–262.

Hassell, M. P., Lawton, J. H., and May, R. M. (1976), Patterns of dynamical behaviour in single species populations, *Journal of Animal Ecology*, **45**, 471–486.

Hassell, M. P., and May, R. M. (1973), Stability in insect host–parasite models, *Journal of Animal Ecology*, **42**, 693–726.

Hassell, M. P., and May, R. M. (1974), Aggregation of predators and insect parasites and its effect on stability, *Journal of Animal Ecology*, **43**, 567–594.

Hassell, M. P., and Varley, G. C. (1969), New inductive population model for insect parasites and its bearing on biological control, *Nature, London*, **223**, 1133–1137.

Hastings, A. (1977), Spatial heterogeneity and the stability of predator-prey systems, *Theoretical Population Biology*, **12**, 37–48.

Hilborn, R. (1975), The effect of spatial heterogeneity on the persistence of predator-prey interactions, *Theoretical Population Biology*, **8**, 346–355.

Hobbie, R. K. (1978), *Intermediate Physics for Medicine and Biology*, Wiley, New York.

Holling, C. S. (1965), The functional response of predators to prey density and its role in mimicry and population regulation, *Memoirs of the Entomological Society of Canada*, **45**, 1–60.

Holling, C. S. (1973), Resilience and stability of ecological systems, *Annual Review of Ecology and Systematics*, **4**, 1–23.

Huffaker, C. B. (1958), Experimental studies on predation: dispersion factors and predator-prey oscillations, *Hilgardia*, **27**, 343–383.

Huffaker, C. B., Shea, K. P., and Herman, S. G. (1963), Experimental studies on predation: complex dispersion and levels of food in an acarine predator–prey interaction, *Hilgardia*, **34**, 305–330.

Hurd, L. E., and Wolf, L. L. (1974), Stability in relation to nutrient enrichment in arthropod consumers of old-field successional ecosystems, *Ecological Monographs*, **44**, 465–482.

Jillson, D. A. (1980), Insect populations respond to fluctuating environments, *Nature, London*, **288**, 699–700.

Kaplan, J. L., and Yorke, J. A. (1975), On the stability of a periodic solution of a differential-delay equation, *SIAM Journal of Mathematical Analysis*, **6**, 268–282.

Kaplan, J. L., and Yorke, J. A. (1977), On the nonlinear differential delay equation $x'(t) = -f(x(t), x(t-1))$, *Journal of Differential Equations*, **23**, 293–314.

Karlin, S., and McGregor, J. (1958), Linear growth, birth and death processes, *Journal of Mathematics and Mechanics*, **7**, 643–662.

Karlin, S., and Taylor, H. M. (1975), *A First Course in Stochastic Processes* (2nd Edition), Academic Press, London.

Keiding, N. (1975), Extinction and exponential growth in random environments, *Theoretical Population Biology*, **8**, 49–63.

Krebs, C. J. (1972), *Ecology: The Experimental Analysis of Distribution and Abundance*, Harper and Row, New York.

Krebs, C. J., Keller, B. L., and Tamarin, R. H. (1969), *Microtus* population biology: Demographic changes in fluctuating populations of *M. ochrogaster* and *M. pennsylvanicus* in southern Indiana, Ecology, **50**, 587–607.

Kyner, W. T., and Sanchez, D. A. (1978), Asymptotic and numerical approximation of the roots of Lotka's equation, *Theoretical Population Biology*, **13**, 112–120.

Langhaar, H. L. (1951), *Dimensional Analysis and the Theory of Models*, Wiley, New York; Chapman and Hall, London.

La Salle, J., and Lefchetz, S. (1961), *Stability by Liapunov's Direct Method with Applications*, Academic Press, London.

Leslie, P. H. (1945), On the use of matrices in certain population mathematics, *Biometrika*, **33**, 183–212.

Leslie, P. H. (1948), Some further notes on the use of matrices in population mathematics, *Biometrika*, **35**, 213–245.

Levin, S. A. (1976), Population dynamic models in heterogeneous environments, *Annual Review of Ecology and Systematics*, **7**, 287–310.

Lewis, E. G. (1942), On the generation and growth of a population, *Sankhya*, **6**, 93–96.

Lighthill, M. J. (1958), *Fourier Analysis and Generalised Functions*, Cambridge University Press.

Lomnicki, A. (1978), Individual differences between animals and the natural regulation of their numbers, *Journal of Animal Ecology*, **47**, 461–476.

Luckinbill, L. S. (1973), Co-existence in laboratory populations of *Paramecium aurelia* and its predator *Didinium nasutum, Ecology*, **54**, 1320–1327.

Luckinbill, L. S. (1974), The effects of space and enrichment on a predator–prey system, *Ecology*, **55**, 1142–1147.

Ludwig, D. (1975), Persistence of dynamical systems under random perturbation, *SIAM Review*, **17**, 605–640.

Ludwig, D., Aronson, D. G., and Weinberger, A. F., (1980), *Spatial Patterning of the Spruce Budworm* (Preprint).

Ludwig, D., Jones, D. D., and Holling, C. S. (1978), Qualitative analysis of insect outbreak systems: the spruce budworm and forest, *Journal of Animal Ecology*, **47**, 315–332.

MacArthur, R. H. (1969), Species packing and what interspecies competition minimises, *Proceedings of the National Academy of Sciences, U.S.A.*, **64**, 1369–1371.

MacArthur, R. H., and Wilson, E. O. (1963), An equilibrium theory of insular zoogeography, *Evolution*, **17**,, 373–387.

MacDonald, N. (1976), Time delay in simple chemostat models, *Biotechnology and Bioengineering*, **18**, 805–812.

MacDonald, N. (1978), *Time Lags in Biological Models*, Springer–Verlag (Lecture Notes in Biomathematics, Vol. 27).

Mackey, M. C., and Glass, L. (1977), Oscillations and chaos in physiological control systems, *Science*, **197**, 287–289.

McKinstry, J. (1980), *Material Cycling and Stability in Some Ecosystem Models*, PhD. Thesis, University of Strathclyde.

McMurtrie, R. (1976), On the limit to niche overlap for nonuniform niches, *Theoretical Population Biology*, **10**, 96–107

McMurtrie, R. (1978), Persistence and stability of single-species and prey–predator systems in spatially heterogeneous environments, *Mathematical Biosciences*, **39**, 11–51.

May, R. M. (1972), Limit cycles in predator–prey communities, *Science*, **177**, 900–902.

May, R. M. (1973a), Time-delay versus stability in population models with two and three trophic levels, *Ecology*, **54**, 315–325.

May, R. M. (1937b), Stability in randomly fluctuating versus deterministic environments, *American Naturalist*, **107**, 621–650.

May, R. M. (1974a), On the theory of niche overlap, *Theoretical Population Biology*, **5**, 297–332.

May, R. M. (1974b), *Statility and Complexity in Model Ecosystems*, (2nd Edition), Princeton University Press.

May, R. M. (1974c), Biological populations with non-overlapping generations: stable points, stable cycles, and chaos, *Science*, **186**, 645–647.

May, R. M. (1975), Biological populations obeying difference equations: stable points, stable cycles and chaos, *Journal of Theoretical Biology*, **51**, 511–524.

May, R. M. (1976a), Simple mathematical models with very complicated dynamics, *Nature, London*, **261**, 459–467.

May, R. M. (1976b), Models for single populations, in *Theoretical Ecology: Principles and Applications*, (Ed. R. M. May,) pp. 4–25, Blackwell Scientific Publications, Oxford.

May, R. M. (Ed.) (1976c), *Theoretical Ecology: Principles and Applications*, Blackwell Scientific Publications, Oxford.

May, R. M. (1976d), Estimating r: a pedagogical note, *American Naturalist*, 496–499.

May, R. M. (1976e), Models for two interacting populations, in *Theoretical Ecology, Principles and Applications*, (Ed. R. M. May), Blackwell Scientific Publications, Oxford.

May, R. M. (1977), Thresholds and breakpoints in ecosystems with a multiplicity of stable states, *Nature, London*, **269**, 471–477.

May, R. M. (1978), Host-parasitoid systems in patchy environments: A phenomenological model, *Journal of Animal ecology*, **47**, 833–843.

May, R. M. (1980), Nonlinear phenomena in ecology and epidemiology, *Proceedings of the International Conference on Nonlinear Dynamics*, in *Annals of the New York Academy of Sciences*, **357**, 267–281.

May, R. M., and Anderson, R. M. (1978), Regulation and stability of host–parasite interactions: II, destabilizing processes, *Journal of Animal Ecology*, **47**, 249–267.

May, R. M., Conway, G. R., Hassell, M. P., and Southwood, T. R. E. (1974), Time delays, density dependence and single species oscillations, *Journal of Animal Ecology*, **43**, 747–770.

May, R. M., and Oster, G. F. (1976), Bifurcations and dynamic complexity in simple ecological models, *American Naturalist*, **110**, 573–599.

Maynard Smith, J. (1974), *Models in Ecology*, Cambridge University Press.

Minorsky, N. (1962), *Nonlinear Oscillations*, Van Nostrand, Princeton.

Mollison, D. (1977), Spatial contact models for ecological and epidemic spread, *Journal of the Royal Statistical Society*, Series B, **39**, 283–326.

Monod, J. (1950), La technique de culture continue: theorie et applications, *Annales de l'Institut Pasteur*, **79**, 390–401.

Moran, P. A. P. (1953), The statistical analysis of the Canadian lynx cycle, I: Structure and prediction, *Australian Journal of Zoology*, **1**, 163–173.

Morris, W. D. (1974), *Differential Equations for Engineers and Applied Scientists*, McGraw-Hill, London.

Mortensen, R. E. (1969), Mathematical problems of modelling stochastic nonlinear dynamic systems, *Journal of Statistical Physics*, **1**, 271–296.

Murdoch, W. W., and Oaten, A. (1975), Predation and population stability, *Advances in Ecological Research*, **9**, 1–131.

Murray, J. D. (1974), *Asymptotic Analysis*, Clarendon Press, Oxford.

Namba, T. (1980), Density-dependent dispersal and spatial distribution of a population, *Journal of Theoretical Biology*, **86**, 351–363.

Nemytskii, V. V., and Stepanov, V. V., (1960), *Qualitative Theory of Differential Equations*, Princeton University Press.

Newman, W. I. (1980), Some exact solutions to a non-linear diffusion problem in population genetics and combustion, *Journal of Theoretical Biology*, **85**, 325–334.

Nicholson, A. J. (1954), An outline of the dynamics of animal populations, *Australian Journal of Zoology*, **2**, 9–65.

Nicholson, A. J. (1957), The self-adjustment of populations to change, *Cold Spring Harbor Symposium on Quantitative Biology*, **22**, 153–173.

Nicholson, A. J., and Bailey, V. A. (1935), The balance of animal populations, *Proceedings of the Zoological Society of London*, **3**, 551–598.

Nicolis, G., and Prigogine, I. (1977), *Self-Organisation in Non-Equilibrium Systems; From Dissipative Structure to Order Through Fluctuations*, Wiley, New York.

Nisbet, R. M., and Gurney, W. S. C. (1976), Population dynamics in a periodically varying environment, *Journal of Theoretical Biology*, **56**, 459–475.

Nisbet, R. M., and Gurney, W. S. C. (1976a), Model of material cycling in a closed ecosystem, *Nature, London*, **264**, 633–634.

Nisbet, R. M., Gurney, W. S. C., and Pettipher, M. A. (1977), An evaluation of linear models of population fluctuations, *Journal of Theoretical Biology*, **68**, 143–160.

Nisbet, R. M., Gurney, W. S. C., and Pettipher, M. A. (1978), Environmental fluctuations and the theory of the ecological niche, *Journal of Theoretical Biology*, **75**, 223–237.

Nyholm, N. (1978), Dynamics of phosphate limited algal growth: simulation of phosphate shocks, *Journal of Theoretical Biology*, **70**, 415–425.

Oberhettinger, F. (1973), *Fourier Transforms of Distributions and their Inverses: A Collection of Tables*, Academic Press, London.

Ollason, J. (1977), Freshwater microcosms in fluctuating Environments, *Oikos*, **28**, 262–269.

Oster, G., and Takahashi, Y. (1974), Models for age-specific interactions in a periodic environment, *Ecological Monographs*, **44**, 483–501.

Pankhurst, R. C. (1964), *Dimensional Analysis and Scale Factors*, Chapman and Hall Ltd., London.

Pettipher, M. (1981), *An investigation into the effects of overlap in a two-level model of consumers and resources*, PhD. Thesis, University of Strathclyde.

Phillipson, J. (1966), *Ecological Energetics*, Camelot Press Ltd., Southampton.

Piaggio, H. T. H. (1952), *An Elementary Treatise on Differential Equations and Their Applications*, (revised edition), Bell, London.

Pianka, E. R. (1976), Competition and niche theory, in *Theoretical Ecology: Principles and Applications*, (Ed. R. M. May), Blackwell Scientific Publications, Oxford.

Pielou, E. C. (1969), *An Introduction to Mathematical Ecology*, Wiley–Interscience, New York.

Platt, T., and Denman, K. L. (1975), Spectral Analysis in Ecology, *Annual Review of Ecology and Systematics*, **6**, 189–210.

Pollard, J. H. (1973), *Mathematical Models for the Growth of Human Populations*, Cambridge University Press.

Poole, R. W. (1976), Stochastic difference equation predictors of population fluctuations, *Theoretical Population Biology*, **9**, 25–45.

Poole, R. W. (1977), Periodic, pseudoperiodic, and chaotic population fluctuations, *Ecology*, **58**, 210–213.

Poole, R. W. (1978), A reply to Anderson, *Theoretical Population Biology*, **13**, 190–196.

Pratt, D. M. (1943), Analysis of population development in *Daphnia* at different temperatures, *Biological Bulletin*, **85**, 116–140.

Price, G., and Maynard Smith, J. (1973), The logic of animal conflict, *Nature*, **246**, 15–18.

Prigogine, I. (1980), *From Being to Becoming*, Freeman.

Readshaw, J. L., and Cuff, W. R. (1980) A model of Nicholson's blowfly cycles and its relevance to predation theory, *Journal of Animal Ecology*, **49**, 1005–1010.

Rorres, C. (1976), Stability of an age specific population with density dependent fertility, *Theoretical Population Biology*, **10**, 26–46.

Rorres, C. (1979a), A nonlinear model of population growth in which fertility is dependent on birth rate, *SIAM Journal of Applied Mathematics*, **37**, 423–432.

Rorres, C. (1979b), Local stability of a population with density dependent fertility. *Theoretical Population Biology*, **16**, 283–300.

Rosenzweig, M. L. (1969), Why the prey curve has a hump, *American Naturalist*, **103**, 81–87.

Rosenzweig, M. L., and MacArthur, R. H. (1963), Graphical representation and stability conditions of predator-prey interactions, *American Naturalist*, **97**, 209–223.

Roughgarden, J. (1974), Population dynamics in a spatially varying environment: how population size 'tracks' spatial variation in carrying capacity, *American Naturalist*, **108**, 649–664.

Roughgarden, J. (1975), A simple model for population dynamics in stochastic environments, *American Naturalist*, **109**, 713–736.

Roughgarden, J. (1977), Patchiness in the spatial distribution of a population caused by stochastic fluctuations in resources, *Oikos*, **29**, 52–59.

Roughgarden, J. (1978), Influence of competition on patchiness in a random environment, *Theoretical Population Biology*, **14**, 185–203.

Sanchez, D. A. (1968), *Ordinary Differential Equations and Stability Theory: An Introduction*, Freeman, San Francisco and London.

Schoener, T. (1974), Some methods for calculating competition coefficients from resource utilisation spectra, *American Naturalist*, **108**, 332–340.

Schuss, Z. (1980), Singular perturbation methods in stochastic differential equations of mathematical physics, *SIAM Review*, **22**, 119–155.

Scott, P., and Rines, R. (1975), Naming the Loch Ness Monster, *Nature, London*, **258**, 466–468.

Segal, L. A., and Jackson, J. L. (1972), Dissipative structure: an explanation and an ecological example, *Journal of Theoretical Biology*, **37**, 545–559.

Sharpe, F. R., and Lotka, A. J. (1911), A problem in age distribution, *Philosophical Magazine*, **21**, 435–438.

Singleton, R. C. (1968), An Algol procedure for the fast Fourier transform with arbitrary factors, Algorithm 339, *Communications of the ACM*, **11**, 776–779.

Singleton, R. C. (1969), An algorithm for computing the mixed radix fast Fourier transform, *IEEE Transactions on Audio and Electroacoustics*, **AU-17**, 93–103.

Smith, A. T. (1974), The distribution and dispersal of pikas: consequences of insular population structure, *Ecology*, **55**, 1112–1119.

Smith, R. H., and Mead, R. (1980), The dynamics of discrete-time stochastic models of population growth, *Journal of Theoretical Biology*, **86**, 607–628.

Streifer, W. (1974), Realistic models in population ecology, *Advances in Ecological Research*, **8**, 199–266.

Sutherland, J. P. (1974), Multiple stable points in natural communities *American Naturalist*, **108**, 859–873.

Tamarin, R. H. (1977), Dispersal in island and mainland votes, *Ecology*, **58**, 1044–1054.

Tanemura, M., and Hasegawa, M. (1980), Geometrical models of territory, I: Models for synchronous and asynchronous settlement of territories, *Journal of Theoretical Biology*, **82**, 477–496.

Tanner, J. L. (1975), The stability and the intrinsic growth rate of prey and predator populations, *Ecology*, **56**, 855–867.

Taylor, C. E., and Sokal, R. R. (1976), Oscillations in housefly population sizes due to time lags, *Ecology*, **57**, 1060–1067.

Torrez, W. T. (1979), Calculating extinction probabilities for the birth and death chain in a random environment, *Journal of Applied Probability*, **16**, 709–720.

Turelli, M. (1977), Random environments and stochastic calculus, *Theoretical Population Biology*, **12**, 140–178.

Turelli, M. (1978), A re-examination of stability in randomly varying versus deterministic environments with comments on the stochastic theory of limiting similarity, *Theoretical Population Biology*, **13**, 244–267.

Turelli, M., and Gillespie, J. H. (1980), Conditions for the existence of stationary densities for some two-dimensional diffusion processes with applications in population biology, *Theoretical Population Biology*, **17**, 167–189.

Usher, M. B. (1972), Developments in the Leslie matrix model, in *Mathematical Models in Ecology* (Ed. J. N. R. Jeffers), 12th Symposium of the British Ecological Society, pp. 29–60, Blackwell Scientific Publications, Oxford.

Utida, S. (1967), Damped Oscillation of Population at Equilibrium, *Research in Population Ecology*, **9**, 1–9.

Vandermeer, J. H. (1973), On the regional stabilization of locally unstable predator–prey relationships, *Journal of Theoretical Biology*, **41**, 161–170.

Vansickle, J. (1977), Analysis of a distributed-parameter population model based on physiological age, *Journal of Theoretical Biology*, **64**, 571–586.

Varley, G. C., Gradwell, G. R., and Hassell, M. P. (1973), *Insect Population Ecology: An Analytical Approach*, Blackwell Scientific Publications, Oxford.

Williams, F. M. (1965), *Population Growth and Regulation in Continuously Cultured Algae*, PhD. Thesis, Yale University, USA.

Williams, F. M. (1970), Dynamics of microbial populations, in *Systems Analysis and Simulation in Ecology*, Vol. II, pp. 197–267 (Ed. B. C. Patten), Academic Press, New York.

Williamson, M. (1972), *The Analysis of Biological Populations*, Edward Arnold, London.

Zeigler, B. P. (1976), Persistence and Patchiness of predator–prey systems induced by discrete event population exchange mechanisms, *Journal of Theoretical Biology*, **67**, 677–686.

Author Index

Subject Index